PROGRAMED GENETICS

Volume III *Extension of the Theory*

PROGRAMED GENETICS

Chester A. Lawson
Research Professor, University College
Michigan State University

Mary Alice Burmester
Associate Professor of Natural Science
Michigan State University

D. C. HEATH AND COMPANY BOSTON

CONTENTS

To the Student

This auto-instructional text, or program, makes it possible for you to learn some of the basic principles of genetics without teacher guidance.

Programed Genetics—Extension of the Theory is organized into a number of small sections. Each section should be read very carefully. At the end of the section you are given a problem followed by multiple choice responses only one of which is correct. Incorrect alternatives suggest responses which you might make if you based your answer on incomplete or inexact knowledge. After selecting a response, indicate your choice with a check mark (√) in the proper box and turn to the page indicated beside that response. There you will find out whether you are correct or incorrect. If correct, you may proceed to the next teaching sequence. If incorrect, you will be given further information and then be asked to go back to the original page and try again.

The principle of proceeding by small, carefully graduated steps is incorporated into this program. Dividing the materials into small steps will help you to grasp the subject and to make correct responses. Making frequent responses to the learning material and finding out immediately if you are correct or incorrect provides a constant index of your progress. With this procedure you also do not proceed with concepts that are wrong and so lose your way.

At the beginning of each chapter you will find one or more worksheets. Directions for their use are incorporated in the text. Each chapter also contains a summary and a review section which will help you to unify what you have learned. You may find it helpful to keep, in addition, a list of new terms and definitions for review purposes. Finally, the text includes a series of tests. Your success in completing these tests gives you an indication of how well you have mastered the chief concepts in the unit. Answers to the test questions are in the Appendix.

There is no time limit in using the program. However, you should work as rapidly—and as carefully—as possible. We hope you will enjoy working with this program, and that you will be as successful in learning from it as were the many students who have already used it.

TO THE INSTRUCTOR

PROGRAMED GENETICS appears in three volumes. Volume I, *The Basic Concepts;* Volume II, *Chromosome Behavior;* and Volume III, *Extension of the Theory.* This series of programs was written to increase instructional efficiency in genetics and to place more responsibility for learning on the student. It is the result of a successful experiment in providing improved instructional material for a course in natural science at Michigan State University.

Volume III deals with modern extensions of the theory of genetics. The material, which utilizes the branching or "scrambled" technique of programing, is organized into six chapters. Worksheets are included at the beginning of each chapter which, when completed, help the student attain an overview of the chapter. Instructions for their use are included in the text. Each chapter also contains one or more summary and review sections. The review sections require the student to make written responses which may be checked against correct responses found in the Appendix. Self tests are included at the end of each chapter. The self tests give evidence of how well the student has mastered the concepts presented in the program. These tests are not simply tests of retention but are challenge tests. They were designed to produce mean scores of about 70%. Lowest scores should be about 50%. Answers to self tests are found in the Appendix.

History of Volume III: Development and Testing   The writing of the material for Volume III was completed in the fall of 1961. A mimeographed version was then tested with 200 Freshmen studying Natural Science at Michigan State University. The material was subsequently revised in the light of an error analysis and students' and instructor's comments. Further field tests with Chapters 2–6 were conducted at MSU in the spring of 1962 with a group of 80 second-term, natural science students. Students were asked to take a 30 item true-false test before working on each of these chapters. They were then asked to go through the program and to take the same test again. Mean gain for this group was 68%.

This gain score took into account percentage gain between pre-test and post-test as well as how far the student had to go to attain a perfect score. Thus a gain of 30% from pre-test to post-test could be interpreted differently in the case of two students: For example, Student "A" has a pre-test score of 65% and a post-test score of 95%. His gain is $\dfrac{30\%}{100\% - 65\%} = 86\%$. Student

"B" has a pre-test score of 20% and a post-test score of 50%. His gain is $\dfrac{30\%}{100\% - 20\%} = 37.5\%$. Student "A" gained almost as much as it was possible to gain from the program, while Student "B" gained about one-third as much as was possible to gain.

Students participating in this last field test were asked to state their attitude to the programed text. Their response was

Very favorable	22%
Favorable	47
Neutral	14
Unfavorable	14
Very unfavorable	3

In the fall of 1962 the material comprising Volume III was again used at MSU with 750 students. As a result, much of the material in Chapter 6 was revised. The final revised form of this chapter was tested with a small group of students from Boston University. Student attitude was excellent. Gain in learning and post-test scores were high.

Administrative Suggestions Volume III, *Extensions of the Theory*, has been used in class sessions and also for outside study. It was found that short study sessions of approximately one hour were more effective than long sessions.

At MSU the programed study was effectively augmented with two lecture periods and a one-hour question and answer period. Developmental aspects of the program did not include laboratory experiences. However, the authors believe that properly designed lab experiences would enhance, rather than interfere with the program.

Enthusiasm on the part of the instructor administering the program is essential. Students are likely to be imbued with the same enthusiasm and confidence. Conversely, a negative attitude on the part of the instructor will reduce the effectiveness of the program.

Time Requirements The time required to finish the program varied from student to student; the average time for completing the program was 20 hours.

Prerequisite Knowledge Volume III assumes a knowledge of Mendelian genetics through the two-factor cross. To demonstrate his familiarity with these concepts, the student should be able to assign genetic probabilities by using probability equations or a checkerboard. He should be able to interpret pedigrees. Prerequisite vocabulary includes: genotype, phenotype, dominant and recessive gene, allele, heterozygous, homozygous, and dihybrid. These prerequisites are contained in Volume I of this series, *The Basic Concepts*. A knowledge of meiosis and mitosis is also assumed. The student should be able to define both these processes step by step. Vocabulary prerequisites include: chromosome, meiosis, mitosis, homologous, gamete, zygote, intersex autosome, X-chromosome, and Y-chromosome. This material is included in Volume II of this series, *Chromosome Behavior*.

Objectives   Upon completion of *Extension of the Theory* the student should be able to

1. Relate the behavior of chromosomes in meiosis to the postulated behavior of genes.
2. Recognize the need for revision of hypotheses on the basis of difference between prediction and experimental results.
3. Solve problems involving multiple alleles.
4. Identify and recall terms used in genetics.
5. Use the pedigree method, the breeding method, the family method, and the population method in solving genetic problems.
6. Solve problems involving sex-linked genes, linkage, crossing-over, chromosome mapping, and gene frequencies.
7. Explain the effect of the genetic mechanism on the stability of gene frequencies in populations.

Progress in programed instruction is closely tied to the performance of students using programed materials as well as to the evaluation of student performance by instructors and other subject matter experts. The authors will welcome all comments, suggestions, and data on student performance from teachers or other individuals who have used the program.

WORKSHEET 1-A

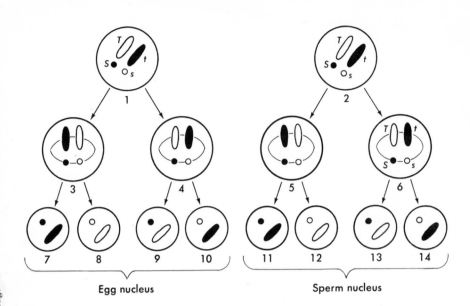

Egg nucleus

Sperm nucleus

Kinds of sperm nuclei

Kinds of egg nuclei

chapter 1

GENES AND CHROMOSOMES

Introduction

The material presented in this chapter assumes that the student is familiar with the processes of mitosis and meiosis and has *some* knowledge of the relationship of chromosomes and sex. The following summaries, however, will serve to review these topics.

Mitosis

Mitosis is a process of cell division that results in the production of two cells where there was only one before and in which the chromosomes of one daughter cell are identical with those in the other daughter cell and also identical with those of the original parent cell. Mitosis consists of two major processes: (1) the duplication of chromosomes and the equal assortment of the chromosomes into the two daughter cells and (2) the division of the cytoplasm.

Duplication of chromosomes occurs during interphase of mitosis when the chromosomes within the nucleus are long and threadlike. After duplication the double chromosomes (each strand now called a chromatid) shorten and thicken. During prophase, while this shortening and thickening process is going on, the nuclear membrane disappears and a spindle forms consisting of two centrioles at the poles with interconnecting fibers. The spindle is shaped somewhat like a football. At metaphase, when the spindle is fully formed, the chromatids become attached at their centromeres to the spindle and become arranged on a midplane which cuts the long axis of the spindle at right angles. This plane is called the equatorial plane. After lining up on the equatorial plane, each centromere divides. At the beginning of anaphase, the two chromosomes of each pair separate and move to opposite poles of the spindle.

As the chromosomes are moving toward the poles a constriction appears in the cytoplasm in the same plane as the equator of the spindle. This constriction deepens until the cell is cut in two.

At the end of anaphase and the beginning of telophase a new nuclear membrane forms, and the chromosomes elongate and thin out until they are again threadlike. Each new cell has a full complement of chromosomes, one centriole which duplicates before the next mitosis, and small fragments of the spindle, which gradually disappear. Thus each new cell contains the same kinds and number of chromosomes as were in the original cell prior to mitosis.

Meiosis

Meiosis is a type of cell division that occurs in immature reproductive cells and that results in the production of gametes. As a result of meiosis the number of chromosomes is reduced by one half. The key process that brings this reduction about is the coupling of homologous chromosomes. The coupled homologous chromosomes line up on the equatorial plane of the spindle and then separate, half of them going into one daughter cell and the other half into the other daughter cell.

The chromosomes duplicate before coupling takes place, and, as a result, a second cell division follows the first. The second cell division separates the sister chromatids that were formed early in the first division.

The gametes, sperm in the male and eggs in the female, contain half the normal number of chromosomes; that is, they are haploid (n) rather than diploid $(2n)$.

In the female, because the division of the cytoplasm is unequal in both the first and second divisions, one large cell (the mature egg) is formed plus three smaller cells called polar bodies. The polar bodies degenerate. The mature egg, if fertilized by a sperm, becomes the zygote for the next generation.

In immature reproductive cells where there are two or more pairs of homologous chromosomes, the coupled homologous chromosomes line up on the equatorial plane independently of each other. One member of a pair of homologous chromosomes is a maternal chromosome and the other member is a paternal chromosome. In some cells during the first division all the chromosomes on one side of the equatorial plane could be paternal chromosomes and all on the other side could be maternal chromosomes. Or any combination of the paternal chromosomes of one pair with the maternal chromosomes of another pair could occur on one side or the other of the equatorial plane. The result is that different kinds of gametes are produced with respect to the distribution of maternal and paternal chromosomes. If there is only one pair of homologous chromosomes, only two different kinds of gametes would be produced. If there are two pairs of homologous chromosomes, four kinds of gametes could be produced. In humans, who have 23 pairs of homologous chromosomes, over 8 million kinds of gametes could be produced, with respect to the combination of chromosomes.

Chromosomes and Sex

The discovery that the chromosomes of the cells of males and females differ supported the hypothesis that genes and chromosomes are intimately related. In insects the sex of an individual apparently depends on a balance between male-determining genes in the autosomes and female-determining genes in the X-chromosomes. If an individual has two X-chromosomes and two sets of autosomes, the X/A ratio expressed as a decimal is 1.0 and the individual is a female. If an individual has one X-chromosome and two sets of autosomes the X/A ratio is .5 and the individual is a male.

In some organisms the male has in addition to the one X-chromosome a hook-shaped chromosome known as the Y-chromosome. That this Y-chromosome is not directly related to sex determination in insects is evident by the occurrence of some organisms in which the Y-chromosome does not appear, e.g., the males having only the one X-chromosome plus the autosomes.

Intersexes in fruit flies have two X-chromosomes but three sets of autosomes. Thus the X/A ratio is .67. The correspondence of the intermediate ratio to the intermediate sex characteristics of these individuals supports the idea that in insects sex is due to a balance between female-determining and male-determining genes contained by the X-chromosomes and the autosomes.

Sex determination in humans differs from that in insects in that the Y-chromosome in humans affects the development of maleness. The X-chromosomes in humans produce femaleness if no Y-chromosome is present.

* * * *

The similarities between the assumed behavior of genes and the observed behavior of the visible chromosomes suggest that the chromosomes are the genes or that they carry the genes. We found the checkerboard a useful device for predicting the outcomes of crosses where the genotypes of parents were known. Will the checkerboard also predict the outcome of crosses if we use chromosomes with genes attached? Diagramed at the top right of Worksheet 1-A is an immature male reproductive cell (#2), a sperm nucleus of a pollen grain containing four chromosomes, two maternal and two paternal. (The chromosome number, n, of the pea is actually 7.) Assume that the

6A   shaded chromosomes represent the maternal ones (the ones received from the mother) and the unshaded ones, the paternal ones. Assume also that this is a cell of an F_1 generation pea plant having a genotype heterozygous for flower arrangement and for stem length. Its phenotype would be axial-flowered, long-stemmed. Its genotype would be *TtSs*. EXAMINE WORKSHEET 1-A. The two alleles *T* and *t* are written adjacent to the long chromosomes and the alleles *S* and *s* adjacent to the short chromosomes.

Which of the chromosomes are homologous?

☐ The two long chromosomes . . . . .page   **8A.**

☐ The two shaded chromosomes . . . . .page   **15D.**

☐ Both of these . . . . .page   **10D.**

6B   **Incorrect.** Since the behavior of the assumed genes corresponds to the observed behavior of chromosomes, does not this at least suggest some relationship between them? _____. Return to page **9A.**

From page **12A.**

6C   **Correct.** The independent behavior of chromosomes during meiosis helps to explain the random or independent assortment of separate pairs of genes during gamete formation. ON WORKSHEET 1-A LABEL THE CHROMOSOMES IN THE EGG NUCLEI NUMBERED 3, 4, 7, 8, 9, AND 10 TO CORRESPOND WITH THOSE IN 5, 6, 11, 12, 13, AND 14. (In this diagram we have ignored the production of polar bodies or their equivalent in plant reproduction, since it is a matter of chance which cell develops into an egg and which becomes a polar body. If a large number of eggs is produced, all four types of eggs should be produced in equal number.) NOW LABEL THE CHROMOSOMES OF THE SPERM AND EGG IN THE CHECKERBOARD. The circles containing four chromosomes in each of the 16 squares of the checkerboard are diagrams representing

☐ gametes . . . . .page   **13A.**

☐ zygotes . . . . .page   **17B.**

Incorrect. Throughout this chapter we have noted that chromosomes assort and recombine, and therefore their observed behavior is similar to the assumed behavior of genes; but we have not found out that genes are chromosomes. Return to page **15C**.

7A

Incorrect. There are two chromosomes in each of the daughter cells. You are associating one gene with each chromosome. How many symbols for genes should you have indicated? _____. Return to page **9C**.

7B

From page **14B**.

Correct. Since the two possible arrangements of the paired chromosomes should occur in equal numbers (50% of each) what would be the ratio of the four kinds of gametes (cells #11, 12, 13, and 14) produced with respect to the combinations of chromosomes?

7C

☐ 1:1.......................................page **9B.**

☐ 1:1:1:1...................................page **12A.**

☐ 9:3:3:1...................................page **15B.**

☐ 3:1.......................................page **17A.**

Incorrect. Cells #13 and 14 were the ones being considered. Did you look at the wrong cells? If not, you have not continued to associate a specific chromosome with a specific gene. The long, unshaded chromosome should carry the gene *T*. Correct your errors on your worksheet and return to page **16C**.

7D

From page **5B.**

8A **Correct.** The two long chromosomes are homologous chromosomes. The two short chromosomes also are homologous. The alleles were placed on

☐ homologous chromosomes . . . . page **11B.**

☐ nonhomologous chromosomes . . . . page **13D.**

8B **Incorrect.** If you toss two coins and consider what lands up as analogous to the chromosomes on one side of the equator and what lands down as analogous to what is on the other side of the equator do you not have just two possibilities — two heads (tails) up and two tails (heads) down, or a head and tail up and the other head and tail down? What would be the chances of two alike being up, compared to two that are different being up? _____. Return to page **14B.**

From page **17B.**

8C **Correct.** The squares represent the possible zygotes and the expected ratios in which these possible zygotes should occur, but they do not represent any particular number of zygotes.

The diagram on Worksheet 1-A represents gamete production, fertilization, and formation of zygotes of an F_2 generation involving the behavior of two pairs of chromosomes. The genes T, t, S, and s have been added to the chromosomes of the immature reproductive cells. LABEL ALL OF THE CHROMOSOMES IN ALL OF THE CELLS OF THE POSSIBLE ZYGOTES IN THE CHECKERBOARD ON WORKSHEET 1-A. DETERMINE THE GENOTYPES AND PHENOTYPES OF THE F_2 GENERATION. T = AXIAL FLOWERS; t = TERMINAL FLOWERS; S = LONG STEMS; s = SHORT STEMS. Axial flowers and long stems are due to dominant genes. What is the phenotypic ratio?

☐ 1:1:1:1 . . . . page **10A.**

☐ 9:3:3:1 . . . . page **15C.**

From page **13B.**

9A

Correct. We have assumed that four kinds of gametes can be produced by a dihybrid.

By assuming genes to be on chromosomes and following the pattern of chromosome behavior in gamete production we achieve the same results as we do by calculating on the basis of gene theory alone.

Does this result support or contradict the assumption that genes are on the chromosomes (or are the chromosomes)?

☐ It supports it.............................page **14B.**

☐ It contradicts it..........................page **6B.**

9B

Incorrect. If there are four different possible events (four different kinds of cells) can the ratio be 1:1? _____ Or even 3:1? _____. These are ratios of two possible events. Return to page 7C.

From page **11B.**

9C

Correct. At cell #5 on Worksheet 1-A you should have the genes t and S on the shaded chromosomes and the genes T and s on the unshaded ones.

After division of the cell at #6, two cells would be produced. ON WORKSHEET 1-A LABEL EACH CHROMOSOME IN CELLS #13 AND 14 WITH THEIR APPROPRIATE GENES. Each of these daughter cells contains two chromosomes. How many symbols for genes does each of these cells contain?

☐ One..page **7B.**

☐ Two..page **16C.**

☐ Four.......................................page **13C.**

10A   **Incorrect.** Did you follow directions? _____. Assign genes to each of the chromosomes as directed; determine the genotypes and their ratios; determine the phenotypic ratio; then return to page **8C**.

From page **16C**.

10B   **Correct.** The other immature germ cell having the other possible arrangement of the chromosomes on the equator is diagramed at cell #5, which you have labeled. NOW LABEL EACH DAUGHTER CELL (#11 and 12) WITH THE GENE SYMBOLS IT SHOULD CONTAIN.

Which two genes are in the daughter cell labeled #11 _____, and which two genes are in the other daughter cell #12 _____? What do you have recorded in these spaces?

☐ *TS* and *ts*...............................page   **17C.**

☐ *tS* and *Ts*...............................page   **13B.**

10C   **Incorrect.** Throughout this chapter we have noted that chromosomes assort and recombine, and therefore their observed behavior is similar to the assumed behavior of genes; but we have not found an exact location for genes. Return to page **15C**.

10D   **Incorrect.** The two shaded chromosomes represent the two maternal chromosomes which were received from this individual's mother; that is, they were assumed to be in the egg from which this individual developed. During meiosis do homologous or nonhomologous chromosomes pair, one of each going into each gamete? Return to page **5B**.

Incorrect. The squares of this checkerboard, like the ones you have used before, represent the possible zygotes that could be produced. Can two parents produce only 16 offspring? _____. Must there always be 16 offspring in any dihybrid cross? _____. The checkerboard gives information only about the expected ratios of offspring or the probability of any one offspring having a particular genotype. Return to page 17B.

From page 8A.

11A

Correct. The alleles T and t were placed on one pair of homologous chromosomes; the alleles S and s were placed on the other pair of homologous chromosomes.

Because homologous chromosomes are arranged as pairs on the equator of the spindle during meiosis, one configuration at this time could be as in the diagram on Worksheet 1-A at #6, where the long chromosome having gene T is on the same side of the equator as the round chromosome having the gene S. DEMONSTRATE THE OTHER POSSIBLE ARRANGEMENT OF THE CHROMOSOMES BY PLACING THE APPROPRIATE SYMBOLS ON THE CHROMOSOMES IN THE CELL MARKED #5. Which of the following do you have recorded for #5?

11B

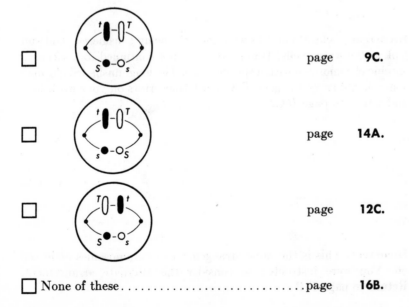

☐   page   **9C.**

☐   page   **14A.**

☐   page   **12C.**

☐ None of these.............................page   **16B.**

From page 7C.

12A **Correct.** The four types of gametes as diagramed in cells #11, 12, 13, and 14 should be in the ratio of 1:1:1:1.

On the basis of the assumptions of the gene theory alone the ratio of the gametes produced by an individual with a genotype heterozygous for two characteristics (*TtSs*) was also predicted to be 1:1:1:1. The correspondence between the ratio of different gametes predicted on the basis of chromosome behavior involving two pairs of chromosomes and the ratio predicted on the basis of the gene theory involving two pairs of genes also supports the hypothesis that genes are on chromosomes. Which of the following assumptions of the gene theory can be explained by the independence of the chromosome pairs when they line up on the equator of the spindle?

☐ Paired genes separate during gamete formation . . . . page   **14C.**

☐ Each gamete has but one gene of a pair . . . . . . page   **17D.**

☐ Genes of different pairs assort at random during gamete formation . . . . page   **6C.**

12B **Incorrect.** Cells #13 and 14 were the ones being considered. Did you look at the wrong cells? If not, you have not continued to associate a specific chromosome with a specific gene. The long, unshaded chromosome should carry the gene *T*. Correct your errors on your worksheet and return to page **16C**.

12C **Incorrect.** This is the same arrangement of chromosomes as in cell #6. You were instructed to consider the alternate arrangement. Return to page **11B**.

Incorrect. Are chromosomes paired in gametes? _____. **13A**
Return to page **6C**.

From page **10B**.

Correct. These two gametes (cells #11 and 12) would contain chromo-   **13B**
somes having the genes *tS* and *Ts* respectively. Thus, considering the
possible gametes as cells #11, 12, 13, and 14, four different chromosome combinations and four different gene combinations (*TS*, *Ts*, *tS*,
ts) can result from the meiotic division of a cell having two pairs of
homologous chromosomes, if we assume that the individual has a
genotype heterozygous for two traits and that the alleles are on the
homologous chromosomes.

On the basis of the assumptions of the gene theory alone how many
kinds of gametes would you expect a plant to produce that had a
genotype heterozygous for two pairs of genes (*TtSs*)?

☐ Two.....................................page   **16D.**

☐ Four....................................page   **9A.**

Incorrect. There are two chromosomes in each of the daughter cells.   **13C**
You are associating one gene with each chromosome. How many symbols for genes should you have indicated? _____. Return to
page **9C**.

Incorrect. Look at cell #2. Are not *T* and *t* alleles? _____.   **13D**
Have they been placed on the two long chromosomes or on the two
shaded ones? _____. Return to page **8A**.

14A   **Incorrect.** Examine cell #2 on the worksheet. The gene labeled
_____ was placed on the long, shaded chromosome; the gene
labeled _____ was placed on the short, shaded chromosome.
In the diagram of cell #5 these are both on the same side of the
equator of the spindle. When a particular gene is associated with a
particular chromosome, that same gene must continue to be associated with that chromosome. Return to page **11B**.

From page **9A**.

14B   **Correct.** The correspondence of the behavior of chromosomes during
meiosis and the assumed behavior of genes supports the hypothesis
that genes are located on chromosomes.

   Study Worksheet 1-A and observe the two possible arrangements of
pairs of chromosomes on the equator of the spindle. In cell #6 the
unshaded long chromosome is on the same side of the equator as the
shaded round chromosome. In cell #5 the two unshaded chromosomes
are on the same side of the equator.

   If the way in which one pair of chromosomes lines up on the equator
is independent of the way the other pair lines up, _____% of
the cells will have one arrangement and _____% will have
the alternative arrangement. What have you recorded in the above
blanks?

☐ 75% and 25%..............................page   **16A.**

☐ 25% and 75%..............................page   **8B.**

☐ 50% and 50%..............................page   **7C.**

14C   **Incorrect.** It is true that this assumption of the gene theory is
explained by the separation of paired chromosomes during meiosis,
but this assumption is concerned with but a single pair of genes, and
not two pairs. Return to page **12A**.

Incorrect. Cells #13 and 14 were the ones being considered. Did you look at the wrong cells? If not, you have not continued to associate a specific chromosome with a specific gene. The round, shaded chromosome should carry the gene S. Correct your errors on the worksheet and return to page 16C.

Incorrect. Think about two coins — a dime and a penny. In what ratio would the four possible combinations obtained by tossing them simultaneously be? _____. Return to page 7C.

From page 8C.

Correct. The phenotypic ratio should be 9 axial-flowered, long-stemmed:3 axial-flowered, short-stemmed:3 terminal-flowered, long-stemmed:1 terminal-flowered, short-stemmed. On the basis of all the evidence presented in this chapter, what would you conclude concerning the relation of genes to chromosomes?

☐ Genes are chromosomes.....................page   **7A.**

☐ Genes are located on chromosomes..........page   **10C.**

☐ Either 1 or 2 is a possibility, but we cannot be
sure on the basis of the evidence presented thus
far.......................................page   **18A.**

Incorrect. The two shaded chromosomes represent the two maternal chromosomes which were received from this individual's mother; that is, they were assumed to be in the egg from which this individual developed. During meiosis do homologous or nonhomologous chromosomes pair, one of each going into each gamete?
Return to page 5B.

16A **Incorrect.** If you toss two coins and consider what lands up as analogous to the chromosomes on one side of the equator and what lands down as analogous to what is on the other side of the equator, do you not have just two possibilities — two heads (tails) up and two tails (heads) down, or a head and tail up and the other head and tail down? What would be the chances of two alike being up, compared to two that are different being up? _____. Return to page **14B**.

16B **Incorrect.** Did you place paired genes on nonhomologous chromosomes? _____. If so, correct your worksheet and return to page **11B**.

From page **9C**.

16C **Correct.** Which two genes would be in the cell labeled #13? _____. Which two would be in the cell labeled #14? _____.
What do you have recorded in the above two spaces?

☐ *TS* and *ts* . . . . page	**10B.**
☐ *Ts* and *tS* . . . . page	**15A.**
☐ *tS* and *Ts* . . . . page	**12B.**
☐ *ts* and *TS* . . . . page	**7D.**

16D **Incorrect.** Genes of different pairs, as *Tt* and *Ss*, are assumed to assort independently of each other. Thus the following combinations are possible in the gametes: *TS, Ts, tS, ts*. Return to page **13B**.

Incorrect. If there are four different possible events (four different kinds of cells) can the ratio be 3:1? _____ Or even 1:1? _____. These are ratios of two possible events. Return to page **7C**. **17A**

From page **6C**.

Correct. Each of the circles in the diagram represents a possible zygote. These 16 squares represent **17B**

☐ 16 zygotes................................page **11A.**

☐ any number of zygotes....................page **8C.**

Incorrect. Did you consider the wrong cells? Look at cells #11 and 12. The long, shaded chromosome has the gene *t* associated with it. Correct your errors and return to page **10B**. **17C**

Incorrect. It is true that this assumption of the gene theory is explained by the separation of paired chromosomes during meiosis, but this assumption is concerned with but a single pair of genes, and not two pairs. Return to page **12A**. **17D**

From page 15C.

18A **Correct.** At this point the conclusion that genes are related to chromosomes can be made, but whether genes are chromosomes or are parts of chromosomes cannot be determined on the basis of the comparison of the observed behavior of chromosomes and the assumed behavior of genes as presented in this chapter. This is the end of this sequence. Continue with the review, which is a point-by-point comparison of chromosome and gene behavior.

REVIEW—Chapter 1

We assumed in Chapter I that genes are transmitted from parents to off-spring in the gametes. Thus any genes contributed by the father presumably were carried by the sperm and any genes contributed by the mother presumably were carried by the egg. We have said that genes are imagined, but this does not mean that we thought of them as having no existence at all. Instead, it means that while we cannot see the genes we postulate that genes actually do exist, that they are carried from parents to offspring, and that they control the development of inherited traits.

Let us compare what we have assumed concerning genes with what we have observed concerning chromosomes during mitosis and meiosis and the production of gametes.

The assumptions that we have made concerning genes are:

A. **Genes are units that control the development of hereditary traits.**

B. **Genes occur in pairs in all somatic cells of each individual; i.e., in each cell there are two genes concerned with the same inherited trait.**

C. **If two genes of the pair differ, one of the two genes may be dominant to the other.**

D. **During gamete formation paired genes separate and go into different gametes; thus each gamete has only one gene of each pair.**

E. **During fertilization the unpaired genes in the male and female gametes are brought together to form new pairs in the zygote. For any one pair the sperm presumably carries one gene of the pair and the egg the other gene of the pair, so that when sperm and egg unite, the two genes that make up the pair are brought together.**

F. **During gamete formation members of different pairs of alleles assort independently of each other. Thus, given an individual with a genotype heterozygous for two pairs of alleles such as Aa and Bb, gene A will separate from gene a. Gene A will go into one gamete while gene a goes into another. Likewise B and b will go into different gametes. The assumption of independent assortment states that it is a matter of chance whether A goes into the same gamete with B or b and whether gene a goes with B or b. Thus, some gametes would contain genes A and B, and some genes A and b; others would contain genes a and B and still others genes a and b. Which combinations occur would be a matter of chance.**

Continue on page 20.

In the following series of questions the assumptions of the gene theory are listed in summary form as a key, below which are statements concerning meiosis; diagrams of the meiotic process are also given. SELECT THE ASSUMPTION ABOUT GENES THAT MATCHES MOST CLOSELY THE STATEMENT ABOUT MEIOSIS AND PLACE THE LETTER OF THE ASSUMPTION IN FRONT OF THE STATEMENT.

Assumptions of the Gene Theory

KEY: A.   Genes are units of heredity.

B.   Genes occur in pairs.

C.   One gene may be dominant to another.

D.   Paired genes separate during gamete formation.

E.   Each gamete has one gene of each pair.

F.   At fertilization unpaired genes are brought together.

G.   There is independent assortment of genes of different alleles.

Homologous chromosomes

___ 1.   In immature reproductive cells the chromosomes occur as individual rodlike bodies.

___ 2.   In immature reproductive cells the chromosomes occur in matched sets. Each chromosome has a homologue, that is, another chromosome like it.

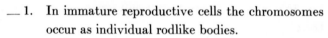

___ 3.   During the first meiotic division the homologous chromosomes come together to form pairs.

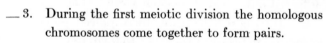

___ 4.   The paired chromosomes become aligned on the equator of the spindle, then separate and move to opposite poles of the spindle, with the result that two daughter cells are produced, each of which receives one set of homologous chromosomes. (Tetrad formation is omitted in this example.)

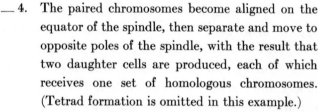

___ 5.   Each gamete produced has one member of each pair of homologous chromosomes.

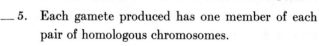

— 6. When paired homologous chromosomes become attached to the equator of the spindle, two arrangements of the paired chromosomes are possible: (1) both maternal chromosomes may be on one side of the equator, with both paternal chromosomes on the other side (diagram *A*), or (2) one paternal and one maternal may be on each side (diagram *B*). When division occurs in the first case one daughter cell contains both maternal chromosomes and the other contains both paternal chromosomes. In the second case, after division, both daughter cells contain one maternal and one paternal chromosome.

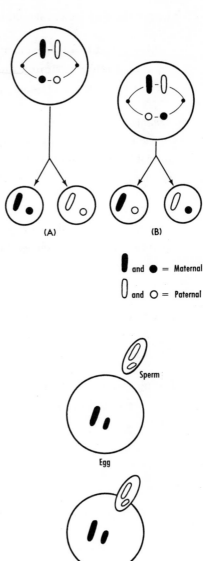

— 7. At fertilization when a sperm from the male unites with an egg from the female the original number of chromosomes is restored. Also, two complete sets of homologous chromosomes are again combined in one cell (the zygote).

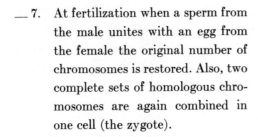

On a separate piece of paper write the sequence of letters you have recorded, and then turn to page **22**.

The sequence of letters should be A, B, B, D, E, G, and F.

Review of Comparison of Assumptions Concerning Genes and Observations Concerning Chromosomes During Meiosis and Fertilization

Assumptions Concerning Genes

1. Genes are units of some sort that control the development of hereditary traits.

2. Genes occur in pairs in all somatic body cells and in immature reproductive cells; i.e., in each cell there are two genes for any one inherited trait.

3. If two genes of a pair differ, one of the two genes may be dominant to the other.

4. During gamete formation paired genes separate and go into different gametes.

5. Each gamete contains but one gene of a pair.

6. During gamete formation members of different pairs of alleles assort independently of each other.

Observations Concerning Chromosomes

1. Chromosomes are individual rod-like bodies contained in the nuclei of cells.

2. In somatic cells and in immature reproductive cells the chromosomes occur in matched sets. Each chromosome has a homologue, i.e., another chromosome like it.

3. Nothing observable in chromosomes can be related to this gene function.

4. During the first meiotic division homologous chromosomes come together to form pairs, which line up on the equator of the spindle and then separate to go into different daughter cells.

5. As a result of the first meiotic division each daughter cell contains one of each homologous pair of chromosomes.

6. Each pair of homologous chromosomes lines up on the equator of the spindle independently of other pairs, and as a result it is a matter of chance which member of one pair of chromosomes will be associated with a member of another pair of homologous chromosomes in a gamete.

7. During fertilization unpaired genes (in gametes) are brought together to form a new pair in the zygote.

7. At fertilization two complete sets of homologous chromosomes are again combined in the zygote.

Continue with the summary of Chapter 1.

SUMMARY—Chapter 1

Additional support for the idea that genes are on chromosomes comes from the fact that the checkerboard can be used for the gene symbols alone or with chromosomes with the same results. When the behavior of two identifiably different things, such as genes and chromosomes, is identical, there is good reason for supposing they are one and the same.

Continue with the self test for Chapter 1.

SELF TEST—Chapter 1

For items 1 through 12 use the following key:

    A.   Chromosome(s)

    B.   Gene(s)

    C.   Both of these

    D.   Neither of these

___ 1.   Occur in pairs in somatic cells.

___ 2.   A hypothesized or imagined unit.

___ 3.   Pair during meiosis.

___ 4.   One of a pair goes to each gamete.

___ 5.   A visible unit.

___ 6.   Transmit hereditary information from generation to generation.

___ 7.   Assort independently of each other.

___ 8.   One of a pair comes from each parent in the formation of a zygote.

___ 9.   Are duplicated at each mitotic division.

___10.   Are referred to as being homologous.

___11.   Are referred to as alleles.

___12.   Two maternal always go into one gamete and two paternal into the other gamete.

___13.   On the basis of the information presented in this chapter one can conclude that

    ___A.   genes are chromosomes.

    ___B.   genes are parts of chromosomes.

    ___C.   either 1 or 2 might be the case.

    ___D.   neither of these is true; there is no relationship between them.

___14.   If one maternal chromosome carries a dominant gene of one allele, the paternal chromosome

    ___A.   must carry the dominant gene of the other allele.

    ___B.   must carry the recessive gene of the other allele.

    ___C.   may carry either gene of the other allele.

    ___D.   will carry neither gene of the other allele.

Turn to page 364 for the correct answers to the questions of this self test.

WORKSHEET 2-A

TABLE 1

Classes	No. of Families	Parents	Offspring
I	200	Taster × Taster	All tasters
II	200	Taster × Taster	75% tasters, 25% nontasters
III	200	Taster × Nontaster	All tasters
IV	200	Taster × Nontaster	50% tasters, 50% nontasters
V	200	Nontaster × Nontaster	All nontasters

TABLE 2

Classes	Parents	Genotypes	Offspring	Genotypes
I	Type A × Type A		100% Type A	
II	Type A × Type A		75% Type A, 25% Type O	
III	Type A × Type O		100% Type A	
IV	Type A × Type O		50% Type A, 50% Type O	
V				
VI	Type B × Type B		100% Type B	
VII	Type B × Type B		75% Type B, 25% Type O	
VIII	Type B × Type O		100% Type B	
IX	Type B × Type O		50% Type B, 50% Type O	
X				

WORKSHEET 2-B TABLE 3

BLOOD TYPE OF PARENTS	GENOTYPES OF PARENTS	GENOTYPE RATIOS OF OFFSPRING	Expected Percentages of Phenotypes of Offspring			
			Type A	Type B	Type AB	Type O
A × A	AA × AA	All AA				
	Ao × AA	1AA:1Ao				
	Ao × Ao	1AA:2Ao:1oo				
B × B	BB × BB	All BB				
	Bo × BB	1BB:1Bo				
	Bo × Bo	1BB:2Bo:1oo				
O × O	oo × oo	All oo				
AB × AB						
A × O	AA × oo	All Ao				
	Ao × oo	1Ao:1oo				
A × B						
A × AB						
B × O	BB × oo	All Bo				
	Bo × oo	1Bo:1oo				
B × AB						
O × AB						

After completing this table turn to page 56C.

chapter 2

INHERITANCE OF BLOOD TYPES

PART I

A-B-O Blood Types

So far we have discussed two methods of investigating inheritance. We started our investigation in Volume I with a study of a single family pedigree and discovered that by making certain assumptions we could explain how taster parents could produce children who were nontasters, and why characteristics can skip one or more generations. This type of study can be called the **pedigree method** of investigation.

The second method discussed in Volume I was similar to that used by Mendel, who first formulated an adequate explanation of inheritance. This method involved mass data on crosses of hybrids which had been produced by crossing individuals of pure lines. Large numbers of individuals were involved; the crosses were controlled, and ratios of individuals with contrasting characteristics in the F_2 were determined. The significance of these ratios was that they led to two new assumptions through the use of an analogy with certain aspects of the theory of probability. This method could be called the **controlled breeding method.**

A third method of studying inheritance is called the **family method.** This method has been used extensively to study inheritance in human beings because it is often difficult to obtain extensive family pedigrees and because it is impossible to employ controlled breeding methods.

In the family method of investigation, data on many sets of parents and their offspring are studied. For example, if we had used the family method to present the material on tasters and nontasters of PTC, we might have given data on a thousand sets of parents and their offspring and presented the data as in Table 1 of Worksheet 2-A.

Continue on page 30A.

29

30A   Of these five classes of families two classes give evidence that the ability to taste PTC is dominant to the lack of this ability. One line of reasoning based on the assumptions of the gene theory which might be used is: When one individual having a homozygous genotype for a characteristic is crossed with an individual having a homozygous genotype for the contrasting characteristic, all of the offspring would have heterozygous genotypes and would express the dominant characteristic. Which of the classes of families would fit this particular kind of cross and thus give some evidence that the gene for ability to taste PTC is dominant?

☐ Class III..............................page   **35B.**

☐ Class IV..............................page   **39A.**

☐ Neither of these classes; this line of reasoning
  does not apply to these data...............page   **41B.**

30B   **Incorrect.** This situation is identical to the one involving determination of dominance and recessiveness for the reaction to PTC. Return to page 29 of this chapter and make sure you understand how dominance and recessiveness are determined by use of the family method, before proceeding with blood type inheritance. Return to page **39C.**

From page **37B.**

30C   **Satisfactory.** Using the symbol B for the gene for Type B, and the symbol b for the gene for Type O, WRITE THE GENOTYPES ON WORKSHEET 2-A FOR ALL THE PARENTS AND ALL OF THE OFFSPRING IN THE FAMILIES HAVING TYPE B AND TYPE O BLOOD. Compare the genotypes you have recorded for Classes VI, VII, VIII, and IX with those you have recorded for Classes I, II, III, and IV. Where you have recorded AA in Class I, have you recorded BB in Class VI, etc.? In other words, except for the letters used, are these the same, class for class, or are there differences?

☐ They are the same.........................page   **32C.**

☐ They are different........................page   **34B.**

30D   **Your answer is correct, but incomplete.** What would be the phenotype of offspring whose parents' genotypes were AA and AA? _____. Return to page **41C.**

Incorrect. We have assumed that antigens A and B are caused by genes *A* and *B*. These Type AB individuals have the antigens; must they not also have the genes? Return to page **40C.**

31A

Incorrect. Study Table 1 of Worksheet 2-A and then start again from page **29.**

31B

Incorrect. Blood types are determined by making observations of the reactions of the blood. Genes, and hence genotypes, can never be observed. Genotypes must be obtained by reasoning from the assumptions of the gene theory. Return to page **36A.**

31C

From page **38D.**

Correct. Your prediction corresponds with the data collected on families where both parents were Type O. It has been found that when both parents have Type O blood, only Type O offspring are produced. ON THE WORKSHEET 2-A ADD THE FOLLOWING DATA AS CLASS V. ALSO WRITE THE GENOTYPES FOR PARENTS AND OFFSPRING.

31D

Parents	Offspring
Type O × Type O	100% Type O

We will now test an assumption regarding the genetic makeup of blood types. We will not be sure whether the assumption is correct until we have tested it.

You have assigned the symbol *A* for the gene for Type A and the symbol *a* for the gene for Type O.

Is it reasonable to assume that genes *A* and *a* are alleles?

☐ Yes......................................page   **37B.**

☐ No.......................................page   **42B.**

☐ I have forgotten the meaning of the term
   allele...................................page   **40B.**

32A   **Why not?** Would not individuals with the genotypes $AaBb \times aabb$ produce some individuals with the genotype $aabb$? _____. Would not these individuals have Type O blood? _____. Return to page **46C**.

32B   **No.** Can the characteristics of parents be recessive when both are the same (Type B) and the combination of both produce offspring having the contrasting characteristic (Type O)? _____. Two non-tasters ($tt \times tt$) cannot produce offspring having the gene T. Return to page **37B**.

From page **30C**.

32C   **Satisfactory.** Is it reasonable to assume that the genes B and b are alleles?

☐ Yes...page   **40C**.

☐ No..page   **55A**.

32D   **Incorrect.** Suppose you did not know which characteristic, ability to taste PTC or lack of this ability, was due to a dominant gene. All of the offspring of Class V are like their parents. Could these be the genotypes? $tt \times tt$ _____ Could these be the genotypes? $TT \times TT$

tt TT

_____. Does the knowledge that the parents are like the offspring give a clue to which gene is dominant? _____. Return to page **35B**.

Incorrect. Blood types are determined by making observations of **33A** the reactions of the blood. Genes, and hence genotypes, can never be observed. Genotypes must be obtained by reasoning from the assumptions of the gene theory. Return to page **36A**.

From page **45A**.

Correct. If the genotype of the Type AB parent were $AABB$ only **33B** Type AB offspring should be produced. If the genotype of the Type AB parent were $AaBb$, you would expect offspring of all four blood types in the ratio of 1:1:1:1.

Keep in mind that in the family method of the study of heredity data are collected on many sets of parents and their offspring.

The following is a completed chart of Type AB × Type O crosses. Check your chart on page 45A with this one and then proceed with the next question.

Type AB		Type O	EXPECTED GENOTYPES OF OFFSPRING	EXPECTED PHENOTYPES OF OFFSPRING
$AABB$	×	$aabb$	$AaBb$	Type AB
$AABb$	×	$aabb$	1 $AaBb$: 1 $Aabb$	½ Type AB, ½ Type A
$AaBB$	×	$aabb$	1 $AaBb$: 1 $aaBb$	½ Type AB, ½ Type B
$AaBb$	×	$aabb$	1 $AaBb$: 1 $Aabb$: 1 $aaBb$: 1 $aabb$	¼ Type AB ¼ Type A ¼ Type B ¼ Type O

If the inheritance of blood types is controlled by two pairs of genes, how many different classes of families should there be if one of the parents is Type AB and the other is Type O?

☐ One . . . . page **56B.**

☐ Two . . . . page **37C.**

☐ Three . . . . page **52C.**

☐ Four . . . . page **46C.**

34A   **Your answer is correct, but incomplete.** What would be the phenotype of offspring of parents whose genotypes were *AA* and *Aa*? _____. Return to page **41C**.

34B   **Incorrect.** Have you assigned the genotype *bb* to all of the Type O individuals in Classes VI, VII, VIII, and IX? _____. Have you assigned the genotype *Bb* to the parents of Class VII? _____. Have you assigned the genotype *BB* to the Type B parents of Class VIII? _____. For Classes VI and VII do you have both homozygous and heterozygous genotypes for the Type B offspring? _____. If you have answered no to any of these questions recheck the genotypes you have assigned for all of the individuals of Class I through Class IX. Then reanswer the question on page **30C**.

34C   **Incorrect.** Blood types are determined by making observations of the reaction of the blood. Any characteristic which can be observed directly or indirectly is a phenotype. Return to page **36A**.

From page **49B**.

34D   **Correct.** The predictions you made concerning possible types of offspring produced by Type AB individuals married to Type O individuals did not correspond with the kinds of offspring actually produced.

   Would this lack of production of Type AB and Type O individuals in these predicted classes of families lead you to question the hypothesis that the inheritance of blood groups is controlled by two pairs of genes?

☐ Yes......................................page   **50B.**

☐ No.......................................page   **52A.**

Incorrect. Study Table 1 of Worksheet 2-A and then start again   **35A**
from page **29**.

From page **30A**.

Correct. The class of families where parents had two contrasting   **35B**
phenotypes, but produced offspring who were like one of the parents,
gave evidence of the mode of inheritance of the trait, since a cross of
two individuals having homozygous genotypes for contrasting characteristics produces individuals with heterozygous genotypes but
expressing the dominant characteristic.

Another line of reasoning, based on the assumptions of the gene
theory, which might be used to determine the mode of inheritance of
two characteristics is: If both parents have the same phenotype and
produce an offspring having the contrasting characteristic, the gene
for that contrasting characteristic is recessive.

Which of the classes of families listed in Table 1 on Worksheet 2-A
would fit this particular kind of cross and thus give some evidence that
the gene for ability to taste PTC is dominant?

☐ Class I. . . . . .page   **43B.**

☐ Class II. . . . . .page   **36A.**

☐ Class V. . . . . .page   **32D.**

☐ None of these classes. . . . . .page   **40A.**

Incorrect. How could individuals with the genotype Aa or AA be   **35C**
produced by a cross of two individuals having the genotype aa? Where
could the gene A have come from? Return to page **38D**.

Incorrect. This situation is identical to the one involving determina-   **35D**
tion of dominance and recessiveness for the reaction to PTC. Return
to page **29** of this chapter and make sure you understand how dominance and recessiveness are determined by use of the family method,
before proceeding with blood type inheritance. Return to page **39C**.

From page 35B.

36A   **You are correct.** The fact that some parents who are tasters produce offspring who are nontasters would enable you to say that nontasting is caused by a recessive gene, even if the data on the other four classes were not given. These examples in relation to determination of dominance and recessiveness for the genes for tasting and nontasting of PTC illustrate the use of the family method of the study of inheritance.

In the study of blood groups in humans, the family method has been used extensively.

Individuals may be typed and classified on the basis of four substances contained in blood. Two of these substances, called **antigens,** are contained in red blood cells. The other two, called **antibodies,** are in the serum or liquid part of the blood in which the red cells float. One of the antigens has been named A, and if a person has this antigen in his red cells he is Type A. A Type B person has antigen B in his red cells. Some people have both antigens and hence have Type AB blood. Others have neither and are Type O.

The antibodies are in the serum. A person with antigen A in the red cells will have antibody b in the serum. And a person with antigen B will have antibody a in his serum. If antigen A comes in contact with antibody a the red blood cells clump. Also if antigen B comes in contact with antibody b the red blood cells clump. This clumping reaction is the basis of the tests for blood types.

Blood-group determinations have many medico-legal applications. Not only can blood groups be used in identifying babies inadvertently exchanged in hospitals and in legal cases of disputed parentage, they can also be used as a means of identification in criminal cases. In blood transfusions, to know the blood types of both donor and recipient is essential because some types of blood are incompatible; that is, one type will cause the clumping of the red cells of another. If this clumping occurs extensively during a transfusion, the recipient dies.

On the basis of blood tests people can be classified as belonging to one of the four possible A-B-O Types. These four blood types are: Type O, Type A, Type B, and Type AB.

Tests can be made by means of which the blood type of a person can be determined. While the determination of blood types is indirect, in the sense that a test must be made, the determination is made on the basis of observation.

The four blood groups, which have been named Type O, Type A, Type B, and Type AB, represent

☐ phenotypes. . . . . .page   **39C.**

☐ genotypes. . . . . .page   **31C.**

☐ both of these. . . . . .page   **33A.**

☐ neither of these. . . . . .page   **34C.**

Incorrect. If you have some other genotypes recorded you have made some serious error. Or did you forget that you had established that the gene for Type A was dominant to the gene for Type O? Check your Worksheet and correct any errors. Return to page **41C.**

37A

From page **31D.**

Satisfactory. Examine the data in Table 2 of Worksheet 2-A on families having Type B and Type O blood types.
    Which gene is dominant?

37B

☐ That for Type B.........................page   **30C.**

☐ That for Type O.........................page   **32B.**

Incorrect. Did you complete the crosses on page 45A? _____. If not, return to that page and do so. If you did complete the crosses, you discovered that the offspring that would be produced by each of these crosses were different. How many classes of families should there be when one parent is Type AB and the other Type O, provided the hypothesis that blood types are controlled by two pairs of alleles is correct? _____. Return to page **33B.**

37C

Incorrect. You assumed that some Type AB individuals should have the genotype *AaBb*. You predicted that if these individuals married Type O individuals four types of offspring should be produced: Type AB, Type A, Type B, and Type O. No Type AB nor Type O individuals are produced. Can you say that your predictions correspond to the actual facts? _____. Return to page **49B.**

37D

38A **Incorrect.** We have assumed in all cases that one gene of a pair comes from one parent and the other from the other parent. How could a Type A parent produce gametes containing the gene *B*? Return to page **47C**.

38B **Incorrect.** Study Table 1 of Worksheet 2-A and then start again from page **29**.

38C **Incorrect.** If Type AB individuals have both antigens, A and B, and if gene *A* is necessary for the production of antigen A and gene *B* is necessary for the production of antigen B, could Type AB individuals have gene *B* only? Return to page **40C**.

From page **42A**.

38D **Correct.** The genotypes of all of the Type O individuals would be *aa*. Did you assign two different genotypes to the Type A offspring in the families of Class II? _____. If not, you probably have forgotten that two parents with heterozygous genotypes produce offspring with genotypic ratios of 1:2:1, and hence a phenotypic ratio of 3:1. Correct your error, if you have made one.

On the basis of the genotypes that you have written, make a prediction concerning the phenotypes and the percentages of these phenotypes that would be produced by a cross between two Type O individuals.

☐ 75% Type A:25% Type O . . . . page **35C.**

☐ 50% Type A:50% Type O . . . . page **43D.**

☐ 100% Type O . . . . page **31D.**

Incorrect. Would persons with the genotype *TT* married to persons with the genotype *tt* produce any nontasting offspring? _____. Return to page **29**.

39A

This is a correct answer in some cases but not here since you did not follow directions. You were asked to use an *o* to represent the recessive gene. Return to page **54C**.

39B

From page **36A**.

You are correct. The blood types, called Type O, Type A, Type B, and Type AB, represent observable characteristics that are inherited. It is true that these characteristics are not directly observable and hence are not observable in the same way that flower color is in peas, nor as coat color in cattle and guinea pigs. However, recall that in determining the phenotypes of tasters and nontasters it was necessary to have the individuals chew a piece of PTC paper. This constituted a kind of chemical test. Similarly in determining the phenotypes of individuals with respect to blood groups, it is also necessary to make a test, because the blood type a person has depends on the presence or absence of chemical substances (antigens) in the blood corpuscles. Since the results of these tests are observable, the blood type of an individual is indirectly an observable characteristic.

39C

It is unfortunate for the student that the biologists who investigated blood types named these types by letters such as A, B, and O and also that they labeled the antigens by letters. The geneticist also uses letters A, B, etc., in symbolizing the genotypes for blood types of the various individuals. *These three sets of letters do not mean the same thing.* When the word "Type" is placed before the letter or letters, it always refers to the indirectly observable phenotype and not to a genotype. In our study of heredity we will not emphasize the names of the antigens and antibodies.

EXAMINE THE DATA PRESENTED IN TABLE 2 OF WORKSHEET 2-A from families having Type A and Type O blood. On the basis of these data which gene is dominant?

☐ The gene for Type A.......................page   **53B.**

☐ The gene for Type O.......................page   **30B.**

☐ There is lack of dominance..................page   **35D.**

40A   **How come?** Is there not one set of data where some of the offspring differ from both parents? ——————. Return to page **35B**.

40B   One definition of alleles is that they are genes for contrasting characteristics. The gene for tasting of PTC and the gene for the lack of this ability are alleles. Are not Type O and Type A bloods contrasting characteristics? ——————. Return to page **31D**.

From page **32C**.

40C   **Satisfactory.** By considering the inheritance of each of the blood types to be due to pairs of genes we were able to write genotypes for the classes of families (1) Type A × Type A, (2) Type O × Type O, and (3) Type A × Type O. We also were able to write genotypes for the parallel classes involving Type B and Type O. Thus the data presented so far can be explained by assuming two sets of single pairs of genes with dominance and recessiveness. Remember we will not be sure whether this assumption is correct or incorrect until we have tested some implications of this assumption.

We have assumed that gene A causes the production of antigen A, and hence the phenotype Type A. We also assumed that gene B causes the production of antigen B, and hence the phenotype Type B. We know on the basis of blood tests that Type O individuals do not have either antigen, A or B. Thus we assigned recessive genes (either a or b) to represent these genotypes.

On the basis of the above it is reasonable to assume that Type AB individuals, who have both antigens A and B

☐ have genes for production of antigen A only . . . . page   **42C.**

☐ have genes for production of antigen B only . . . . page   **38C.**

☐ have genes for production of both antigens A and B . . . . page   **45A.**

☐ have genes for the production of neither antigen A nor antigen B . . . . page   **31A.**

Incorrect. We have assumed in all cases that one gene of a pair comes from one parent and the other from the other parent. How could a Type B parent produce gametes containing the gene *A*? Return to page **47C**.

Incorrect. The two classes of individuals with homozygous genotypes would have the genotypes *TT* and *tt*. What would be the genotypes of offspring of parents with the genotype *TT* and the genotype *tt*? _____. What would be the phenotypes? _____. Return to page **29**.

From page **53B**.

Correct. The families of Class III give evidence that the gene for Type A blood is dominant to the gene for Type O, because all of the offspring of these crosses have Type A blood. Class II families also give evidence that the gene for Type A is dominant, since some Type O offspring are produced by crosses of Type A individuals.

If we assign the symbol *A* to represent the gene for Type A and the symbol *a* to represent the gene for Type O, what would be all of the possible genotypes for the parents and for the offspring in Classes I, II, III and IV? FILL IN THESE GENOTYPES AT THE PROPER PLACES ON WORKSHEET 2-A. (Reminder: More than one combination of genotypes may be possible.)

What genotypes did you record for the parents of Class I?

☐ *AA* × *AA* .... page   **34A.**

☐ *AA* × *Aa* .... page   **30D.**

☐ Both of these .... page   **42A.**

☐ Neither of these .... page   **37A.**

From page 41C.

42A **Correct.** The Type A parents who have only Type A offspring might both have homozygous genotypes, or one might have a homozygous genotype and the other might have a heterozygous genotype.

Do you have the same genotype recorded for all of the Type O individuals?

☐ Yes......................................page   **38D.**

☐ No.......................................page   **49C.**

42B **Incorrect.** One definition of alleles is that they are genes for contrasting characteristics. The gene for tasting of PTC and the gene for the lack of this ability are alleles. Are not Type O and Type A bloods contrasting characteristics? _____. Return to page **31D.**

42C **Incorrect.** If Type AB individuals have both antigens, A and B, and if gene *A* is necessary for the production of antigen A and gene *B* is necessary for the production of antigen B, could Type AB individuals have gene *A* only? Return to page **40C.**

42D **Why not?** Scientists are obliged to abandon hypotheses and seek new ones when data and predictions conflict. You found a conflict. You have agreed to give up the hypothesis that A, B, O blood types are controlled by two pairs of genes — so now you are obliged to substitute another hypothesis. You may feel that, because you had assigned the symbol *a* to a gene in one case and the symbol *b* in the other case, these must be different genes. It is essential to keep in mind that these are only symbols, and that you have assigned them. Return to page **48B.**

43A

Incorrect. Alleles can be defined as genes for contrasting characteristics. Are not Type A and Type O contrasting characteristics? Return to page **53A**.

43B

Incorrect. Suppose you did not know which characteristic, ability to taste PTC or lack of this ability, was due to a dominant gene. All of the offspring of Class I are like their parents. Could these be the genotypes? *tt* × *tt* _____. Could these be the genotypes?

$$tt$$

TT × *TT* _____. Does the knowledge that the parents are

$$TT$$

like the offspring give a clue to which gene is dominant? _____.
Return to page **35B**.

From page **52B**.

43C

Correct. An individual with the genotype *AB* should be a Type AB individual.

We have already established that the gene for Type A is dominant to the gene for Type O and also that the gene for Type B is dominant to the gene for Type O. What is the relationship with respect to dominance of genes *A* and *B*?

☐ *A* is dominant to *B* ....page **54D.**

☐ *B* is dominant to *A* ....page **44C.**

☐ Neither *A* nor *B* is dominant to the other ......page **51B.**

43D

Incorrect. How could individuals with the genotype *Aa* or *AA* be produced by a cross of two individuals having the genotype *aa*? Where could the gene *A* have come from? Return to page **38D**.

44A   **Correct but incomplete.** Return to page **56A**.

From page **48B**.

44B   **Correct.** The assumption that only one kind of gene is involved in Type O inheritance is an alternate hypothesis. Whether it is an adequate hypothesis can only be determined by making predictions from it and determining whether these predictions correspond to the data. If there is but one pair of genes, and not two pairs, involved in the production of a Type O individual, then we have assigned two different symbols, a and b, to the same gene. Let us assume that there is only one kind of gene for Type O, assign a single symbol to it, and see if we can develop an explanation that will fit the data. Let us use the symbol o. Thus the genotype for a Type O individual would be oo.

Notice that in using the symbol o for the recessive gene we have departed from the traditional method of designating genes, namely the capital and lower case of a single letter. Since the symbols for genes are purely arbitrary and a matter of convenience, such deviations from the traditional pattern are employed when they clarify the meaning.

Recall that we previously wrote the genotype Aa for a Type A individual with a heterozygous genotype. On the basis of the new symbol for the gene for Type O, how should the genotype of such an individual be written?

☐ Ao . . . . .page   **54C.**

☐ $Aooo$ . . . . .page   **49A.**

44C   **Incorrect.** If A were dominant to B, then individuals with the genotype AB would be Type A individuals, or if B were dominant to A, then individuals with the genotype AB would be Type B individuals. There would be no combination which could produce Type AB individuals. What assumption can you make about the relationship of the gene A to the gene B which would produce a Type AB phenotype? _____. Return to page **43C**.

From page **40C.**

Satisfactory. It is reasonable to assume that Type AB individuals have genes for production of both antigen A and antigen B.

Families in which one parent is Type A and the other Type B have children some of which are Type AB. If we assume that the Type AB children are the result of the combination of gene *A* from the Type A parent and the gene *B* from the Type B parent it might be possible to explain the inheritance of all four blood types as due to two pairs of alleles *A*, *a* and *B*, *b*. Let us follow the consequences of this hypothesis to see if it explains the data. If this hypothesis is correct, the genotype of a Type AB individual could be *AABB*, *AABb*, *AaBB*, or *AaBb*. Type A genotypes could be *AAbb* or *Aabb*. Type O individuals would have the genotype *aabb*.

On the basis of the hypothesis that the A, B, O blood types are controlled by two pairs of alleles, *A* and *a* and *B* and *b*, one can predict the number of *expected* classes of families that could be produced in crosses where one parent is Type AB and the other parent is Type O. In order to make such a prediction, consider the possible types of offspring and the percent of each that could be produced by each of the following crosses. COMPLETE THE FOLLOWING TABLE.

Type AB	Type O	EXPECTED GENOTYPES OF OFFSPRING	EXPECTED PHENOTYPES OF OFFSPRING
AABB ×	*aabb*		
AABb ×	*aabb*		
AaBB ×	*aabb*		
AaBb ×	*aabb*		

If the genotypes of the parents were *AaBB* and *aabb* the genotypic ratio of the children should be 1 *AaBb* : 1 *aaBb*. Therefore _____% of the offspring should be Type AB and _____% would be Type B.

If the genotypes of the parents were *AABB* and *aabb* what proportion of the children should be Type AB?

☐ 50% . . . . .page   **47A.**

☐ 75% . . . . .page   **51C.**

☐ 100% . . . . .page   **33B.**

46A This is not an unreasonable response if it is assumed that gene B is dominant to gene A, but if this were the case how could one explain the presence in the population of Type AB individuals? What is the other possibility? _____. Return to page **52B**.

46B Incorrect. Think about the relation of genes to chromosomes. We have observed that chromosomes occur in pairs. We have assumed that genes are paired and that alleles are on homologous chromosomes.

Which of the two following statements would be more consistent with the theory we have developed thus far? (1) There are three homologous chromosomes instead of two in each individual. (2) Any one person would have only two of the three possible kinds of chromosomes. _____. Return to page **54A**.

From page **33B**.

46C Good. If the hypothesis that blood types are controlled by two pairs of genes were correct, you would expect that in families in which one parent was Type AB and the other was Type O, the offspring could be grouped into four classes. If the genotype of the Type AB parent were $AABB$ you would expect 100% Type AB offspring. If the genotype of the Type AB parent were $AABb$ or $AaBB$, you would expect 50% of the offspring to be Type AB in each case, and the other 50% to be Type A or Type B depending upon the genotype of the Type AB parent. In families in which one parent is Type O and the other is Type AB and the Type AB parent had the genotype $AaBb$, _____% should be Type AB, _____% should be Type A, _____% should be Type B, _____% should be Type O.

Thus on the basis of assuming that two pairs of genes are involved in the inheritance of blood types in all of the four predicted classes, there should be some children with Type AB blood. If this hypothesis were correct, should some Type AB individuals married to Type O individuals produce Type O offspring?

☐ Yes . . . . page **49B.**

☐ No . . . . page **32A.**

Incorrect. If the Type O individual had the genotype *aabb* he could **47A** produce but one kind of gamete with respect to blood type, *ab*. How many kinds of gametes could a person produce if his genotype were *AABB*? _____. How many kinds of offspring could be produced? _____. What blood type would they be? _____. Return to page **45A**.

You have made some error in calculations. Return to page **56C** so **47B** that you can compare Table 4 with Worksheet 2-B. Compare the genotypes you have recorded for the parents on the Worksheet with the genotypes in Table 4. Are they the same? _____. If not, correct the errors and recalculate the genotypic ratios for the offspring. If you made no errors in recording the genotypes of the parents, compare the genotypic ratios you calculated with those in Table 4. Are they the same? _____. If not, recalculate them. If they are the same your error was in translating genotypic ratios to phenotypic ratios.

From page **53A**.

Correct. The genes *A* and *o* are alleles but the gene *o* is also an allele **47C** of the gene *B*.

Assume that an individual with a genotype heterozygous for Type A (*Ao*) married someone with the genotype *Bo*. What types of gametes, with respect to blood type, would the Type A individual produce? _____; the Type B individual? _____. If a gamete containing the gene *A* united with one containing the gene *B* what would be the genotype of the offspring?

☐ *AA* ....page **41A**.

☐ *AB* ....page **52B**.

☐ *BB* ....page **38A**.

48A   Correct but incomplete. Return to page **53A.**

From page **50B.**

48B   **Correct.** The hypothesis that the A, B, O blood types are controlled by two pairs of genes had to be discarded because prediction from this hypothesis did not correspond to the data.

You may question the value of presenting an explanation for the inheritance of blood types that turned out to be inadequate and so had to be discarded. The reason for doing so is to impress upon you that scientific explanations may change and that these changes are a legitimate and necessary part of the growth of scientific understanding. All scientific explanations are not equally good. Some are the best possible in light of the available data, but they may be changed as more data become known. All scientific explanations are at best only approximations of truth and never absolute in the sense of absolute certainty. Thus all scientific theories are in some degree tentative and subject to change as more facts become known. The best theories hold a sufficient degree of truth to persist even though changed. Some theories, however, are found to be totally inadequate to account for new knowledge and these are then discarded and replaced if better explanations can be invented.

In order to discover a reasonable alternative explanation of the inheritance of blood types let us go back over the reasoning which led us to assume two pairs of genes. Recall that for the classes of families where the parents were Type A and Type O we explained the data by assuming a gene A for Type A and its recessive allele a for Type O. Also in families where the parents were Type B and Type O we assumed that the gene B caused the phenotype Type B and the gene b caused Type O. Thus we assigned two different symbols to the genes which presumably controlled the Type O phenotype. These were genes a and b.

Since the phenotypes of all Type O individuals are the same, is it reasonable to assume that only one kind of gene causes the development of the Type O phenotype?

☐ Yes . . . . page   **44B.**

☐ No . . . . page   **42D.**

Incorrect. You have retained the original hypothesis of two pairs
of genes and have substituted an *o* for *a* and for *bb*, as if *Aabb* = *Aooo*.
Return to page **44B.**

49A

From page **46C.**

Satisfactory. If the hypothesis we have accepted were correct, then
we would expect that some Type AB individuals married to Type O
individuals would have Type O offspring.

Remember that you have tentatively accepted the hypothesis that
there are two pairs of genes which control the phenotype with respect
to A, B, O blood groups. On this basis you predicted four classes of
families, and you predicted that there would be some offspring with
Type AB blood in each of the four classes. These were predictions.
To test any hypothesis the predictions must be compared with the
data. The data are: In all families where one parent is Type AB and
the other Type O, there are but two types of offspring. Some of the
offspring are Type A, some are Type B; no Type O and no Type AB
individuals are ever produced in those families where one parent is
Type AB and the other is Type O. Do these data correspond to your
predictions or are they contradictory to your predictions?

☐ They correspond to predictions..............page   **37D.**

☐ They do not correspond to predictions.......page   **34D.**

49B

Incorrect. You have discovered that the gene for Type A is dominant
to the gene for Type O, and you were directed to use *A* for the gene
for Type A and *a* for the gene for Type O, so the genotype of a Type O
person could neither be *AA* nor *Aa*. If it were *AA* or *Aa* the individual
would have Type A blood. Did you forget to assign two genes to each
individual? _____. If so, correct your error and reanswer the
question on page **42A.**

49C

Incorrect. Although there are four phenotypes, was it necessary to
assume a separate kind of gene for the Type AB individual? _____.
Return to page **51B.**

49D

50A **Correct but incomplete.** Return to page **53A**.

From page **34D**.

50B **Correct.** The lack of correspondence between the prediction from the hypothesis and the data obtained from family histories led scientists to question the hypothesis that two pairs of genes were involved in the production of the antigens which caused the various blood types. So, the problem was "How are blood types inherited?"

Outstanding geneticists struggled with this problem for a number of years. One of the reasons why it was difficult to decide on an adequate explanation for the inheritance of blood types was the inadequacy of the data. Although data on Type A and Type O crosses were plentiful, data on families where one or both parents were Type B or Type AB were not plentiful. The reason for this is that very few people have Type B blood, and even fewer have Type AB blood.

Since the classification of the family matings is made on the basis of the kinds of offspring produced, records from many families were required before classes could be established. So, when only a few records were available for families where one parent was Type AB and the other parent Type O, it could have been assumed that the lack of Type AB and Type O offspring was due to the small sample.

However, when adequate data were available it was found that there was but one class of families where one parent was Type AB and the other was Type O; not four classes as would be the case if two pairs of genes were involved. In this one class of families all of the offspring were either Type A or Type B. The ratio of Type A to Type B among the offspring was 1:1. ENTER THESE DATA ON WORK-SHEET 2-A:

Class	Parents	Offspring
X	Type AB × Type O	50% Type A, 50% Type B

There were never any Type AB offspring nor were there even any Type O offspring as would have been expected in such crosses if two pairs of alleles were involved. Therefore, the hypothesis that blood groups were determined by two pairs of alleles had to be discarded because

☐ the data were not adequate or the data were inaccurate...................................page **53C.**

☐ predictions from the hypothesis did not corre-spond with the data.......................page **48B.**

From page **43C**.

51B

Correct. The assumption that the genes A and B each cause the production of an antigen when present in one individual, that is, that neither is dominant, explains the presence of individuals who have Type AB blood.

How many different kinds of genes are involved in the inheritance of the A, B, AB, O blood types?

☐ Two . . . . .page   **52D.**

☐ Three . . . . .page   **54A.**

☐ Four . . . . .page   **49D.**

51C

Incorrect. If the Type O individual had the genotype *aabb* he could produce but one kind of gamete with respect to blood type, *ab*. How many kinds of gametes could a person produce if his genotype were *AABB*? _____. How many kinds of offspring could be produced? _____. What blood type would they be? _____.
Return to page **45A**.

51D

Incorrect. You have forgotten, or ignored, one assumption of the gene theory that we have used since the first chapter. Do we assume that genes occur singly or in pairs? _____. Return to page **54A**.

52A **Why not?** The structure of science is built upon the idea of prediction from a hypothesis. If the observations do not correspond with the prediction from the hypothesis one starts questioning, first the observations, then the reasonableness of the prediction, and finally the hypothesis itself. Return to page **34D**.

From page 47C.

52B **Correct.** Since half of the gametes produced by an individual with the genotype *Ao* should contain the gene *A* and half of the gametes produced by an individual having the genotype *Bo* would contain the gene *B*, the genotype of some of the offspring should be *AB*. If the genotype of an individual is *AB* what would you expect the phenotype to be?

☐ Type A.................................page   **54B.**

☐ Type B.................................page   **46A.**

☐ Type AB................................page   **43C.**

52C **Incorrect.** Did you complete the crosses on page 45A? _____.
If not, return to that page and do so. If you did complete the crosses, you discovered that the offspring that would be produced by each of these crosses were different. How many classes of families should there be when one parent is Type AB and the other Type O, provided the hypothesis that blood types are controlled by two pairs of alleles is correct? Return to page **33B**.

52D **Incorrect.** We have assumed one gene for Type A, the gene *A*; one gene for Type O, the gene *o*; there is also a Type B. We have symbolized the gene for this as *B*. Return to page **51B**.

From page **54C.**

Correct. The genotype of an individual with a genotype heterozygous   **53A**
for Type B blood would be symbolized as *Bo*, if the symbol *o* is used to
represent the recessive gene. A Type A individual could have the genotype *AA* or *Ao*, a Type B individual the genotype *BB* or *Bo*, and a
Type O individual would have the genotype *oo*.
   Which of the following are alleles?

☐ *A* and *o* . . . . .page   **48A.**

☐ *B* and *o* . . . . .page   **50A.**

☐ Both of these . . . . .page   **47C.**

☐ Neither of these . . . . .page   **43A.**

From page **39C.**

Correct. You were able to determine that the gene for Type A is   **53B**
dominant to the gene for Type O.
   Which of the classes of families in Table 2 gave this evidence?

☐ Classes I and III . . . . .page   **38B.**

☐ Classes II and III . . . . .page   **41C.**

☐ Classes II and IV . . . . .page   **31B.**

☐ Classes I and IV . . . . .page   **35A.**

Incorrect. The data were inadequate at first, therefore the hypothesis   **53C**
that two pairs of genes controlled blood types could be entertained,
but eventually sufficient accurate data were collected to indicate that
no Type AB nor Type O individuals were produced in crosses where
one parent was Type O and the other Type AB. Return to page **50B.**

From page **51B.**

54A **You are correct.** We have now assumed that there are three genes involved. These are *A*, *B*, and *o*.

How many of these three genes may be present in any one individual?

☐ One.....................................page **51D.**

☐ Two.....................................page **56A.**

☐ Three...................................page **46B.**

54B This is not an unreasonable response if it is assumed that gene *A* is dominant to gene *B*, but if this were the case how could one explain the presence in the population of Type AB individuals? What is the other possibility? _____. Return to page **52B.**

From page **44B.**

54C **You are correct.** The genotype for a Type A individual with a heterozygous genotype would be *Ao* on the basis of the assumption that there is only one kind of gene which is recessive. Type O individuals would have the homozygous genotype *oo*. What would be the genotype of an individual with Type B blood whose genotype was heterozygous for this trait?

☐ *Bo*.....................................page **53A.**

☐ *Bb*.....................................page **39B.**

54D **Incorrect.** If *A* were dominant to *B*, then individuals with the genotype *AB* would be Type A individuals, or if *B* were dominant to *A*, then individuals with the genotype *AB* would be Type B individuals. There would be no combination which could produce Type AB individuals. What assumption can you make about the relationship of the gene *A* to the gene *B* which would produce a Type AB phenotype? _____. Return to page **43C.**

_____. Return to page **32C**.

From page **56A**.

Correct. The genes *A*, *B*, and *o* are all alleles. Notice that we have   **55B** introduced a new concept concerning the relations of genes to each other. Prior to this we had assumed that for paired genes there were only two alleles, such as *A* and *a*. Now we discover that there may be more than two different genes involved in forming single pairs. Where any characteristic is controlled by three or more different genes that occur in various combinations of pairs, the alleles involved in the combinations are called **multiple alleles.**

The concept of multiple alleles requires that we conceive of genes as being present in populations of organisms. Among individuals in human populations the three alleles for blood types are contained as paired genes; thus some genotypes will be *AB*, some *Ao*, some *AA*, etc. While there are three different genes available in a population, we assume that only two of the three are present in any one person.

Some characteristics in organisms have multiple alleles consisting of more than three genes. For example, in Drosophila the eye-color trait has at least 14 different genes which are alleles.

Recall that at first we had assumed that two pairs of alleles were involved in blood type inheritance. This hypothesis led to conflict between predictions and data. In order to discover whether the alternate hypothesis of multiple alleles is adequate, COMPLETE TABLE 3 ON WORKSHEET 2-B. This table is partially filled out. At the top are headings indicating what is to be filled in under the headings. In the left-hand column are given a total of ten different matings of various blood types. The second column contains spaces where you are to fill in the possible genotypes of the parents. The genotypes that you have already determined have been entered in Table 3. For example, the first cross, Type A × Type A, is represented by three different genotypes. FOR EACH CROSS FILL IN THE POSSIBLE GENOTYPES. IN EACH CASE RECORD THE HOMOZYGOUS PARENTS AS THE FIRST PAIR OF GENOTYPES. RECORD THE HETEROZYGOUS POSSIBILITIES AS THE SECOND AND THIRD. IN THE THIRD COLUMN FILL IN THE GENOTYPES AND THE RATIOS OF GENOTYPES OF THE OFFSPRING. IN THE LAST FOUR COLUMNS RECORD THE PERCENTAGES OF THE VARIOUS POSSIBLE PHENOTYPES OF THE OFFSPRING. When you have completed this table turn to page **56C**.

From page **54A**.

56A **Correct.** There would be two genes for this trait in each individual. Alleles are more precisely defined as genes that always segregate at meiosis. On the basis of this definition, which of the genes A, B, and o are alleles?

☐ Only A and B . . . . .page   **44A.**

☐ Only A and o, and B and o . . . . .page   **51A.**

☐ All three genes A, B, and o are alleles . . . . .page   **55B.**

56B **Incorrect.** Did you complete the crosses on page **45A**? _____. If not, return to that page and do so. If you did complete the crosses, you discovered that the offspring that would be produced by each of these crosses were different. How many classes of families should there be when one parent is Type AB and the other Type O, provided the hypothesis that blood types are controlled by two pairs of alleles is correct? _____. Return to page **33B**.

56C From page **55B**.

COMPARE TABLE 3 ON WORKSHEET 2-B WITH TABLE 4, NEXT PAGE.

In making the comparison of the genotypes you have recorded for the parents with those in Table 4, you will probably find that you have not used exactly the same order of genotypes. If you followed directions, however, they should correspond quite closely. Check the predicted ratio of phenotypes of offspring with the data that have been obtained in actual crosses.

Does the hypothesis of multiple alleles produce results which correspond with the data?

☐ Yes . . . . .page   **58A.**

☐ No . . . . .page   **47B.**

TABLE 4

Blood Type of Parents	Genotypes of Parents	Genotype Ratios of Offspring	Observed Percentages of Phenotypes of Offspring			
			Type A	Type B	Type AB	Type O
A × A	AA × AA	All AA	100	0	0	0
	Ao × AA	1AA:1Ao	100	0	0	0
	Ao × Ao	1AA:2Ao:1oo	75	0	0	25
B × B	BB × BB	All BB	0	100	0	0
	Bo × BB	1BB:1Bo	0	100	0	0
	Bo × Bo	1BB:2Bo:1oo	0	75	0	25
O × O	oo × oo	All oo	0	0	0	100
AB × AB	AB × AB	1AA:2AB:1BB	25	25	50	0
A × O	AA × oo	All Ao	100	0	0	0
	Ao × oo	1Ao:1oo	50	0	0	50
A × B	AA × BB	All AB	0	0	100	0
	AA × Bo	1AB:1Ao	50	0	50	0
	Ao × BB	1AB:1Bo	0	50	50	0
	Ao × Bo	1AB:1Ao:1Bo:1oo	25	25	25	25
A × AB	AA × AB	1AA:1AB	50	0	50	0
	Ao × AB	1AB:1AA:1Ao:1Bo	50	25	25	0
B × O	BB × oo	All Bo	0	100	0	0
	Bo × oo	1Bo:1oo	0	50	0	50
B × AB	BB × AB	1BB:1AB	0	50	50	0
	Bo × AB	1BB:1AB:1Bo:1Ao	25	50	25	0
O × AB	oo × AB	1Ao:1Bo	50	50	0	0

From page 56C.

58A   **Good.** This is the end of Part I. Continue with the review.

REVIEW—Chapter 2, Part I

Individuals can have any one of four blood types: Type A, Type B, Type O, or Type AB. These blood types are (*genotypes, phenotypes*) _____. The inheritance of blood types is assumed to be controlled by (#) _____ genes; any one individual, however, can have only (#) _____ of these genes. This situation where there are more than two alleles is called (*wds*) _____ inheritance. The genotype of a Type A individual can be (*lts*) _____ or (*lts*) _____. The genotype of a Type B individual could be (*lts*) _____ or (*lts*) _____. All Type O individuals would have the genotype (*lts*) _____ and all of the Type AB individuals would have the genotype (*lts*) _____. There are (#) _____ classes of families where both parents are Type A, those that produce all Type (*lt*) _____ individuals and those that produce both Type A individuals and Type (*lt*) _____ individuals. The offspring of two Type O parents would be Type (*lt*) _____. If one parent is Type O and the other is Type AB, (#) _____ types of offspring can be produced; they are: (*wds*) _____.

To check your responses to the review of Part I, turn to page 356 and then continue with the summary.

SUMMARY—Chapter 2, Part I

In the investigation of blood groups the family method was used. This method involved the collection of data concerning parents and offspring of human families, the determination of dominance and recessiveness of contrasting characteristics on the basis of the appearance of the contrasting phenotypes in the parents and children of specific families.

On the basis of the family method it was discovered that the gene for Type A blood was dominant to the gene for Type O, and that the gene for Type B also was dominant to the gene for Type O. We attempted to explain the inheritance of blood groups by assuming that two pairs of genes were involved, one of the pair determining Type A with the recessive allele determining Type O. Another gene presumably determined Type B blood and its recessive allele determined Type O. Thus, according to this scheme, gene A caused Type A blood, gene B caused Type B blood, while their respective alleles a and b each caused Type O blood. According to this scheme Type AB blood would result when any combinations of A and B genes occurred, such as $AABB$, $AABb$, $AaBB$, and $AaBb$. From such a scheme we would expect that at least some crosses between Type AB individuals and Type O individuals would produce children having Type O. No such families were ever discovered. In fact only Type A and Type B offspring were produced.

An alternate hypothesis was presented that blood groups were controlled by three different genes (multiple alleles). Thus gene A caused Type A blood, gene B caused Type B blood while gene o, recessive to both A and B, caused Type O blood. The combination AB would produce Type AB. The combinations AA and Ao would produce Type A and the combinations BB and Bo would produce Type B blood. This scheme of multiple alleles satisfied all of the data from human families and is accepted as the correct explanation of inheritance of blood groups.

Continue with Part II of Chapter 2.

60A   In addition to the presence or absence of the various antigens related to the A, B, O blood types, other antigens may be present in the red blood cells. One of these is the Rh factor. Since its discovery in 1939 the Rh factor has been the subject of much research and of much general interest.

In addition to being classified as Type AB, A, B, or O, people also are classified as being either Type Rh positive (Rh+) or Type Rh negative (Rh−). Thus a person could be Type A, Rh+ or Type A, Rh−. The 85% of the population who are Type Rh+ have an antigen present in their red cells. The 15% who are Type Rh− lack this antigen. While several antigens are involved in making persons Type Rh positive, one particular Rh antigen accounts for 95% of the Type Rh positive group. In the following discussion of Rh blood-type inheritance we will limit ourselves to this major Rh antigen, which can be detected in human blood by observation of results of a chemical test.

Which of the following represents a phenotype and not a genotype?

☐ Type Rh+ . . . . .page   **63A.**

☐ Type Rh− . . . . .page   **64D.**

☐ Both . . . . .page   **66B.**

☐ Neither . . . . .page   **68C.**

60B   **Incorrect.** How many different genotypes can individuals who are Type Rh+ have? _____. Individuals who are Type Rh− all have the genotype *rr*. Then how many types of crosses are there between Type Rh+ and Type Rh− individuals? Return to page **68A.**

60C   **Incorrect.** You apparently assigned the genotype *BoRr* to the woman. This was correct, but how about the man? From his phenotype you could write *A?R?*. Could it be *AoRr*? _____. Return to page **64B.**

Correct but incomplete. Return to page **65A**.   **61A**

From page **62B**.

What is your solution to the problem?   **61B**

☐ This child could not have been the offspring of
either this man or this woman . . . . page   **70B**.

☐ This woman could have been the mother but
the man could not have been the father . . . . . . page   **64C**.

☐ This man could have been the father but this
woman could not have been the mother . . . . . . page   **67C**.

☐ This child could have been the offspring of this
man and this woman . . . . page   **69A**.

You are partially correct. One of these individuals could be the   **61C**
parent of this child, but you can be more specific. Could the man be
the father? _____ . Could the woman be the mother? _____ .
Return to page **67B**.

From page **66B**.

Correct. The gene for Type Rh+ is dominant to the gene for Type   **61D**
Rh−. Use R for the gene for Type Rh+ and r for the gene for
Type Rh−.
What would be the genotype of Type Rh− individuals?

☐ Rh− . . . . page   **67A**.

☐ Rr . . . . page   **64A**.

☐ rr . . . . page   **70A**.

62A   **Correct but incomplete.** Return to page 65A.

From page **68A.**

62B   **Correct.** There would be two classes of families in marriages between Type Rh+ and Type Rh− individuals. These would be either *RR* × *rr* or *Rr* × *rr*.

As was mentioned in the introduction, knowledge of inheritance of blood types is often important in legal cases. The following is an example of a case of disputed parentage. A couple might claim that babies had been switched in a hospital. Suppose that the man was Type A and Type Rh+ and the woman was Type B and Type Rh+ and the child was Type O and Type Rh−. If you were on a jury, what decision would you make concerning whether this child could be the offspring of this man and woman?

If you can solve the problem and can reach a decision on this case without help, do so and then turn to page **61B.** If you need help in the solution of this problem, continue.

In order to solve the problem concerning the parentage of the child it would be necessary to establish possible genotypes for all of the individuals.

What is the genotype of the child?

☐ *ooRr* . . . . .page   **66C.**

☐ *oorr* . . . . .page   **64B.**

☐ It cannot be determined completely from the
data given . . . . .page   **68D.**

62C   **Incorrect.** What genotypes do you have assigned for the man and the woman? _____. Could the man have the genotype *AoRr*? _____. Could the woman have the genotype *BoRr*? _____. Could these individuals produce a child with the genotype *oorr*? _____. Return to page **64B.**

Incorrect. Could not some other man and woman with the same   **63B** phenotypes or even with some other phenotype have produced this child, for example, two Type O, Type Rh— individuals? _____. Return to page **69A**.

From page **67B**.

Correct. A man having the Type AB and Type Rh— blood and a   **63C** woman having Type O and Type Rh + blood could not produce a child who had Type AB blood, since all of the gametes produced by the mother would contain the gene *o*. But a woman of Type A, or Type B, or Type AB and Rh + married to this man could have produced a child who was Type AB and Type Rh +. Therefore the man could theoretically have been the father.

Now consider the data which follow the key.

KEY

A. The child could be the offspring of this man and this woman.
B. This woman could be the mother of the child but the man could not be the father.
C. The man could be the father of the child, but the woman could not be the mother.
D. One of the individuals could be the parent but not both.
E. Neither of these individuals could be the parent of this child.

In each of the following cases select your answer from the key and record it in the right-hand column.

MAN	WOMAN	CHILD	Answer from Key
a. Type A, Type Rh+	Type O, Type Rh+	Type O, Type Rh—	_____
b. Type O, Type Rh—	Type O, Type Rh—	Type O, Type Rh+	_____
c. Type AB, Type Rh+	Type AB, Type Rh+	Type O, Type Rh+	_____

Turn to page **70D** to check your answers.

64A **Incorrect.** The gene for Type Rh− is recessive to the gene for Type Rh+. An *Rr* individual would exhibit the dominant phenotype. Is Rh+ or Rh− dominant? What would be the genotype of an Rh− individual? _____. Return to page **61D**.

From page **62B**.

64B **Correct.** The child's genotype would be *oorr*. The man was Type A and Type Rh+; the woman was Type B and Type Rh+. You can write part of the genotypes of these two individuals on the basis of their phenotypes. ASSIGN TO THE MAN AND TO THE WOMAN ONE GENE FOR EACH OF THE TWO TRAITS (A, B, O TYPE AND RH TYPE) ON THE BASIS OF THEIR PHENOTYPES.

$$\text{— — — —} \times \text{— — — —}$$
Child *oorr*

To determine whether these individuals could be the parents of this child, attempt to complete the genotypes of the two parents assuming that this is their child.

Now what decision would you make if you were on the jury?

☐ The child could be the offspring of this man
and this woman . . . . page **69A.**

☐ This woman could be the mother of the child
but the man could not be the father . . . . page **60C.**

☐ The man could be the father but the woman
could not be the mother . . . . page **66D.**

☐ Neither could be the parent . . . . page **62C.**

64C You jumped to a hasty conclusion. Go back to page **62B** and answer the question "What is the genotype of the child?"

64D **Correct but incomplete.** Return to page **60A**.

From page **70A.**

Correct. In marriages between two Type Rh− individuals all of the **65A** offspring should have Type Rh− blood.

What would be a possible genotype of the individuals who are Type Rh+?

☐ *Rr*..page **62A.**

☐ *RR*..page **61A.**

☐ Both of these............................page **68A.**

Incorrect. How many different genotypes can individuals who are **65B** Type Rh+ have? _____. Individuals who are Type Rh− all have the genotype *rr*. Then how many types of crosses are there between Type Rh+ and Type Rh− individuals? Return to page **68A.**

Incorrect. Can the characteristics of parents be recessive when both **65C** are the same (Rh+) and the combination of both parents produces offspring having the contrasting characteristic (Rh−)? _____. Two nontasters (*tt* × *tt*) cannot produce offspring having the gene *T*. Return to page **66B.**

Incorrect. With respect to the O, A, B blood types the woman's **65D** genotype would be *oo*. Therefore the offspring would have to have at least one gene which is (*A*, *B*, *o*) _____. Can a Type O individual ever produce a Type AB offspring? _____. Return to page **67B.**

66A   **Incorrect.** You have stated that the genotype of Type Rh− individuals would be rr. What kind of offspring would a cross between two Type Rh negative individuals produce, that is, $rr \times rr$? _____ . Return to page **70A**.

From page **60A**.

66B   **Correct.** In some marriages between two Type Rh + individuals all of the offspring are Type Rh+, while in other marriages of two Type Rh + individuals 75% of the offspring are Type Rh + and 25% are Type Rh −.

Which is controlled by a dominant gene?

☐ Type Rh +................................page   **61D.**

☐ Type Rh −................................page   **65C.**

☐ Neither................................page   **68B.**

66C   **No.** The child is Type O and Type Rh−. Both of these are recessive. What blood type with respect to Rh would the child have if it had the genotype Rr? _____ . Return to page **62B**.

66D   **Incorrect.** You apparently assigned the genotype $AoRr$ to the man. This was correct, but how about the woman? From her phenotype you could write $B?R?$. Could it be $BoRr$? _____ . Return to page **64B**.

Incorrect. Rh− represents a phenotype, not a genotype. Return to **67A** page **61D**.

From page **69A**.

You are correct. Although these two individuals could have been **67B** the parents of this child, it does not follow that they are the parents. Some other pair of individuals might have been the parents. Suppose that in this case where two children were suspected of being changed in the hospital the other possible parents were both Type O and Type Rh−. This child could equally well have been theirs. Knowledge of blood group inheritance is, however, useful in cases where the evidence indicates that an individual could *not* have been the parent of that child.

Now consider a situation in which the man is Type AB and Type Rh− while the woman is Type O and Type Rh+. If the child were Type AB and Type Rh+, what conclusion could you draw concerning the possible relationship of this child to this man and this woman? Could the man be the father? _____. Could the woman be the mother? _____.

☐ The child could be the offspring of this man
and this woman...........................page **70C.**

☐ This woman could be the mother of the child
but the man could not be the father.........page **65D.**

☐ The man could be the father of the child, but
the woman could not be the mother.........page **63C.**

☐ One of the individuals could be the parent
but not both..............................page **61C.**

☐ Neither the man nor the woman could be a
parent of this child........................page **69B.**

You jumped to a hasty conclusion. Go back to page 62B and answer **67C** the question "What is the genotype of the child?"

From page **65A**.

68A   **Correct.** Individuals having Rh+ blood types could have the genotype *RR* or the genotype *Rr*.

   In marriages between Type Rh+ (*RR* or *Rr*) and Type Rh− (*rr*)
individuals how many classes of families should there be?

☐ One . . . . page   **65B.**

☐ Two . . . . page   **62B.**

☐ Four . . . . page   **60B.**

68B   **Incorrect.** Can the characteristics of parents be recessive when both
are the same (Rh+) and the combination of both parents produces
offspring having the contrasting characteristic (Rh−)? _____.
Two nontasters (*tt* × *tt*) cannot produce offspring having the gene *T*.
Return to page **66B**.

68C   **Incorrect.** The symbols Rh+ and Rh− refer to the reaction of the
blood of the individual to certain chemical substances. Tasting of
PTC was also a phenotype which could not be "seen" but which
represents a reaction to a chemical substance. Phenotype refers to
characteristics of the individual which are directly or indirectly
observable. Rh blood types can be established without any reference
to heredity or genetic makeup. Return to page **60A**.

68D   **Incorrect.** Have you forgotten that the genes for both Type O and
Type Rh− are recessive? If an individual exhibits the recessive
characteristic it is always possible to write the genotype on the basis
of the phenotype. Return to page **62B**.

From page **61B** or **64B**.

You are correct. This man and this woman could have been the   **69A**
parents of the child.

On the basis of the phenotypes given for the man and the woman
you could write

$$A?R? \times B?R?$$

The genotype of the child was *oorr* because the genes for both Type O
and Type Rh − are recessive. All of these genes of the child could have
come from these two parents, as follows:

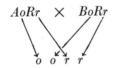

Does the above mean that these two people were necessarily the
parents of this child?

☐ Yes...................................page   **63B.**

☐ No....................................page   **67B.**

Incorrect. If the man were married to a Type A, or Type B, or Type   **69B**
AB woman, could he have a child who was Type AB? _____.
And if that woman were Type Rh + could he not have an Rh + child?
_____. Of course, a woman who is Type O could not have a
Type AB child. Return to page **67B.**

Incorrect. You have stated that the genotype of Type Rh − indi-   **69C**
viduals would be *rr*. What kind of offspring would a cross between
two Type Rh negative individuals produce, that is, $rr \times rr$? _____.
Return to page **70A.**

From page **61D.**

70A   **You are correct.** The genotype for a Type Rh− individual would be *rr*.

In marriages between two Type Rh− individuals what kinds of offspring and what percentage of each would you expect?

☐ 100% Type Rh+........................page   **66A.**

☐ 100% Type Rh−........................page   **65A.**

☐ Neither of these........................page   **69C.**

70B   You jumped to a hasty conclusion. Go back to page **62B** and answer the question "What is the genotype of the child?"

70C   **Incorrect.** With respect to the O, A, B blood types the woman's genotype would be *oo*. Therefore the offspring would have to have at least one gene which is (*A, B, o*) _____. Can a Type O individual ever produce a Type AB offspring? _____. Return to page **67B.**

From page **63C.**

70D   Answers:
   (a) .... A
   (b) .... D
   (c) .... E

If you have made any errors, return to page **63C** and rework the problems you missed. If you have made no errors, continue with the review for Part II.

REVIEW—Chapter 2, Part II

Each person can be classified on the basis of his A, B, O blood type and also on the basis of his Rh blood type. The two contrasting characteristics with respect to this latter trait are (wd) _____ and (wd) _____. The gene for Rh+ is dominant to the gene for Rh−; therefore, the genotype of anyone who is Rh− is (lts) _____, while the person who is Rh+ has the genotype (lts) _____ or (lts) _____.

To check your responses to the review of Part II, turn to page 356 and then continue with the summary.

SUMMARY—Chapter 2, Part II

In addition to blood types AB, A, B, and O there is the Rh blood type. Persons can be Rh positive (Rh+) or Rh negative (Rh−). The gene for Rh+ is dominant to the gene for Rh−. Knowledge of the mode of inheritance of blood types AB, A, B, O and Rh can be used in cases where there is some question concerning the parentage of children. Because we know that two Rh− parents could not produce a child that is Rh+, we would know in a particular case that a certain couple could not have been the parents of a certain child. However, if according to our knowledge of inheritance we could say that two parents *could* have produced a given child we could not be certain that they, in fact, were the parents. Two other people being able to produce a child of the same blood group might have been the actual parents.

Continue with the self test for Chapter 2.

SELF TEST—Chapter 2

How many different phenotypes of offspring could be produced by the following types of parents? Use the key to answer the questions.

KEY: A. One   B. Two   C. Three   D. Four
       E. More than four

— 1. Both parents Type A.
— 2. Both parents Type O.
— 3. One parent Type A, one Type B.
— 4. One parent Type AB, the other Type O.
— 5. Both parents Type AB.

Items 6–10 refer to the inheritance of blood groups. Fill in the blanks with the proper answer from the following key.

KEY: A. Only Type A; Type B
       B. Only Type A; Type O
       C. Only Type B; Type O
       D. Any of the four blood groups
       E. None of the combinations listed

— 6. If both parents are Type A the children could be _____.
— 7. If one parent were an O Type and the other Type AB the children could be _____.
— 8. If one parent were an A Type and the other parent a B Type the children could be _____.
— 9. If one parent were Type AB and the other Type A the children could be _____.
—10. If both parents are Type AB the children could be _____.

Items 11–16 are statements describing the probable blood groups of offspring resulting from matings of individuals of different blood groups. In each case select the response from the key indicating the mating which could be expected to produce offspring as described in the item.

KEY: A. Type A × Type B, both with heterozygous genotypes
       B. Type AB with Type AB
       C. Type O with Type A (homozygous genotype)
       D. Type O with Type B (heterozygous genotype)
       E. Type O with Type AB

—11. One-half Type B and one-half Type O.
—12. One-fourth of the offspring Type AB, one-fourth Type A, one-fourth Type B, and one-fourth Type O.

___13. All the offspring are Type A.

___14. One-fourth of the offspring are Type A, one-half Type AB, one-fourth Type B.

___15. One-half Type A, one-half Type B.

___16. Only one genotype for blood groups in the offspring.

For items 17–19 select your response from the key below:

KEY: A. Blood Type O
      B. Blood Type A
      C. Blood Type AB
      D. Blood Type B
      E. Blood type cannot be definitely determined

___17. The blood type to which neither parent could belong if their child was blood type O.

___18. Parents belonging to Type A have one child of Type O. To what blood group will their next child belong?

___19. A woman of Type A whose mother was Type O married a man of Type AB. There is a 50% chance that this couple's first child will have which one of the above blood types?

In items 20–27 the first two columns list the blood types of the mother and father of 8 families. In the third column are listed the blood types of the *present* (already born) children in each family.

What is the probability, in percent, that the next child this couple has will have the blood type listed in column 4 marked "next child." Select your answers from the key.

KEY: A. 100%   B. 75%   C. 50%   D. 25%
      E. 0%

	MOTHER	FATHER	PRESENT CHILDREN	NEXT CHILD
___20.	Type A	Type A	Types A and O	Type A
___21.	Type B	Type O	Types B and O	Type O
___22.	Type A	Type B	Types A, B, O, and AB	Type AB
___23.	Type AB	Type AB	Types A, B, and AB	Type O
___24.	Type AB	Type AB	Types A and B	Type AB
___25.	Type O	Type O	Type O	Type O
___26.	Type AB	Type AB	Types B and AB	Type B
___27.	Rh+	Rh+	Rh+ and Rh−	Rh−

73

For the next 7 items use the following key to select your response.

KEY: A. Woman could be mother but man could not be father
      B. Man could be father but woman could not be mother
      C. Child could be offspring of man and woman
      D. One or the other but not both could be parents
      E. Neither could be parents

	Man	Woman	Child
__28.	Type A	Type B	Type O
__29.	Type O	Type AB	Type AB
__30.	Type B	Type O	Type AB
__31.	Type AB, Rh+	Type A, Rh+	Type B, Rh−
__32.	Type O, Rh−	Type O, Rh−	Type A, Rh−
__33.	Type AB, Rh−	Type AB, Rh−	Type O, Rh−

A Type A, Rh− man whose mother was Type AB and Rh+ was married to a Type B, Type Rh+ woman. They had two children. One, a daughter, had Type AB and Type Rh− blood; and the other, a son, had Type O and Rh+ blood. To determine the genotype of the woman certain facts must be used and certain deductions must be made.

Respond to statements 34–45 using the following key.

KEY: A. Given and necessary to solve the problem
      B. Given but not necessary to solve the problem
      C. Not given, can be determined, necessary to solve problem
      D. Not given, can be determined, but not necessary to solve problem
      E. Not given and cannot be determined

__34. The genotype of the woman's mother with respect to her A, B, O Type.

__35. The phenotype of the woman with respect to A, B, O Type.

__36. The phenotype of the daughter with respect to her Rh Type.

__37. The phenotype of the son with respect to his Rh Type.

__38. The phenotype of the father.

__39. The genotype of the father.

__40. The phenotype of the son with respect to his A, B, O Type.

__41. The phenotype of the daughter with respect to her A, B, O Type.

__42. The genotype of the son with respect to his Rh Type.

__43. The genotype of the son with respect to his A, B, O Type.

__44. The genotype of the daughter with respect to her A, B, O Type.

__45. The genotype of the daughter with respect to her Rh Type.

Correct answers to the questions on the self test for Chapter 2 are on page 364.

WORKSHEET 3-A

TABLE I

COLUMN 1	COLUMN 2	COLUMN 3	COLUMN 4	COLUMN 5
	The Expected Distribution		The Actual Distribution	
100 F_2 flies	50% males	50% females	50% males	50% females
red-eyed				
white-eyed				

TABLE II

P_1 Phenotypes RED-EYED FEMALE $\times$ WHITE-EYED MALE

Genotypes _____ _____

F_1 Phenotypes RED-EYED FEMALE $\times$ RED-EYED MALE

Genotypes _____ _____

Gametes _____ _____

Eggs \ Sperm	W ⚥	⚥
W ⚥	Genotype: Eye color: Sex:	Genotype: Eye color: Sex:
w ⚥	Genotype: Eye color: Sex:	Genotype: Eye color: Sex:

F_2 generation

Genotypic ratio for females_____.

Phenotypic ratio for females_____.

Genotypic ratio for males_____.

Phenotypic ratio for males_____.

WORKSHEET 3-B

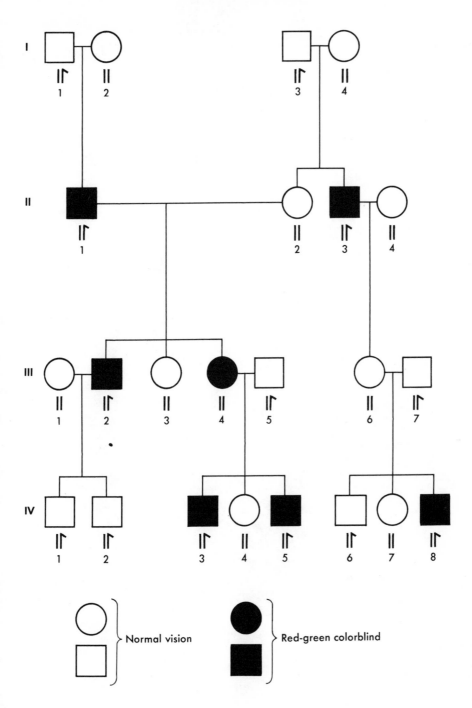

Normal vision

Red-green colorblind

77

chapter 3

SEX LINKAGE

PART I

For many years it has been known that colorblindness is not uncommon in human males but that it is very rare in females. Colorblindness is inherited, but because it appears more frequently in males than in females it does not follow the pattern of inheritance that we have described for other characteristics. This chapter will be concerned with a type of inheritance where the sex of the individual is related to the expression of the trait.

To inquire into the nature of this kind of inheritance we will examine the data concerning inheritance of white eye in Drosophila, the fruit fly. The normal eye color of the fruit fly is red, but there are also some fruit flies that have white eyes.

Crosses of red-eyed female flies by white-eyed male flies produce F_1 offspring all of which are red-eyed. Therefore we assume the gene for red eye to be dominant to the gene for white.

From a cross between two F_1 red-eyed flies one could expect the F_2 offspring to be in the ratio of

☐ 3 red-eyed:1 white-eyed . . . . page **83A.**

☐ 1 red-eyed:3 white-eyed . . . . page **80A.**

☐ 1 red-eyed:1 white-eyed . . . . page **87A.**

☐ 1 red-eyed:2 pink-eyed:1 white-eyed . . . . page **85A.**

80A   **Incorrect.** If W represents the gene for red eyes and w the recessive allele, you would expect the genotypic ratio to be $1WW:2Ww:1ww$. If the gene for white is recessive, what should the phenotypic ratio be? _____. Return to page **79**.

80B   **Incorrect.** We have assumed that all chromosomes except the X-chromosomes are paired in all somatic cells, and that the X-chromosomes are paired in females. Autosomes are all chromosomes other than the X- and Y-chromosomes. Return to page **85D**.

80C   **No.** The symbol $W\!\!\mid$ represents the gene for red eye. If a male had this gene could he be white-eyed? _____. Return to page **84A**.

From page **83A**.

80D   **Correct.** The expected distribution would be

100 F₂ FLIES	50% MALES	50% FEMALES
75 red-eyed	38	37
25 white-eyed	12	13

COMPLETE COLUMNS 2 AND 3 OF TABLE I OF WORKSHEET 3-A.

However, when two of the red-eyed F₁ flies were crossed it was found that the actual distribution was 25 red-eyed males, 25 white-eyed males, 50 red-eyed females and no white-eyed females. ADD THESE DATA IN COLUMNS 4 AND 5 OF TABLE I ON WORKSHEET 3-A.

For the total 100 flies (red-eyed plus white-eyed) the sex distribution was

☐ 75% males; 25% females..................page   **88C.**

☐ 50% males; 50% females..................page   **86C.**

Incorrect. We symbolized the male as | ↑, and the female as | |. **81A**
Return to page **90B**.

Return to page **90B**.

From page **86C**. **81B**

Correct. The distribution of red-eyed flies was $33\frac{1}{3}\%$ males; $66\frac{2}{3}\%$
females.
    The distribution of sex among the white-eyed flies was

☐ 50% males; 50% females..................page   **86B.**

☐ 100% males; 0% females..................page   **82B.**

From page **89A**.

Correct. Since the symbols w↑ ↓w represented a pair of autosomes   **81C**
and since both males and females have paired autosomes, you could
not decide whether this particular genotype represented a male or a
female. It could be either. By assuming that the genes for eye color of
the fruit fly are on the autosomes we could predict an F_2 generation
that could contain white-eyed flies, but nothing followed from the
assumption which would tell us about the sex of the individuals.
    The hypothesis that the genes for eye color are on the autosomes

☐ explains the fact that all the white-eyed flies
  in the F_2 generation were males.............page   **93B.**

☐ fails to explain the fact that all white-eyed flies
  in the F_2 generation were males.............page   **88B.**

Incorrect. Males have only one X-chromosome and one Y-chromo-   **81D**
some. Return to page **95A**.

Return to page **95A**.

82A   **Incorrect.** Males have only one X-chromosome and one Y-chromosome. Return to page **95A.**

82B   From page **81B.**

Correct. All the white-eyed flies were males. None were females. Thus, although the normal 50:50 distribution of sex appeared in this F_2 generation, there were more red-eyed females than expected and there were less white-eyed females than expected — there were none.

In all of our previous studies of an F_2 generation of a one-factor cross we have found that the dominant and recessive characteristics appeared in a 75:25 or 3:1 ratio. Also we found that the sex ratio was 50:50 or 1:1. That is, among the F_2 offspring exhibiting the dominant characteristic, 50% were males and 50% were females. Also among the recessives, 50% were males and 50% were females. Because of the difference between the dominant:recessive and the male:female ratios, it is reasonable to conclude that the cause of sex is independent of the cause of the dominant and recessive characteristics. In the cross between red-eyed and white-eyed flies the distribution of males and females was 1:1 for the entire F_2 generation, but it was not 1:1 in both phenotypes. REEXAMINE TABLE I OF WORKSHEET 3-A. Among the red-eyed flies $66\frac{2}{3}\%$ were female and $33\frac{1}{3}\%$ were male, while among the white-eyed flies no females appeared; all were males.

Can you conclude from these data that in this case sex and eye color are somehow related and not independent of each other?

☐ Yes. . . . . .page   **85D.**

☐ No. . . . . .page   **88D.**

82C   **Incorrect.** There were 25 red-eyed males and 50 red-eyed females. Is 25:50 a 1:1 ratio? _____. Return to page **86C.**

82D   **Incorrect.** A male has but one X-chromosome. If one rod (|) represents one X-chromosome and an individual is symbolized as | |, what sex is symbolized? _____. Return to page **88B.**

From page **79**.

Correct. The F_2 offspring should be in the ratio of 3 red-eyed:1 white-eyed. In an actual cross it was found that 75% of the F_2 offspring were red-eyed and 25% were white-eyed.

Fruit flies are bisexual; there are males and females. The normal ratio of males to females is 1:1; that is, in a population of flies 50% are males and 50% are females.

The 1:1 ratio of males and females that appears among the dominant and recessive forms of an F_2 generation can be illustrated by assuming that the F_2 generation consists of 100 flies. Of the 100 individuals, 75 would have the dominant phenotype and 25 would have the recessive phenotype. Among the 75 dominant forms approximately 50% (that is, 38) would be males and approximately 50% (37) would be females. Among the 25 recessive flies approximately 50% (12) would be males and 13 would be females.

This relationship may be seen better in the following table.

100 FLIES	50% MALES	50% FEMALES
75 dominant	38	37
25 recessive	12	13

It is doubtful that in any actual F_2 generation you would obtain these exact numbers. However, the numbers would be *approximately* the same as these.

We have already established that the F_2 generation of a cross between red-eyed and white-eyed flies contained 75% red-eyed flies and 25% white-eyed flies. RECORD 75 RED-EYED AND 25 WHITE-EYED FLIES IN COLUMN 1 OF TABLE I ON WORKSHEET 3-A. If this cross follows the normal pattern of sex distribution would you expect the following pattern of sex distribution among the F_2 offspring?

100 F_2 FLIES	50% MALES	50% FEMALES
75 red-eyed	38	37
25 white-eyed	12	13

☐ Yes......................................page **80D.**

☐ No.......................................page **84D.**

From page **90B**.

84A   **Correct.** W⧧ ⧧w would represent a female with red eyes. The sex and eye color of an individual symbolized as W⧧ ⌐ would be

☐ male, red-eyed . . . . .page   **96C.**

☐ male, white-eyed . . . . .page   **80C.**

☐ female, red-eyed . . . . .page   **87B.**

☐ female, white-eyed . . . . .page   **100A.**

84B   **Incorrect.** The genotype of the female is W⧧ ⧧w. If at meiosis the chromosome with the gene for red eyes goes into one cell the chromosome with the gene for white eyes would go into another cell. What would be the ratio of the two types of gametes? _____. Do not confuse ratios of gametes with phenotypic ratios. Return to page **97B**.

From page **88B**.

84C   **Correct.** An individual symbolized | | would be a female. What sex would an individual have that was symbolized by | | ?

☐ Male . . . . .page   **87C.**

☐ Female . . . . .page   **90D.**

84D   **Why not?** If half of the flies are males and half are females would you not expect the ratio of red : white to be 3 : 1 for each sex? _____. Return to page **83A**.

Incorrect. If there were lack of dominance the F_1 individuals should have been pink. Return to page **79.**

Return to page **79.**

85A

Incorrect. We are testing an hypothesis; namely, that the alleles for red and white eye color of the fruit fly are carried on the X-chromosomes *only*. If we assume they are only on the X-chromosomes we do not assume they are also on the Y-chromosomes. Return to page **87C.**

85B

Incorrect. One-half of the gametes produced by the female with a heterozygous genotype would contain a gene for white eye color; the other half would contain a gene for red eyes. Isn't this a difference? Return to page **93A.**

85C

From page **82B.**

85D

Correct. The unequal distribution of sex among the two phenotypes suggests that eye color and sex are interdependent and not independent.

In order to understand the material which follows, certain concepts of chromosome behavior are essential. The next few questions are a review of these aspects.

Recall that female fruit flies have two X-chromosomes in each somatic (body) cell. Male fruit flies have one X-chromosome and one Y-chromosome in each body cell. The X-chromosomes and the Y-chromosomes are called sex chromosomes. The other chromosomes in the cells of both males and females are called autosomes; these occur in pairs in all individuals.

In fruit flies and other insects the sex of the individual is thought to depend on the ratio between female-determining genes in the X-chromosomes and male-determining genes in the autosomes.

Autosomes appear in pairs in

☐ males only . . . . page   **80B.**

☐ females only . . . . page   **92A.**

☐ both males and females . . . . page   **95A.**

From page **97B.**

86A   **Correct.** The ratio of the gametes produced by the female with the heterozygous genotype would be 1:1.

   The F_1 male was symbolized as $W \blacklozenge \upharpoonright$. Half of the gametes produced by this male would contain the X-chromosome and the other half would contain the Y-chromosome, but would these gametes differ with respect to the genes for eye color?

☐ Yes . . . . page   **92C.**

☐ No . . . . page   **90C.**

86B   **No.** There were no white-eyed females. So how could the ratio of white-eyed males to females be 1:1? Return to page **81B.**

From page **80D.**

86C   **Correct.** For the total population of flies the sex distribution was 50% males; 50% females. EXAMINE TABLE I OF WORKSHEET 3-A. Among the red-eyed flies of the F_2 generation the distribution of males and females was

☐ 50% red-eyed males; 50% red-eyed females . . . page   **82C.**

☐ $33\frac{1}{3}$% red-eyed males; $66\frac{2}{3}$% red-eyed females . page   **81B.**

86D   **Incorrect.** The assumption of the gene theory concerning dominance refers to pairs of genes. We assumed that when a single recessive allele is present on the X-chromosome of a male it can be expressed; we also have assumed that if an individual has the recessive genes for a characteristic on paired chromosomes, the characteristic is expressed. Neither of these situations denies that the presence of the dominant allele "masks" the effect of the recessive. Return to page **91D.**

No. The question asked what the ratio should be in the F₂ generation if two F₁ individuals were crossed. We assume the gene for red to be dominant to the gene for white. Red-eyed (WW) flies were crossed with white-eyed flies (ww). What would you expect the genotypes of the F₁ offspring to be? _____. If you crossed two of these F₁ offspring what would be the genotypes and the ratio of these genotypes? _____. What would you expect the phenotypes and phenotypic ratios to be? _____. Return to page **79**.

Incorrect. We have already accepted the symbols | | as representing a female and the symbols | ⌐ as representing a male. Return to page **84A**.

From page **84C**.

Correct. The symbol | represents an X-chromosome and the symbol ⌐ represents a Y-chromosome, hence the symbols | ⌐ represent a male. We rejected the hypothesis that the alleles for red and white eye color are on the autosomes. Let us test the hypothesis that the X-chromosomes carry genes that affect eye color. The gene symbols W and w for eye color can be placed on the symbols for the X-chromosomes contained in the F₁ females and males. An F₁ female having a genotype heterozygous for eye color would thus be symbolized as W┃ ┃w; the red-eyed male as W┃ ⌐. The hypothesis we are testing is that the alleles for red and white eye color are on the X-chromosomes only. Genes which are carried on an X-chromosome are called **sex-linked.**

Thus we have made the assumption that genes for eye color of the fruit fly are carried on

☐ the X-chromosomes........................page **90B.**

☐ the Y-chromosomes........................page **94A.**

☐ both X- and Y-chromosomes................page **85B.**

No. The symbols W┃ stand for an X-chromosome and a gene for red eyes. We have established that the gene for red eyes is dominant to the gene for white eyes. Return to page **95C**.

88A **No.** Although the symbols | | represent a female, we have established that the gene for red (W) is dominant to the gene for white (w). Return to page **90B**.

From page **81C**.

88B **Good.** The hypothesis that the eye color genes are on a pair of autosomes is unsatisfactory.

Let us reason from the hypothesis that the genes for red and white eye color are alleles and are on the X-chromosomes to see if this will explain the F_2 generation where all of the white-eyed flies were males.

Let us again use the rod but this time to designate the X-chromosome. For the Y-chromosome we will use a rod with a hook on one end as | .

A female would be symbolized as | | .

A male would be symbolized as | | .

In using a rod to represent an X-chromosome the rod would also represent the sex-determining power of the X-chromosome. Thus an individual symbolized as | | would be

☐ male....................................page **82D**.

☐ female...................................page **84C**.

88C **Incorrect.** The question asked about the distribution of sex in the 100 flies. You have confused eye-color ratio with the sex ratio. Return to page **80D**.

88D **How come?** We know that when the sex of the individual is independent of the trait in question, the ratio of males to females in an F_2 generation is the same for both the dominant and recessive phenotypes. In the case of red-eyed and white-eyed flies the ratio of males to females is not 1:1, but 1 male:2 female in the red-eyed flies and 1 male: 0 female in the white-eyed flies. Does this variation not suggest some relation between the inheritance of sex and the inheritance of eye color? Return to page **82B**.

From page **95A.**

Correct. Females have two X-chromosomes while males have but one X-chromosome.

If eye color of the fruit fly and sex are related, perhaps the genes for eye color are related in some fashion to the genes for sex. One possible relation would be that the genes for eye color are on the same chromosomes as the genes for sex.

One explanation for sex determination makes the assumption that the autosomes carry genes for maleness and that the X-chromosomes carry genes for femaleness. Assuming that the alleles for red and white eye color were on the same chromosome with the sex genes, it might be possible that (1) the alleles for eye color are on the auto- somes and thus associated with the male sex genes, or (2) the genes for eye color are on the X-chromosomes.

Let us follow out the implications of the hypothesis that the genes for eye color are on one pair of autosomes. Recall that autosomes are paired in both males and females. Let us diagram these two auto- somes as rods ($\dagger$ $\dagger$), and indicate the genes for eye color by the attached symbols W and w, where W represents the gene for red eye color and w the gene for white eye color.

Using these symbols the genotype of the red-eyed F_1 individuals would be

$$W\dagger \ \dagger w$$

A cross of two such individuals ($W\dagger \ \dagger w \times W\dagger \ \dagger w$) would be dia- gramed as

	$W\dagger$	$w\dagger$
$W\dagger$	$W\dagger \ \dagger W$ ¼ Red	$W\dagger \ \dagger w$ ¼ Red
$w\dagger$	$W\dagger \ \dagger w$ ¼ Red	$w\dagger \ \dagger w$ ¼ White

(F_2) $W\dagger \ \dagger W$ $W\dagger \ \dagger w$ $W\dagger \ \dagger w$ $w\dagger \ \dagger w$

    ¼ Red-eyed,   ¼ Red-eyed,   ¼ Red-eyed,   ¼ White-eyed

Examine the above symbols for the F_2 individuals. What sex is represented by $w\dagger \ \dagger w$?

☐ Male. . . . . .page   **90A.**

☐ Female. . . . . .page   **98D.**

☐ Either male or female. . . . . .page   **81C.**

90A   **Incorrect.** Did you confuse $w\dagger$ $\dagger w$ with X- and Y-chromosomes? The upright bars were meant to represent a pair of autosomes. No X- or Y-chromosome was included in the diagram of the cross, so how could you tell whether any individual was male or female? Return to page **89A**.

From page **87C**.

90B   **Correct.** In stating that we are testing the hypothesis that the genes for eye color are carried on the X-chromosomes only, we were obliged to assume that genes for eye color are not carried on the Y-chromosome. We make this same assumption about all sex-linked genes, namely that they are carried by the X-chromosomes only. We assume that the Y-chromosome does not ever carry any sex-linked genes. Some genes are found on the Y-chromosome only. Such inheritance is known as Y-chromosome inheritance. If alleles are on both the X- and Y-chromosomes, these genes are called incompletely sex-linked. However, in the case of the genes for red and white eye we are assuming that they are on the X-chromosomes only.

   The sex and eye color of a fruit fly having the chromosomes symbolized as $W\dagger$ $\dagger w$ would be

☐ male, red-eyed............................page   **81A.**

☐ male, white-eyed..........................page   **96A.**

☐ female, red-eyed..........................page   **84A.**

☐ female, white-eyed........................page   **88A.**

90C   **Incorrect.** We have hypothesized that the Y-chromosome does not carry genes for eye color. If half of the gametes receive a Y-chromosome, and hence no genes for eye color, would not these gametes be different with respect to genes for eye color from the gametes receiving the X-chromosome which we have assumed does carry a gene for eye color? _____. Is not something different than nothing? _____. Return to page **86A**.

90D   **No.** We symbolized the female as | |. Return to page **84C**.

Incorrect. A ratio of 1:0 would indicate that all the gametes were alike. Are they? _____. Return to page **92C**.

No. REEXAMINE WORKSHEET 3-A. In how many squares have you recorded the word "white" after eye color?

☐ One................................page **97C**.

☐ Two................................page **98A**.

☐ More than two.........................page **93D**.

No. Dominance of a gene always refers to the masking of the effect of one gene by another gene. How many genes for white eye does each cell of the male have? _____. Is this gene masking the effect of some other gene? _____. Can the gene for white eyes be considered dominant in the male? _____. Return to page **100C**.

From page **93C**.

Correct. The cross of an F_1 red-eyed female with a white-eyed P_1 male should produce both red-eyed and white-eyed females in the ratio of 1:1. When such crosses were made half of the females produced were red-eyed, half were white-eyed.

The hypothesis that genes for eye color of the fruit fly are located on the X-chromosome adequately explains the data obtained from an actual cross. However, this hypothesis suggests that one of the assumptions of the theory of the gene which we have accepted thus far must be modified.

Which assumption of the gene theory must be modified?

☐ Genes control the development of inherited characteristics.............................page **97A**.

☐ Genes always occur in pairs in all somatic cells. .page **98B**.

☐ One gene of a pair can be dominant to the other gene of the pair.............................page **86D**.

92A   **Incorrect.** We have assumed that all chromosomes except the X-chromosomes are paired in all somatic cells, and that the X-chromosomes are paired in females. Autosomes are all chromosomes other than the X- and Y-chromosomes. Return to page **85D.**

92B   **Incorrect.** You know that all of the white-eyed flies would be males. You also know that red-eyed females should be produced. Then how could 100% of red-eyed flies be males? Return to page **100B.**

From page **86A.**

92C   **Correct.** All of the sperm produced by the F₁ male ($W \dagger \upharpoonright$) that contained the X-chromosome would also contain the gene for red eye color. The sperm that contained the Y-chromosome would not have a gene for eye color.

These two kinds of gametes also would be produced in a

☐ 1:0 ratio. . . . . page   **91A.**

☐ 1:1 ratio. . . . . page   **94C.**

☐ 3:1 ratio. . . . . page   **96B.**

92D   **This is not an adequate statement.** What other genes, besides autosomal genes, occur in pairs? Return to page **98B.**

From page **96C.**

Correct. All the gametes would contain one X-chromosome and they   **93A**
would not differ with respect to their ability to determine sex.
    Would the gametes $(W\!\uparrow)$ and $(\uparrow w)$ produced by the female differ
with respect to the genes for eye color?

☐ Yes . . . . page   **97B.**

☐ No . . . . page   **85C.**

Incorrect. Could not individuals with the genotype $w\!\uparrow$ $\uparrow w$ be white-   **93B**
eyed females? _____, and could they not be males? _____.
So how could this explain why all of the white-eyed flies were males?
Return to page **81C.**

From page **95C.**

Correct. The genotype of a white-eyed female would be $w\!\uparrow$ $\uparrow w$.   **93C**
EXAMINE WORKSHEET 3-A. Which of the following crosses would
produce some white-eyed females?

☐ A cross of two F_1 individuals . . . . page   **99B.**

☐ A cross of an F_1 female with the P_1 male . . . . page   **91D.**

☐ A cross of an F_1 male with the P_1 female . . . . . page   **94B.**

In the two top squares you should have recorded $W\!\uparrow$ $\uparrow W$ and $W\!\uparrow$ $\uparrow$.   **93D**
What would be the eye colors of the females $W\!\uparrow$ $\uparrow W$ and males $W\!\uparrow$ $\uparrow$
with these genotypes? _____. In the lower two squares you
should have recorded $W\!\uparrow$ $\uparrow w$ and $w\!\uparrow$ $\uparrow$. Red is dominant to white.
What would be the eye color of the females? _____. Return to
page **94C.**

94A   **Incorrect.** We are testing an hypothesis; namely, that the alleles for red and white eye color of the fruit fly are carried on the X-chromosomes *only*. If we assume they are only on the X-chromosomes we do not assume they are also on the Y-chromosomes. Return to page **87C**.

94B   **No.** The F_1 male had the genotype $W{\dagger}\,\lceil$. The P_1 female had the genotype $W{\dagger}\,{\dagger}W$. Could this cross produce a female with the genotype $w{\dagger}\,{\dagger}w$? _____. Return to page **93C**.

From page **92C**.

94C   **Correct.** A male having the genotype $W{\dagger}\,\lceil$ would produce two kinds of gametes in a ratio of 1:1. One kind would contain an X-chromosome carrying the gene W the other would contain the Y-chromosome which would not carry any genes for eye color.

     When fertilization occurs between the F_1 male, $W{\dagger}\,\lceil$, and the F_1 female, $W{\dagger}\,{\dagger}w$, four kinds of F_2 offspring should result. COMPLETE THE CHECKERBOARD ON WORKSHEET 3-A TO DETERMINE THE GENOTYPES OF THESE OFFSPRING. ALSO DETERMINE THE GENOTYPIC RATIOS FOR EACH SEX AND RECORD THESE BELOW THE CHECKERBOARD. ASSIGN EYE COLOR AND SEX AS INDICATED ON THE CHECKERBOARD AND DETERMINE THE PHENOTYPIC RATIOS FOR BOTH SEXES FOR THE INDIVIDUALS OF THE F_2 GENERATION.

What would be the sex of the F_2 white-eyed flies?

☐ Male....................................page   **100B.**

☐ Female..................................page   **99A.**

☐ Some male, some female....................page   **91B.**

94D   **Incorrect.** The genotype of the female is $W{\dagger}\,{\dagger}w$. If at meiosis the chromosome with the gene for red eyes goes into one cell the chromosome with the gene for white eyes would go into another cell. What would be the ratio of the two types of gametes? _____. Do not confuse ratios of gametes with phenotypic ratios. Return to page **97B**.

From page **85D.**

From page **85D.**

Correct. Autosomes occur in pairs in both males and females. The **95A** sex chromosomes (X-chromosomes) occur in pairs in

☐ males. . . . . .page **82A.**

☐ females. . . . . .page **89A.**

☐ both males and females. . . . . .page **81D.**

This is not the best answer. This statement does not specify when **95B** genes occur in pairs and when they do not occur in pairs. Return to page **98B.**

From page **100C.**

Correct. A single recessive gene can express itself if the dominant **95C** allele is not present. The original P_1 female had a genotype that was homozygous for the dominant gene and was red-eyed. Hence, her genotype was $W{\restriction}\ {\restriction}W$. The P_1 male was white-eyed so his genotype was $w{\restriction}\ {\upharpoonleft}$. RECORD THESE TWO GENOTYPES IN THE PROPER PLACES IN TABLE II ON WORKSHEET 3-A.

A question which arises from the foregoing discussion is "Can females with white eyes be produced"? If they can, what would be the genotype of the white-eyed female fly?

☐ $W{\restriction}\ {\restriction}w$. . . . . .page **87D.**

☐ $w{\restriction}\ {\restriction}w$. . . . . .page **93C.**

☐ $w{\restriction}\ {\upharpoonleft}$. . . . . .page **96D.**

Incorrect. You have established that ¼ of the flies would be white- **95D** eyed and male. All of the remaining flies with genotypes, $W{\restriction}\ {\restriction}W$, $W{\restriction}\ {\restriction}w$, and $W{\restriction}\ {\upharpoonleft}$ would be red eyed. Of these red-eyed flies what would be the ratio of females to males? _____. What percent would be female? _____, male? _____. Return to page **100B.**

96A **Incorrect.** We symbolized the male as | ↾ , and the female as | |. Return to page **90B**.

96B **Incorrect.** Do not confuse a 3:1 phenotypic ratio with a ratio of genes. Have we ever assumed gametes to be produced in a 3:1 ratio? _____. An individual with a heterozygous genotype produces gametes in a ratio of _____ : _____. Would not an individual with the genotype W⧫ ↾ be heterozygous? _____. Return to page **92C**.

From page **84A**.

96C **Correct.** W⧫ ↾ represents a red-eyed male.

The red-eyed female with a heterozygous genotype (W⧫ ⧫w) represents one of the F_1 red-eyed flies produced by the cross of a red-eyed fly with a white-eyed fly. The red-eyed male (W⧫ ↾) is also an F_1 fly. Thus a cross between this female and this male would produce the F_2 generation. Let us diagram this cross as

Red-eyed female   ×   Red-eyed male

W⧫ ⧫w W⧫ ↾

RECORD THE CHROMOSOME AND GENE SYMBOLS FOR THE F_1 MALE AND FEMALE IN TABLE II ON WORKSHEET 3-A. ALSO RECORD ON THE WORKSHEET OPPOSITE "GAMETES" THE KINDS OF EGGS THAT WOULD BE PRODUCED BY THE FEMALE AND THE KINDS OF SPERM PRODUCED BY THE MALE.

Would the gametes (W⧫) and (w⧫) produced by the female (W⧫ ⧫w) differ in their ability to determine the sex of an offspring?

☐ Yes . . . . page **98C.**

☐ No . . . . page **93A.**

96D **No.** The symbol ↾ stands for a Y-chromosome. What would be the sex of an individual with the genotype w⧫ ↾ ? _____. Return to page **95C**.

97A

Why? Did we not assume that there were genes for red eyes and genes for white eyes and that the phenotypic characteristic of the individual was controlled by them? Return to page **91D**.

From page **93A**.

97B

Correct. Two kinds of gametes would be produced — those containing the X-chromosome with the gene for red eye color and those containing the X-chromosome with the gene for white eye color.

What would be the ratio of these two kinds of gametes? (See Worksheet 3-A.)

☐ 1:1, i.e. 50% (W↕) and 50% (w↕) . . . . page   **86A.**

☐ 2:1, i.e. 67% (W↕) and 33% (w↕) . . . . page   **94D.**

☐ 3:1, i.e. 75% (W↕) and 25% (w↕) . . . . page   **84B.**

97C

If you only have "white" recorded in one square, how could you have answered "some males and some females" to the previous question? An individual with two X-chromosomes would be a female, one with one X-chromosome and one Y-chromosome would be a male. In which square have you recorded "white," one having | ↑ or one having | |? _____. Which sex is represented by | |? _____, by | ↑? _____. Return to page **94C**.

97D

Why not? When predictions from an hypothesis, such as the hypothesis that the alleles for red eyes and white eyes are on the X-chromosomes, agree with observational facts we accept the hypothesis, at least until one which is better is suggested. And in this case the prediction from the hypothesis agreed with the observational facts. Return to page **99C**.

98A　In the two top squares you should have recorded $W\dagger$ $\dagger W$ and $W\dagger$ $\lceil$. What would be the eye colors of the females $W\dagger$ $\dagger W$ and males $W\dagger$ $\lceil$ with these genotypes? _____. In the lower two squares you should have recorded $W\dagger$ $\dagger w$ and $w\dagger$ $\lceil$. Red is dominant to white. What would be the eye color of the females? _____.

Return to page **94C**.

98B　**Correct.** The assumption that genes always occur in pairs must be modified. Which of the following is the best statement of the modification of this assumption?

☐ Genes sometimes occur in pairs but there is no relationship between the chromosomes on which they are located and the paired or unpaired condition of these genes...................page **95B.**

☐ Only those genes carried by autosomes occur in pairs. All genes on sex chromosomes are unpaired....................................page **92D.**

☐ Autosomal genes and genes on the paired sex chromosomes occur in pairs, but the genes on the sex chromosomes, where only one of the sex chromosomes occurs, are unpaired...........page **100D.**

98C　**Incorrect.** All of the gametes produced by the female have an X-chromosome. If the X-chromosome is important in the determination of sex of the offspring how could a gamete containing one X-chromosome differ with respect to sex determination from some other gamete also containing an X-chromosome? Return to page **96C.**

98D　**Incorrect.** Did you mistake the symbols $w\dagger$ $\dagger w$ for X-chromosomes? The upright bars were meant to represent a pair of autosomes. No X- or Y-chromosome was included in the diagram of the cross so how could you tell whether any individual was male or female? Return to page **89A**.

Incorrect. REEXAMINE WORKSHEET 3-A. Look at the square containing the symbols $w\dagger\upharpoonright$, recorded as the genotype. The symbol $\upharpoonright$ represents a Y-chromosome. What sex is an individual who has only one X-chromosome? _____. What would the eye color be? _____. Would any of the other genotypes represent white-eyed flies? _____. Return to page **94C**.

99A

Incorrect. The F_1 individuals had the genotypes $W\dagger\dagger w$ and $W\dagger\upharpoonright$. Could this cross produce a female with the genotype $w\dagger\dagger w$? _____. Return to page **93C**.

99B

From page **100B**.

Correct. $33\frac{1}{3}\%$ of the red-eyed flies would be males.   **99C**

Now let us return to the original data. These data are given again in the table below. Boxes have been added under the numbers of red-eyed and white-eyed flies produced out of a total of 100. In these boxes write the genotypes that you predicted would be produced on the assumption that the eye-color genes are on the X-chromosomes. These were $25\% W\dagger\dagger W$, $25\% W\dagger\dagger w$, $25\% W\dagger\upharpoonright$, $25\% w\dagger\upharpoonright$.

100 FLIES	50% MALE	50% FEMALE
75 red-eyed	25	25 + 25 = 50
	[ ]	[ ]
25 white-eyed	25	0
	[ ]	[ ]

Would you agree that the hypothesis, "the genes for eye color are on the X-chromosomes," could explain the unusual sex distribution in this cross?

☐ Yes..page   **100C**.

☐ No...page   **97D**.

100A **Incorrect.** We have already accepted the symbols | | as representing a female and the symbols | ↾ as representing a male. Return to page 84A.

From page **94C**.

100B **Correct.** All of the white-eyed flies should be male. What percentage of the red-eyed flies would you expect to be male?

☐ 100% . . . . page **92B.**

☐ 50% . . . . page **95D.**

☐ 33⅓% . . . . page **99C.**

From page **99C**.

100C **Correct.** If the genes for eye color were located on the X-chromosome you would predict (1) that all of the white-eyed flies of the F_2 generation should be males, and (2) that of the total number of red-eyed flies, 33⅓% should be males, 66⅔% should be females.

The assumption that sex-linked genes are on the X-chromosomes, but not on the Y-chromosome, can explain the data in relation to certain kinds of crosses. This assumption implies that

☐ the gene for white eyes is dominant in the
male . . . . page **91C.**

☐ a single recessive gene can express itself if the
dominant allele is not present . . . . page **95C.**

From page **98B**.

100D **Correct.** In order to explain the type of ratio obtained from a cross of red-eyed $\dot{F}_1$ males with red-eyed F_1 females, the assumption that genes always occur in pairs had to be modified to include the idea that autosomal genes and genes on paired sex chromosomes occur in pairs, but that in the males having but one X-chromosome the genes are unpaired. This is the end of the sequence. Continue with the review.

REVIEW—Chapter 3, Part I

In a cross between two F_1 individuals where there is dominance the ratio of the dominant characteristic to the recessive characteristic is $3:1$. If the genes for this particular trait are carried on the autosomes the ratio of males to females for those with dominant phenotypes will be _____ : _____, and the ratio of males to females for those with the recessive phenotype will be _____ : _____.

Some genes are sex-linked, that is, some genes are located on (*autosomes, sex chromosomes*) _____. It is assumed that the X-chromosome (*does, does not*) _____ carry genes and that the Y-chromosome (*does, does not*) _____ carry sex-linked genes.

By assuming that the genes for red and for white eye color are located on the (*X, Y*) _____ chromosome, the sex ratios of individuals of the F_2 generation of a cross between two F_1 flies can be explained. In this cross there were no (*males, females*) _____ with the (*dominant, recessive*) _____ characteristic. The genotype of the original red-eyed female parent (P_1) was (*lts*) _____ while the genotype of the white-eyed male parent (P_1) was (*lts*) _____. The F_2 females had the genotype (*lts*) _____ and the F_2 males had the genotype (*lts*) _____. There were no white-eyed females in the F_2 generation, but white-eyed females could be produced by crossing a white-eyed male with a female having the genotype (*lts*) _____.

Sex-linked inheritance differs from other types of inheritance in that the (*male, female*) _____ has but one gene for the trait. Thus the assumption of the gene theory that genes always occur in pairs must be modified. The assumption can be modified as: Genes occur in (*wd*) _____ on all (*autosomes, sex chromosomes*) _____ and on the sex chromosome of the sex that has (*one, two*) _____ sex chromosomes. Thus a single recessive gene (*can, cannot*) _____ be expressed in the sex which has but one X-chromosome.

To check your responses to the review turn to page 356, and then continue with the summary.

SUMMARY—Chapter 3, Part I

The observation that some characteristics such as colorblindness appear more frequently in males than in females suggested a relation between the genes that determine the characteristic and the genes that determine sex.

The explanation for this relationship between sex and certain other characteristics was sought through the data obtained from crosses of red-eyed by white-eyed fruit flies. In the F_2 generation of such a cross, while the normal 1:1 ratio of males to females appeared, there were no white-eyed females. All of the white-eyed individuals were males.

Because genes on autosomes caused maleness and genes on X-chromosomes caused femaleness, it was possible to hypothesize that the genes for eye color (1) were linked on the autosomes with the male-determining genes or (2) were linked on the X-chromosome with the female-determining genes. By using each hypothesis to calculate consequences we learned that the second hypothesis, i.e., that the eye color genes were on the X-chromosome, satisfied the data and thus presumably was the correct explanation.

Genes which affect parts of the body not concerned with sex but linked on the X-chromosome with sex-determining genes are said to be sex-linked.

Also because such sex-linked genes occur singly in males, because the male has only one X-chromosome per cell, it was necessary to modify the assumption of the gene theory that all genes occur in pairs. Genes on autosomes occur in pairs, but those on X-chromosomes in the male do not.

Continue with Part II.

The pedigree on Worksheet 3-B is that of a human family in which **103A** colorblindness occurs. Various types of colorblindness have been found, the most frequent being red-green colorblindness in which individuals have difficulty distinguishing red from green. This condition is much more frequent in males than in females. The shaded squares and circles represent red-green colorblind individuals. The unshaded squares and circles represent the persons with normal color vision. The squares represent males and the circles females. Under the squares are the symbols for the one X- and one Y-chromosome. Under the circles are the symbols for two X-chromosomes.

Examine the data presented in the pedigree for Individuals I-1, I-2, and II-1. Individuals I-1 and I-2 are the parents of II-1. On the basis of these three individuals which of the genes for the two contrasting characteristics, normal vision and colorblindness, is dominant? The gene for

☐ normal color vision . . . . page   **105D.**

☐ colorblindness . . . . page   **107D.**

☐ cannot be determined on the basis of the information given . . . . page   **110C.**

Incorrect. How many X-chromosomes does the male have? _____ .   **103B**
The female? _____ . Return to page **107A.**

Incorrect. Count the number of colorblind males and females on the   **103C**
pedigree. Return to page **110B.**

Incorrect. If all females get one X-chromosome from their mother   **103D**
and one from their father, and if the single X-chromosome of the father carries a recessive gene, what can you say about the daughters? Return to page **108C.**

104A Incorrect. Return to page **106D**.

104B Incorrect. If all females get one X-chromosome from their mother and one from their father, and if the single X-chromosome of the father carries a recessive gene, what can you say about the daughters? Return to page **108C**.

104C Incorrect. Assume that the genotype of the woman is homozygous dominant $(A\!\!\uparrow\ \uparrow\!\!A)$. The man has one gene for the sex-linked recessive and has one Y-chromosome $(a\!\!\uparrow\ \uparrow)$. What would be the genotype of the sons? _____. Of the daughters? _____. Return to page **106D**.

From page **107A**.

104D Correct. Since each somatic cell of a male would contain but one X-chromosome the male would have only one gene for a sex-linked characteristic, while the female having two X-chromosomes would have a pair of genes for the trait.

Our next problem is to discover whether the gene for red-green colorblindness is or is not sex-linked. Since genes cannot be observed we must obtain related data on the basis of which we can answer this question.

If a human characteristic were recessive and sex-linked, that is, if its gene were carried on the X-chromosome, which of the following should be true?

☐ The characteristic should be more frequent in men than in women........................page **110B**.

☐ The characteristic should be more frequent in women than in men........................page **112B**.

☐ There should be no sex difference in the frequency of the characteristic..................page **109B**.

Incorrect. If the characteristic were due to a recessive sex-linked **105A** gene and the father did not have this characteristic, while the mother did, what would be the genotype of the daughters?

☐ A┊ ┊a . . . . .page   **110A.**

☐ a┊ ┊a . . . . .page   **114A.**

☐ a┊ ┊ . . . . .page   **113D.**

Correct. The genotype of the daughters should be A┊ ┊a. Should any **105B** of them have the characteristic due to the recessive gene? _____. Return to page **116A.**

Incorrect. Suppose both mother and father had a recessive sex-linked **105C** characteristic, could the son have the characteristic caused by the dominant allele? _____. Return to page **110D.**

From page **103A.**

Correct. The gene for normal vision is dominant to the gene for red- **105D** green colorblindness.

   If the alleles for red-green color vision are carried on autosomes, how many genes for red-green color vision should a colorblind male have in each somatic cell? _____, a colorblind female have? _____.

   What numbers do you have recorded in the above blanks?

☐ 1 and 2 . . . . .page   **108A.**

☐ 2 and 1 . . . . .page   **117A.**

☐ 1 and 1 . . . . .page   **111A.**

☐ 2 and 2 . . . . .page   **107A.**

106A **Incorrect.** Would the genotype a⊦⌐ be a female? _____.
Return to page **88B** of Part I.

106B **Incorrect.** How many X-chromosomes have we assumed the male to
have? _____. Return to page **121A**.

106C **Incorrect.** Return to page **107A**.

From page **110B**.

106D **Correct.** Colorblindness is more frequent in the males of this family
than in the females.

However, higher frequency of occurrence of a characteristic is not
in itself an adequate criterion for determining that a characteristic is
sex-linked; that is, that the gene for the characteristic is carried on the
X-chromosome. For example baldness, though more frequent in
males than in females, is not assumed to be due to a sex-linked gene.
It is assumed that the gene for baldness is expressed in a male having
a heterozygous genotype but not in a female with a heterozygous
genotype. So other criteria for determining whether a characteristic
is due to a sex-linked gene must be established.

Consider a man having a characteristic due to a sex-linked recessive
gene, married to a woman who does not have the characteristic and
who does not have relatives having this characteristic. Which of the
following should be true of the children of this man and this woman?

☐ Half of their sons should have the character-
istic . . . . .page   **104C.**

☐ Half of their daughters should have the charac-
teristic . . . . .page   **111B.**

☐ Half of their sons and half of their daughters
should have the characteristic . . . . .page   **118B.**

☐ None of their children should have the charac-
teristic . . . . .page   **108C.**

From page **105D.**

From page **105D.**

Correct. If the alleles for red-green color vision are carried on auto-   **107A**
somes, each individual should have a pair of genes for this trait in each
somatic cell. If the alleles are not on the autosomes but instead are
sex-linked, each somatic cell of the male should contain (#)_____
gene(s) for red-green color vision and each cell of a female should
contain (#)_____.
  What do you have recorded in the above blanks?

☐ 1 and 2 . . . . page   **104D.**

☐ 2 and 1 . . . . page   **103B.**

☐ 2 and 2 . . . . page   **114D.**

Incorrect. Choose another answer on page **115C.**   **107B**

From page **110D.**

From page **110D.**

Correct. A characteristic due to a recessive sex-linked gene could   **107C**
appear in the sons only if the gene for this characteristic were carried
by the mother. The mother herself might or might not have the characteristic. If the mother did have the characteristic due to a recessive
sex-linked gene but the father did not, what prediction would you
make about her sons?

☐ All of her sons would have the characteristic . . page   **116A.**

☐ Half of her sons would have the characteristic . . page   **112C.**

☐ None of her sons would have the characteristic . page   **115A.**

Incorrect. The parents both have normal vision. They produce an   **107D**
offspring unlike themselves. Can two individuals with the recessive
characteristic produce one with the dominant characteristic? _____.
Return to page **103A.**

108A **Incorrect.** Autosomes are paired in both males and females, so how many genes for characteristics due to autosomal genes would individuals of both sexes have? _____. Return to page **105D**.

108B **Incorrect.** You can assign one gene for normal vision to Individual IV-7 on the basis of her phenotype. You know that she received one X-chromosome from her father that carried a gene for normal vision. You know that her mother has one X-chromosome with a gene for normal vision and one with a gene for colorblindness. Can you tell which gene was on the X-chromosome she received from her mother? _____. Return to page **115C**.

From page **106D**.

108C **Correct.** The children of men with characteristics due to recessive sex-linked genes do not have this characteristic if the wife does not have a gene for the characteristic. The sons cannot receive the gene from the father since the gene is carried on the X-chromosome; the daughters do not show the characteristic because it is due to a recessive gene and its effects are masked by the dominant gene received from the mother.

What statement can be made about the daughters of a man having a characteristic due to a recessive sex-linked gene?

☐ All of the daughters have a gene for this characteristic .... page **113C**.

☐ Half of the daughters have a gene for this characteristic .... page **103D**.

☐ None of the daughters have a gene for this characteristic .... page **104B**.

108D **Incorrect.** These individuals are all males so they would have (*1, 2*) _____ X-chromosome(s). They are all colorblind. What symbol (*C* or *c*) have you used for the gene for red-green colorblindness? _____. Correct your worksheet and return to page **119B**.

From page **122B.**

Good. Since males have only one X-chromosome their genotypes can **109A**
be completely determined on the basis of their phenotypes. Thus all of
the individuals for whom it is impossible to complete the genotype are
females with normal vision. To each of these females it was

☐ possible to assign one gene for colorblindness . . . page **114B.**

☐ possible to assign one gene for normal vision . . . page **112A.**

☐ impossible to assign any gene; that is, it was
    necessary to write two "?'s" . . . . page **122C.**

Incorrect. How many genes does a male have for a sex-linked char- **109B**
acteristic? _____. If a male has such a gene is it not always
expressed? _____. If a female has only one recessive sex-
linked gene is it expressed? _____. Would the frequency of the
observable characteristic be greater in males or in females? _____.
Return to page **104D.**

Incorrect. If the characteristic were due to a recessive sex-linked **109C**
gene and the father did not have this characteristic, while the mother
did, what would be the genotype of the daughters?

☐ A⊦ ⊦a . . . . page **105B.**

☐ a⊦ ⊦a . . . . page **112D.**

☐ a⊦ ⎰ . . . . page **106A.**

You are cautious, and since the data are limited, you are justified in **109D**
being cautious about drawing a conclusion. However, you were asked
to make an hypothesis, that is, a tentative conclusion. It is always
possible to make an hypothesis on the basis of insufficient data. Return to page **118C.**

110A **Correct.** The genotype of the daughters should be Aɫ ɫa. Should any of them have the characteristic due to the recessive gene? _____.
Return to page **116A**.

From page **104D**.

110B **Correct.** If a characteristic is recessive and sex-linked it should be more frequent in males than in females. EXAMINE THE PEDIGREE ON WORKSHEET 3-B. Is colorblindness more frequent in males than in females?

☐ Yes . . . . .page **106D.**

☐ No . . . . .page **103C.**

110C **Incorrect.** There is information given which should enable you to make the decision. The parents produced an offspring with the contrasting characteristic. If you assume that there are but two contrasting characteristics you cannot conclude that there is lack of dominance. Return to page **103A**.

From page **113C**.

110D **Correct.** Consider a man with a characteristic due to a sex-linked, recessive gene married to a woman who did not have the recessive gene. None of the offspring of the couple would have the sex-linked characteristic, but half of the daughters' sons would have it.
A characteristic caused by a recessive sex-linked gene

☐ could appear in both father and son only if the characteristic appeared in the family of the mother, or if the mother had the characteristic
. . . . .page **107C.**

☐ could never appear in both father and son . . . . . page **105C.**

Incorrect. The question referred to somatic cells, not to gametes. **111A**
Return to page **105D**.

Incorrect. Assume that the genotype of the woman is homozygous **111B**
dominant $(A\uparrow\ \uparrow A)$. The man has one gene for the sex-linked recessive
and has one Y-chromosome $(a\uparrow\ \uparrow)$. What would be the genotype of the
sons? _____. Of the daughters? _____. Return to
page **106D**.

Incorrect. It is true that you could assign one gene for normal vision **111C**
to Individuals II-2 and III-1. But to assign a second gene is it not
necessary to have evidence of a father or son having the contrasting
characteristic? _____. Return to page **112A**.

From page **117C**.

Correct. Since Individual III-4 is a colorblind female, and since **111D**
she has two X-chromosomes, and since we have assumed colorblindness to be recessive, she would have to have two genes for colorblindness in order to be colorblind.

How many genes for colorblindness did you assign to Individual I-4?

☐ None.......................................page **117B**.

☐ One..page **114C**.

☐ Two..page **119A**.

From page **109A.**

112A **Correct.** All of the individuals for whom it is impossible to determine the complete genotype can be assigned one gene on the basis of their phenotype. All of these individuals were normal-visioned females so you should have C⊦ ⊦? assigned to each of them.

For which of the following normal-visioned females could you *not* determine the complete genotype?

☐ II-2 . . . . .page **121C.**

☐ III-1 . . . . .page **115C.**

☐ Both of these . . . . .page **117D.**

☐ Neither of these . . . . .page **111C.**

112B **Incorrect.** How many genes does a male have for a sex-linked characteristic? _____. If a male has such a gene is it not always expressed? _____. If a female has only one recessive sex-linked gene is it expressed? _____. Would the frequency of the observable characteristic be greater in males or in females? _____. Return to page **104D.**

112C **Incorrect.** If the mother had a characteristic which was due to a recessive sex-linked gene, how many genes for the characteristic would she have?

☐ One . . . . .page **118A.**

☐ Two . . . . .page **121B.**

112D **Incorrect.** If the father did not have the characteristic caused by the recessive gene and if the genes for the trait are carried by the X-chromosome, how could any of the gametes produced by such a male have the chromosome ⊦a? Return to page **109C.**

If only one X-chromosome had a gene for colorblindness then the **113A** other X-chromosome would have to have a gene for normal vision. If Individual III-4 had one gene for normal vision, which is dominant, what would her phenotype be? _____. Return to page **117C**.

Incorrect. Return to page **88B**, Part I.   **113B**

From page **108C**.

Correct. All of the daughters of a man having a characteristic caused **113C** by a recessive sex-linked gene would have one gene for this characteristic, because they all receive one of their X-chromosomes from their father. Such females are often referred to as "carriers."

Since we cannot observe genes we cannot determine by observation of the individual which individuals are "carriers." One criterion which we have recognized which would suggest that a characteristic was due to a recessive sex-linked gene is the higher frequency of the characteristic in males. A second criterion would be:

☐ The characteristic should be transmitted through a man's sons (who do not have the characteristic) to half of his sons' sons . . . . page   **123A**.

☐ The characteristic should be transmitted through a man's sons (who do not have the characteristic) to all of his sons' sons . . . . page   **104A**.

☐ The characteristic should be transmitted through a man's daughters (who do not have the characteristic) to half of the daughters' sons . . . . page   **110D**.

☐ The characteristic should be transmitted through a man's daughters (who do not have the characteristic) to all of the daughters' sons . . . . page   **119C**.

Incorrect. Would the genotype $a\uparrow\uparrow$ be a female? _____. **113D** Return to page **88B** of Part I.

114A   **Incorrect.** If the father did not have the characteristic caused by the recessive gene and if the genes for the trait are carried by the X-chromosome, how could any of the gametes produced by such a male have the chromosome $\dagger a$? Return to page **105A**.

114B   **Incorrect.** These individuals for whom the genotype cannot be determined are all normal-visioned females. Since normal is dominant would you not have to assign one gene on the basis of the phenotype? _____. If you could also assign one gene for colorblindness the genotype would be completely determined. Correct your worksheet and reanswer the question on page **109A**.

From page **111D**.

114C   **Correct.** Individual I-4 should have one gene for colorblindness. CHECK WORKSHEET 3-B. You should also have one gene for color-blindness assigned to Individuals I-2, II-2, III-3, III-6 and IV-4. If you do not have one gene for normal vision and one gene for color-blindness assigned to each of these individuals, correct your errors.

What information could you use to conclude that Individual II-2 had one gene for colorblindness?

☐ She had a son who was colorblind . . . . page **116D.**

☐ She had a daughter who was colorblind . . . . . . page **120A.**

☐ Either 1 or 2 above would have been sufficient . . page **123D.**

114D   **Incorrect.** How many X-chromosomes does the male have? _____. The female? _____. Return to page **107A**.

Incorrect. If the mother had a characteristic which was due to a re-   **115A**
cessive sex-linked gene, how many genes for the characteristic would
she have?

☐ One . . . . .page   **113B.**

☐ Two . . . . .page   **122D.**

Incorrect. Since the males have only one X-chromosome, and since   **115B**
the gene for colorblindness, or its allele the gene for normal vision, is
on the X-chromosome only, males can have either a gene for colorblindness or a gene for normal vision, but not both. Thus it is possible
to establish the genotype for all of the males on the basis of their
phenotype. Correct your worksheet and then reanswer the question
on page **122B.**

From page 112A.

Correct. It was not possible to determine the complete genotype for   **115C**
Individual III-1. For which of the following could you determine the
complete genotype?

☐ II-4 . . . . .page   **116C.**

☐ IV-7 . . . . .page   **108B.**

☐ Both of these . . . . .page   **107B.**

☐ Neither of these . . . . .page   **121D.**

Incorrect. Individual II-1 is colorblind. You should have assigned   **115D**
him at least one gene for colorblindness, *c*, on the basis of his phenotype. Return to page **121D.**

From page **107C.**

116A **Correct.** All of the sons of a woman having a characteristic due to a recessive sex-linked gene should have the characteristic because both of her X-chromosomes would carry such genes and each of her sons would have one of these X-chromosomes plus the Y-chromosome from the father.

A woman has a recessive sex-linked characteristic. She is married to a man who does not have this characteristic. What prediction would you make about their daughters?

☐ All of their daughters should have the characteristic.....................................page **105A.**

☐ Half of their daughters should have the characteristic.....................................page **109C.**

☐ None of their daughters should have the characteristic.....................................page **118C.**

116B **Incorrect.** Did you not answer yes to all of the questions about the relationship of the information in the pedigree to the criteria for establishing a characteristic as sex-linked? _____. If not, go back and study the questions and the pedigree. You might hesitate to say that it is sex-linked but how can you say that it is not sex-linked? Return to page **118C.**

116C **Incorrect.** Individual II-4 is normal-visioned so you know she has one gene for normal vision, but what else do you know about her? Was her father normal-visioned or was he colorblind? _____. Does she have sons who are colorblind? _____. Do you have any evidence which permits you to assign a second gene to Individual II-4? _____. Return to page **115C.**

116D **Correct but incomplete.** Return to page **114C.**

Incorrect. Autosomes are paired in both males and females, so how **117A** many genes for characteristics due to autosomal genes would individuals of both sexes have? _____. Return to page **105D**.

Incorrect. If Individual I-4 had no genes for colorblindness h er **117B** genotype would have to be $C\!\!\!/ \;\; \!\!\!/C$. Her husband, I-3, is normal-visioned, and so his genotype is $C\!\!\!/ \;\; \uparrow$. They have a son, II-3, who is colorblind, hence he has the genotype $c\!\!\!/ \;\; \uparrow$. He received his Y-chromosome from his father, so he had to receive his X-chromosome from his mother. Where would the chromosome $c\!\!\!/$ have come from if his mother's genotype was $C\!\!\!/ \;\; \!\!\!/C$? Return to page **111D**.

From page **121A**.

Correct. Individuals II-3, III-2, IV-3, IV-5 and IV-8 should have the **117C** genotype $c\!\!\!/ \;\; \uparrow$.

How many genes for colorblindness did you assign to Individual III-4?

☐ None . . . . page   **122A.**

☐ One . . . . page   **120B.**

☐ Two . . . . page   **111D.**

Incorrect. Individual II-2 has a son who is colorblind. Colorblindness **117D** is carried on the X-chromosome. From which parent did he get his one X-chromosome? _____. So what does that tell you about the genotype of this parent? _____. Return to page **112A**.

118A Incorrect. Return to page **88B**, Part I.

118B Incorrect. Assume that the genotype of the woman is homozygous dominant $(A \mathrel{\vdash} \mathrel{\dashv} A)$. The man has one gene for the sex-linked recessive and has one Y-chromosome $(a \mathrel{\vdash} \lceil \,)$. What would be the genotype of the sons? _____. Of the daughters? _____. Return to page **106D**.

From page **116A**.

118C Correct. None of the daughters of a woman having a characteristic due to a sex-linked recessive gene should have the characteristic provided the husband did not have this characteristic. All of the daughters however would have heterozygous genotypes and hence be carriers.

So far we have discovered four criteria for determining whether a characteristic is due to a recessive sex-linked gene; thus a characteristic is probably recessive and sex-linked (1) which is more frequent in men than in women, (2) which is present in a man, not present in his daughter but is present in half of her sons, (3) which rarely appears in both father and son, and (4) which is present in all of the sons but none of the daughters of a woman having the characteristic and a man not having the characteristic. EXAMINE THE PEDIGREE ON WORKSHEET 3-B. The characteristic is more frequent in the males than in the females. Is the characteristic present in a man, not present in a daughter, but present in half of her sons? _____. Is there colorblindness in the family of the mother in the instance where a colorblind man had a colorblind son? _____. Is the characteristic present in a woman, not in her husband, in all of her sons but none of her daughters? _____. What hypothesis would you make concerning the type of inheritance involved in the inheritance of red-green colorblindness?

☐ It is sex-linked . . . . page **120D.**

☐ It is not sex-linked . . . . page **116B.**

☐ I cannot make any hypothesis about the type of inheritance involved . . . . page **109D.**

No. If Individual I-4 had two genes for colorblindness, which is re- **119A** cessive, she should have been colorblind. She was not colorblind. Return to page **111D**.

From page **121D**.

Correct. Since Individual II-1 is a male, he has but one X-chromo- **119B** some in each cell and can therefore have but one gene for colorblind- ness in each cell. Therefore his genotype would be $c\!\mid\uparrow$.

EXAMINE YOUR WORKSHEET. Have you assigned the same genotype to Individuals II-3, III-2, IV-3, IV-5, and IV-8?

☐ Yes . . . . page **121A**.

☐ No . . . . page **108D**.

Incorrect. A man having a characteristic due to a recessive sex-linked **119C** gene would produce daughters all of whom had a heterozygous geno- type $(A\!\mid\ \mid a)$. What percent of the gametes produced by such a female should have the recessive sex-linked gene? _____. If the gamete is fertilized by a sperm containing a Y-chromosome the off- spring should be a male. What percent of the males would receive the recessive gene? _____. Return to page **113C**.

Incorrect. These individuals are colorblind males. What symbol, C or **119D** c, is used to represent a recessive gene? _____. Correct your worksheet and return to page **121A**.

120A **Correct but incomplete.** Return to page 114C.

120B **Incorrect.** You have assumed that colorblindness is recessive. Individual III-4 is colorblind. You have assumed the genes for colorblindness are on the X-chromosomes. How many X-chromosomes does Individual III-4 have?

☐ One . . . . page **123C.**

☐ Two . . . . page **113A.**

120C **Incorrect.** Since the males have only one X-chromosome, and since the gene for colorblindness, or its allele the gene for normal vision, is on the X-chromosome only, males can have either a gene for colorblindness or a gene for normal vision, but not both. Thus it is possible to establish the genotype for all of the males on the basis of their phenotype. Correct your worksheet and then reanswer the question on page **122B.**

From page **118C.**

120D **Correct.** This pedigree gives evidence that the gene for red-green colorblindness is recessive and sex-linked. Not only is red-green colorblindness more frequent in the males than in the females, Individual II-1 is colorblind and half of his grandsons are colorblind; Individual II-1 has a colorblind son, but there is colorblindness in his wife's family, and Individual III-4 has no colorblind daughters but all of her sons are colorblind.

How many genes for red-green color vision (for normal, for colorblind or for both) should each male in the pedigree have?

☐ One . . . . page **122B.**

☐ Two . . . . page **106C.**

From page **119B**.

Correct. You should have the same genotype assigned to Individuals **121A** II-3, III-2, IV-3, IV-5, and IV-8. What genotype have you assigned them?

☐ c†‖ . . . . .page   **117C.**

☐ C†‖ . . . . .page   **119D.**

☐ c† †c . . . . .page   **106B.**

Correct. She would have two genes for the characteristic. Would not **121B** each of the homologous X-chromosomes carry a gene for the characteristic? _____. From whom do her sons obtain their X-chromosome? _____. Return to page **107C.**

Incorrect. Individual II-2 has a son who is colorblind. Colorblindness **121C** is carried on the X-chromosome. From which parent did he get his one X-chromosome? _____. So what does that tell you about the genotype of this parent? _____. Return to page **112A.**

From page **115C**.

Correct. The genotypes of Individuals II-4 and IV-7 cannot be com- **121D** pletely determined.

   How many genes for colorblindness did you assign to Individual II-1?

☐ None . . . . .page   **115D.**

☐ One . . . . .page   **119B.**

☐ Two . . . . .page   **123B.**

122A Incorrect. Individual III-4 is colorblind, is she not? _____.
Can you not always assign at least one gene on the basis of the phenotype of the individual? _____. Return to page **117C**.

From page **120D**.

122B Correct. Since each male has but one X-chromosome he should have
only one gene for red-green color vision. Recall that the assumption
has been made that the Y-chromosome does not carry sex-linked genes.

On the assumption that the X-chromosomes carry the gene for
colorblindness, c, and its allele the gene for normal vision, C, COM-
PLETE THE GENOTYPES FOR ALL THE INDIVIDUALS IN THE PEDIGREE
ON WORKSHEET 3-B. In case you have no evidence to determine any
particular genotype completely, use a question mark (?) for the un-
determined gene. Be sure to assign one gene to each individual on the
basis of the phenotype. For example, the genotype of Individual I-1
can be indicated as $C \vdash \lceil$.

On the assumption that the gene for red-green colorblindness is
recessive and also sex-linked, it is not possible to determine the complete genotype for certain individuals in the pedigree. Which of the
following is true?

☐ These individuals are all males . . . . page   **115B**.

☐ These individuals are all females . . . . page   **109A**.

☐ Some of these individuals are males and some
    are females . . . . page   **120C**.

122C Incorrect. These individuals are all normal-visioned females. You
can always assign at least one gene on the basis of the phenotype of
the individual. Correct your worksheet and reanswer the question on
page **109A**.

122D Correct. She would have two genes for the characteristic. Would not
each of the homologous X-chromosomes carry one gene for the characteristic? _____. From whom do her sons obtain their X-
chromosome? _____. Return to page **107C**.

Incorrect. Return to page **106D**. **123A**

Incorrect. Return to page **88B** of Part I. **123B**

Incorrect. Return to page **88B** of Part I. **123C**

From page 114C.

Correct. This is the end of this chapter. Continue with the Review **123D**
of Part II.

REVIEW—Chapter 3, Part II

If a characteristic is sex-linked (1) it is more frequent in (*males, females*)
_____ (2) it is transmitted through a (*son, daughter*) _____ to
(½, *all*) _____ of (*her, his*) _____ (*sons, daughters*) _____
and (3) it should appear only in father and son if the characteristic had appeared in the family of the (*father, mother*) _____. The family showing
red-green colorblindness exhibited all of these three points, therefore colorblindness was assumed to be due to a recessive and (*wd*) _____ gene; the
gene being located on the (*X, Y*) _____-chromosome. The genotypes
of (*all, some*) _____ of the males could be determined from the phenotypes because the males are assumed to have (#) _____ X-chromo-
some(s), so any gene on that chromosome (*would, would not*) _____ be
expressed since there is no other gene to "mask" its effect. The genotype of
the one colorblind female (*could, could not*) _____ be completely
determined from her phenotype, because colorblindness was assumed to be
(*dominant, recessive*) _____. If the sperm fertilizing an egg contains
an X-chromosome the resulting child will be a (*male, female*) _____,
therefore if a normal-visioned female has a father who is colorblind, her genotype (*can, cannot*) _____ be completely determined. The X-chromosome of a male comes from the (*father, mother*) _____ so if a normal
visioned female has a colorblind son her complete genotype (*can, cannot*)
_____ be determined.

To check your responses to the review of Part II turn to page 357; then continue with the summary of Part II.

SUMMARY—Chapter 3, Part II

Characteristics are probably sex-linked (1) when they are more frequent in males than in females, (2) when the characteristic is transmitted through a daughter who does not have the characteristic to half of her sons, and (3) the characteristic appears in the father and son only when the characteristic also appeared in the family of the mother.

By assuming that the pedigree of red-green colorblindness represented a sex-linked recessive characteristic it was possible to assign genotypes to most of the individuals of the pedigree.

Continue with the self test for Chapter 3.

SELF TEST—Chapter 3

Give the probability of each of the following; that is, what is the probability that their *first* child will be the child listed as "expected child"?

KEY: A. 1 B. ¾ C. ½ D. ¼ E. 0

	Father	Mother	Expected Child
__ 1.	Normal vision	Colorblind	A colorblind child
__ 2.	Colorblind	"Carrier"	A colorblind daughter
__ 3.	Normal vision	"Carrier"	A normal vision child
__ 4.	Normal vision	"Carrier"	A colorblind son
__ 5.	Colorblind	"Carrier"	A colorblind child
__ 6.	Normal vision	Colorblind	A colorblind daughter

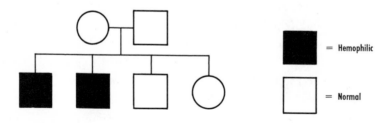

The gene for hemophilia is recessive and sex-linked. A family has four children. Two of the three sons are hemophilic (bleeders). The daughter is not hemophilic. Evaluate the statements 7–13 using the following key.

__ 7.   The father has a gene for hemophilia, but is not a hemophilic.

__ 8.   The hemophilic sons each have two genes for hemophilia.

__ 9.   The mother is a bleeder.

__10.   The mother has two genes for hemophilia.

__11.   The nonbleeder son carries a gene for hemophilia.

__12.   The mother carries a gene for hemophilia but is not a bleeder.

__13.   The daughter carries a gene for hemophilia.

In man, in the fruit fly, and in most other organisms the sex chromosomes are paired in the female but single in the male. However, in birds, butterflies, and moths the opposite is the case. This type of inheritance is often referred to as WZ inheritance instead of XY inheritance. To distinguish a WZ cross, use a bar ($|$) to represent a W-chromosome and a Z to represent a Z-chromosome. It is difficult to tell the sex of newly hatched chicks, but it is often easy to distinguish phenotypic characteristics of the newly hatched chicks. Two such phenotypic characteristics are called barred and nonbarred. Assume barred to be due to a dominant sex-linked gene, B. Use the following crosses as a key to answer questions 14–20.

KEY: *Male*   *Female*

           A. $B| \ |B \times b|Z$

           B. $b| \ |b \times B|Z$

           C. $B| \ |b \times b|Z$

           D. $B| \ |b \times B|Z$

           E.   None of these

__14.   Which cross would produce males with one characteristic and females with the contrasting characteristic?

__15.   Which cross would produce all barred offspring?

__16.   Which cross would produce both barred and nonbarred females but all barred males?

__17.   Which cross would produce offspring in which both sexes were 50% barred, 50% nonbarred?

__18.   Which cross would produce all barred males and all nonbarred females?

__19.   Which cross would produce all nonbarred males and all barred females?

__20.   Which cross would produce offspring in the ratio of 3 barred:1 nonbarred?

Assume that brown eye color is dominant to blue eye color. Mr. and Mrs. Smith are both brown-eyed. Joe, their son, has brown eyes and is colorblind, and Mary, their daughter, has blue eyes. Listed as items 21–25 are descriptions of certain genetic makeups. Choose from the key the person to whom they could belong.

> KEY: A. Joe
> B. Mary
> C. Mrs. Smith
> D. Mr. Smith
> E. Mrs. Smith's father

__21. The single X-chromosome of this individual carries a gene for color-blindness. This individual has at least one gene for brown eyes.

__22. This person has two genes for blue eyes and the single X-chromosome carries a gene for colorblindness.

__23. This person has one gene for blue eyes, one gene for brown eyes, one of the X-chromosomes carries a gene for colorblindness.

__24. This person carries one gene for brown eyes, one gene for blue eyes, and has one X-chromosome which carries the gene for normal vision.

__25. This individual has two X-chromosomes, two genes for blue eyes.

Items 26–32 are concerned with a family in which the first generation father was red-green colorblind. The mother had normal vision. The marriages of their three children are indicated. Assume that individual II-6 has a genotype homozygous for normal vision. (Hint: Determine the genotypes of all the individuals for whom the genotypes can be determined before answering the questions.) Use the key which follows the pedigree to respond to the items.

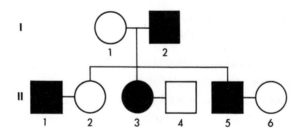

> KEY: A. II-1 and II-2
> B. II-3 and II-4
> C. II-5 and II-6
> D. All of these couples.
> E. None of these couples.

___26. All of the sons of this couple but none of the daughters of this couple will be colorblind.

___27. Some or all of the daughters of this couple will be "carriers".

___28. None of the sons of this couple will be colorblind.

___29. The probability that a son of this couple will be colorblind is $\frac{1}{2}$.

___30. No children of this couple will be colorblind.

___31. All of the children of this couple will be colorblind.

___32. The probability that a daughter of this couple will be colorblind is $\frac{1}{2}$.

For items 33–43 use the information given in the two following crosses.

Cross 1: A pure-line black male cat was crossed with a pure-line yellow female. Three female kittens were produced, they were all spotted (called tortoise)

Cross 2: Each of these spotted females was later crossed with a pure-line black male. Of the kittens in these three litters 11 were black males, 10 were yellow males, 9 were black females and 11 were spotted females.

To answer items 33–43 use the following key.

KEY: A. Cross 1 gives evidence for this statement.
      B. Cross 1 gives evidence against this statement.
      C. Cross 2 gives evidence for this statement.
      D. Cross 2 gives evidence against this statement.
      E. Neither cross gives evidence for or against this statement.

___33. The gene for black is dominant to the gene for yellow.

___34. There is lack of dominance in the inheritance of this trait.

___35. The genes for yellow and for black are alleles.

___36. The genes for yellow and for black are located on the X (sex)-chromosomes.

___37. The spotted kittens had heterozygous genotypes.

___38. No spotted males can be produced.

___39. If there had been any males produced in the first cross they would have been spotted.

___40. If there had been any males produced in the first cross they would have been yellow.

___41. All yellow cats have two genes for yellow.

___42. All black females have two genes for black.

___43. Fifty percent of the males produced by a spotted female and a yellow male would be black, the other 50% of the males would be yellow.

Correct answers to the questions on the self test for chapter 3 are on page 364.

WORKSHEET 4-A

Parents

Phenotypes: gray, normal $\times$ black, jaunty

Genotypes: _____ _____

Gametes: _____ _____

1. Gametes	2.	3. Expected genotypes	4. Probability	5. Expected phenotypes	6. Probability	7. Actual phenotypes	8.	9.
BJ	_____	_____	_____	_____	_____	_____	_____	_____
Bj	_____	_____	_____	_____	_____	_____	_____	_____
bJ	_____	_____	_____	_____	_____	_____	_____	_____
bj	_____	_____	_____	_____	_____	_____	_____	_____

Expected phenotypic ratio: _____

Actual phenotypic ratio: _____

129

WORKSHEET 4-B

Parents :

Phenotypes: normal eye, normal wing × kidney-shaped eye, short wing

Genotypes: *KkSs* × *kkss*

If independent assortment

Gametes	Expected genotypes	Ratio	Expected phenotypes	Ratio	Observed phenotypes	Ratio
KS	_____	_____	_____	_____	_____	_____
Ks	_____	_____	_____	_____	_____	_____
kS	_____	_____	_____	_____	_____	_____
ks	_____	_____	_____	_____	_____	_____

If linkage

Gametes of *KkSs*	Gametes of *kkss*	Expected genotypes	Expected phenotypes
_____	_____	_____	_____
_____	_____	_____	_____

chapter 4

LINKAGE AND CROSSING–OVER

PART I

    In considering the inheritance of two traits simultaneously we **133A** assumed that the genes for the two traits assorted independently of each other. We found that in an individual heterozygous for two pairs of genes *AaBb*, when the two pairs of genes assort independently and at random, *A* might go into a gamete with *B* or with *b*, and likewise *a* might occur in a gamete with *B* or with *b*. Thus an individual heterozygous for two traits, having the genotype *AaBb*, should produce

☐ two kinds of gametes.....................page   **146A.**

☐ four kinds of gametes.....................page   **137A.**

Incorrect. We assumed that the gametes produced by the parent **133B** having the dominant characteristics with the genotype *AaBb* were *AB*, *Ab*, *aB*, and *ab*. The parent having the genotype *aabb* produces but one kind of gamete *ab*. How many kinds of offspring would be produced and in what ratio? _____. Does this ratio correspond to the ratio of gametes produced by the individual having the genotype *aabb*? _____. If you are unable to answer these two questions, review the two-factor cross; then return to page **134C.**

Incorrect. There were 26 gray-bodied normal-winged and 24 black- **133C** bodied jaunty-winged flies produced. Isn't this approximately a 1:1 ratio? _____. What is a 1:1 ratio expressed as a probability equation? _____. Return to page **152C.**

From page **152C.**

134A   **Correct.** The equation expressing the actual results of the cross is: ½ gray normal + ½ black jaunty = 1. Expressed as a ratio this is: 1 gray normal:1 black jaunty. RECORD THIS RATIO OF ACTUAL PHENO-TYPES PRODUCED ON WORKSHEET 4-A.

Compare your predicted phenotypic ratio with the ratio obtained from an actual cross. What conclusion can you make on the basis of this comparison?

☐ Fifty is too small a number to obtain a ratio. If 500 offspring were obtained, the ratio would be 1:1:1:1 . . . . .page **151B.**

☐ There was some mistake in the experiment itself; the wrong cross was reported or there was an error in counting. The ratio of the phenotypes must be 1:1:1:1 . . . . .page **142C.**

☐ The results contradict the prediction; there-fore some new explanation for the results should be found . . . . : . . . . .page **137C.**

134B   **Incorrect.** Can two alleles go into one gamete? You have forgotten that pairs of genes segregate during gamete formation. Return to page **137A.**

From page **154B.**

134C   **Correct.** An individual with the genotype *aabb* could produce but one type of gamete (*ab*), while the individual having the genotype *AaBb* produces four types of gametes in equal numbers.

If a large number of offspring are produced by a cross between an individual having the genotype *AaBb* and one having the genotype *aabb* the offspring of the cross should reflect the ratio of gametes produced by

☐ the parent having both dominant characteris-tics . . . . .page **139C.**

☐ the parent having both recessive characteris-tics . . . . .page **133B.**

From page 137C.

Correct. No gray-bodied jaunty-winged nor black-bodied normal-winged flies appeared among the offspring. **135A**
There were only two types of offspring produced: gray normal and black jaunty. What two genotypes were produced in the cross $BbJj \times bbjj$ that resulted in gray normal and black jaunty offspring? (Gray-body is dominant to black, normal-wing to jaunty.)

☐ $Bbjj$ and $bbJj$ . . . . page **138A.**

☐ $BbJj$ and $bbjj$ . . . . page **148D.**

☐ $BBJJ$ and $bbjj$ . . . . page **136A.**

No. You assumed two chromosomes, but how many chromosomes are **135B** there per pair? _____. Return to page **141D.**

From page 141B.

Correct. You predicted that four types of gametes should be produced on the assumption that during gamete formation genes of **135C** different pairs assort independently of each other.
If there is independent assortment the four types of gametes should be produced in the ratio of

☐ 9:3:3:1 . . . . page **149B.**

☐ 1:1:1:1 . . . . page **154B.**

Incorrect. What are the four gametes produced by an individual **135D** with the genotype $BbJj$? _____ _____ _____ _____. Are these not produced in equal number? _____. Does not the individual with the genotype $bbjj$ produce but one type of gamete, bj? _____. So what would be the ratio of the offspring? _____. Expressed as a probability equation this would be _____ $BbJj +$ _____ $Bbjj +$ _____ $bbJj +$ _____ $bbjj = 1.$ Return to page **145A.**

136A **Incorrect.** The cross was gray-body normal-wing (*BbJj*) × black-body jaunty-wing (*bbjj*). Could any of the offspring of such a cross have the genotype *BBJJ*? _____. Return to page **135A**.

136B **Wrong.** You predicted four genotypes: *BbJj*, *Bbjj*, *bbJj*, and *bbjj*. Check your worksheet to make sure you have not made a mistake in these. Of these only *BbJj* and *bbjj* were represented in the 50 offspring. Which two genotypes were not produced? _____. Therefore which of the gametes listed on your worksheet for the parent with the genotype *BbJj* were not produced? _____. Return to page **148D**.

From page **147A**.

136C **Correct.** IN COLUMN 5 OF WORKSHEET 4-A RECORD THE TRANSLATION OF EACH OF THE GENOTYPES INTO ITS EXPECTED PHENOTYPE, KEEPING IN MIND THAT THE GENE *B* STANDS FOR GRAY BODY, THE GENE *b* STANDS FOR BLACK BODY, THE GENE *J* STANDS FOR NORMAL WING, AND THE GENE *j* STANDS FOR JAUNTY WING. IN COLUMN 6 RECORD THE EXPECTED PROBABILITY OF EACH OF THE PHENOTYPES.

The expected phenotypic ratio would be

☐ 9 gray-bodied normal-wing : 3 gray-bodied jaunty-wing : 3 black-bodied normal-wing : 1 black-bodied jaunty-wing..................page   **151D**.

☐ 1 gray-bodied normal-wing : 1 gray-bodied jaunty-wing : 1 black-bodied normal-wing : 1 black-bodied jaunty-wing..................page   **152C**.

136D **No.**

3 dominant   :1 recessive

Return to page **144B**.

From page **133A.**

Correct. Assuming independent assortment of genes, four kinds of **137A** gametes should be produced by an individual with the genotype *AaBb*. The four types of gametes produced should be

☐ *Aa, Bb, Ab, aB* . . . . .page   **134B.**

☐ *AB, Ab, aB, ab* . . . . .page   **141B.**

Incorrect. All of the offspring were either gray-bodied (*B*) and   **137B** normal-winged (*J*) with the genotype *BbJj* or they were black-bodied (*b*) and jaunty-winged (*j*) with the genotype *bbjj*. Which gene was in the same gamete with the gene *B*? _____. With the gene *b*? _____. Therefore, which two genes were on one chromosome of the individual with the heterozygous genotype? _____, and which two genes were on the other chromosome? _____. Return to page **138B.**

From page **134A.**

Correct. The offspring produced by the cross were in a ratio of 1:1.   **137C** These results did not conform to prediction; therefore some new explanation of the results should be found.

Again compare the **expected** phenotypes in column 5 with the record of observations of **actual** phenotypes recorded in column 7. Which two phenotypes did **not** appear in the offspring of the cross?

☐ Gray-bodied normal-winged and black-bodied
   normal-winged . . . . .page   **148C.**

☐ Gray-bodied jaunty-winged and black-bodied
   jaunty-winged . . . . .page   **140C.**

   Gray-bodied jaunty-winged and black-bodied
   normal-winged . . . . .page   **135A.**

Wrong. The heterozygous individual has the genotype *Aa*. If one   **137D** gene goes into one gamete and the other gene into another gamete, in what ratio would they be? _____. Return to page **150C.**

138A **Incorrect.** The dominant genes are those for gray body and for normal wing. What would be the phenotype of an individual with the genotype *Bbjj*? _____. Of *bbJj*? _____. Were these two types produced? _____. Return to page **135A**.

From page 149A.

138B **Correct.** An individual having the genotype *BbJj* in which both pairs of alleles are on the same pair of homologous chromosomes might be symbolized as $\dfrac{B}{b}\ \ \dfrac{J}{j}$ or as $\dfrac{B}{b}\ \ \dfrac{j}{J}$

If the genes for body color and wing tilt were on different sets of homologous chromosomes they could be diagrammed as

$$\dfrac{B}{b} \qquad\qquad\qquad\qquad \dfrac{J}{j}$$

However, the 1:1 phenotypic ratio of the offspring of the cross *BbJj* × *bbjj* (Worksheet 4-A) led us to hypothesize that a single pair of homologous chromosomes was involved and not two pairs of homologous chromosomes.

Which of the following diagrams could represent the genes and chromosomes for the gray, normal parent, on Worksheet 4-A, having the genotype *BbJj*? (Remember that in a cross of this individual with a fly having the genotype *bbjj*, only two types of offspring were produced. They were gray-bodied normal-winged and black-bodied jaunty-winged. We have interpreted this to mean that only two types of gametes were produced by the parent having the heterozygous genotype.)

☐ $\dfrac{B\quad b}{J\quad j}$ ....page **137B**.

☐ $\dfrac{B\quad J}{b\quad j}$ ....page **140B**.

☐ Both of these.............................page **148A**.

138C **Why not?** If the genes assorted independently there should have been four types of offspring. There were not. How could we explain the facts? Return to page **150A**.

From page **146C**.

From page **146C**.

Correct. One half of the gametes of an individual with the genotype **139A**
$\dfrac{A \quad B}{a \quad b}$ should contain the chromosome $\underline{A \quad B}$; the other

half should contain the chromosome $\underline{a \quad b}$.
If the arrangement of the genes on the homologous chromosomes of
an individual with the genotype *AaBb* were $\dfrac{A \quad b}{a \quad B}$,which of the

following equations would represent the probability equation of the
gametes?

☐ ½ *AB* + ½ *ab* = 1...................... page **154A.**

☐ ½ *Ab* + ½ *aB* = 1...................... page **149A.**

☐ Either of these........................... page **142A.**

Wrong. In an individual with the genotype *AaBb* there are two pairs **139B**
of genes, or four genes. Previously we have equated one gene with one
chromosome, hence there would be four chromosomes, or two pairs.
Return to page **149C**.

From page **134C**.

From page **134C**.

Correct. The offspring of the cross *AaBb* × *aabb* should reflect the **139C**
ratio of gametes produced by the parent showing the dominant characteristics. A test cross reflects the ratio of gametes produced by the
parent having the dominant characteristics because

☐ if one of the parents has a genotype which is
homozygous for the recessive genes, all of the
genes present in the parent with the heterozygous genotype will be expressed in the offspring.................................. page **145A.**

☐ none of the recessive genes produced by the
individual showing the dominant characteristics
will be expressed in the offspring........... page **142B.**

140A **Incorrect.** Suppose one gene *A* caused *both* gray body and normal wing, and its allele *a* was the gene for *both* black body and jaunty wings. Could any individual ever have gray body and jaunty wings? _____. Some individuals do have gray body and jaunty wings; others have gray body and normal wings. How many pairs of genes must be involved? _____. Return to page **151A**.

From page **138B**.

140B **Correct.** If we assume that the genes for body color and wing form are on one pair of homologous chromosomes and also that the genes *B* and *J* are on one of the chromosomes and the genes *b* and *j* on the other as $\dfrac{B\quad\;\; J}{b\quad\;\; j}$,we can explain the appearance in the offspring of the two phenotypes gray-body normal-wing and black-body jaunty-wing.

   The transmission of two characteristics which stay together generation after generation is called **linkage.** Linkage can also be defined as the association of two genes on a single chromosome. Thus the assumption that genes always assort independently must be restricted to the condition where genes are on

☐ homologous chromosomes . . . . page **143D.**

☐ nonhomologous chromosomes . . . . page **154C.**

140C **Incorrect.** You have not properly recorded the results of the experiment or you have not filled in your worksheet. Return to page **152C** and correct your worksheet.

140D **Wrong.** You predicted four genotypes: *BbJj*, *Bbjj*, *bbJj*, and *bbjj*. Check your worksheet to make sure you have not made a mistake in these. Of these only *BbJj* and *bbjj* were represented in the 50 offspring. Which two genotypes were not produced? _____. Therefore which of the gametes listed on your worksheet for the parent with the genotype *BbJj* were not produced? _____. Return to page **148D**.

Partially correct. You have recognized that a new symbolization is **141A** necessary to differentiate genes of two pairs which are on the same chromosome from genes of two pairs which assort independently; but you have not realized that the gene *A* might be on the same chromosome as the gene *B*, but that in some other individual the gene *A* might be on the same chromosome as the gene *b*. Return to page **153B**.

From page 137A.

Correct. The four types of gametes produced by the individual having **141B** the genotype *AaBb* should be *AB, Ab, aB, ab.*
   Which postulate of the gene theory directed you to predict that four kinds of gametes should be produced by the individual with the heterozygous genotype?

☐ At gamete formation genes separate, and only
   one of the pair goes into one gamete.........page   **143C.**

☐ During gamete formation genes of different
   pairs assort independently of each other......page   **135C.**

☐ At fertilization genes come together to form
   new pairs................................page   **145D.**

Incorrect. These would be the gametes if the genes assorted inde- **141C** pendently. The symbol *A____B* represents the idea that these genes are on a single chromosome. Return to page **146C.**

From page 149C.

Correct. You assumed two pairs of homologous chromosomes to be **141D** involved in a cross where two pairs of alleles were involved, when you obtained a 1:1:1:1 ratio of gametes.
   In the formation of gametes by the individual having a genotype heterozygous for one trait (*Aa*) how many pairs of homologous chromosomes did you assume to be involved?

☐ One.....................................page   **142D.**

☐ Two.....................................page   **135B.**

142A **Incorrect.** If the genes A and b are on one chromosome as $\underline{\quad A \quad\quad b \quad}$ and the alleles are on the other chromosome of the homologous pair as $\underline{\quad a \quad\quad B \quad}$ would not A and b go together into one gamete and a and B go together into the other gamete? Return to page **139A**.

142B **Incorrect.** If an individual with a heterozygous genotype is crossed with an individual having a genotype homozygous for the recessive genes, all the genes of the heterozygous parent, i.e., both the dominant and the recessive genes, will be expressed in the offspring. For example, since the individual with the genotype *AaBb* produces some gametes with the genes *ab* and since the parent with the genotype *aabb* produces only gametes containing the genes *ab*, some of the offspring should have the genotype *aabb*. Return to page **139C**.

142C **No.** The experiment was repeated, and in no case for this particular cross was the expected $1:1:1:1$ ratio obtained. Return to page **134A**.

From page **141D**.

142D **Correct.** You assumed one pair of homologous chromosomes to be involved in the inheritance of one pair of alleles *Aa*. Thus on the basis of the two pairs of characteristics involved in this cross, we would assume that two pairs of chromosomes are involved; but on the basis of the offspring produced by the test cross, we would assume that only one pair of chromosomes is involved. How do we resolve this dilemma?

   The fruit fly has only four pairs of chromosomes, yet it has been discovered that there are at least 3,000 inherited traits in this insect. How can so many traits be transferred from parents to offspring with so few chromosomes?

☐ Many genes are on a single chromosome.......page **145C**.

☐ Each gene is on a separate chromosome......page **152B**.

Partially correct. You have recognized that a new symbolization is necessary to differentiate genes of two pairs which are on the same chromosome from genes of two pairs which assort independently; but you have not realized that the gene *A* might be on the same chromosome as the gene *B*, but that in some other individual the gene *A* might be on the same chromosome as the gene *b*. Return to page **153B**.

143A

From page **150C**.

Correct. An individual with the genotype *Aa* produces only two types of gametes in the ratio of 1:1 with respect to this trait.

143B

Because the results of the cross between gray-bodied, normal-winged flies and black-bodied, jaunty-winged flies suggested that gametes were produced in a 1:1 ratio, it is possible that only one pair of genes was involved, and that this one pair of genes controls the development of both body color and wing tilt.

Some genes are known to produce multiple effects. For example, a single gene of fowl causes both "frizzled" feathers and enlarged heart.

If any two traits are controlled by a single pair of genes, any cross involving these traits should produce the same two combinations of characteristics.

If a single gene produced both black body and jaunty wing, no individuals having

☐ gray body and normal wings should ever be produced . . . . .page   **144A.**

☐ black body and normal wings should ever be produced . . . . .page   **151A.**

Wrong. This postulate tells you how many genes of a single pair are assumed to be present in each gamete, and therefore is involved in the assigning of four kinds of gametes to an individual heterozygous for two traits, but it is not the principal assumption involved. Return to page **141B**.

143C

Incorrect. We have assumed that independent assortment occurs only when genes are not linked, that is, when the genes are on non-homologous chromosomes. Return to page **140B**.

143D

144A **Incorrect.** If one kind of gene, as *a*, produced both black body and jaunty wing in the homozygous condition, as *aa*, what would be the phenotype of an individual with the genotype *Aa* or *AA*? _____. Return to page **143B**.

From page **150A**.

144B **Correct.** Because the phenotypic ratio of the offspring was 1:1 instead of the expected 1:1:1:1 we could conclude that the gametes were produced in a 1:1 ratio. Therefore, something must have prevented the random assortment of genes in gamete formation.

In this cross the two kinds of offspring that were produced were in a 1:1 ratio. What type of cross that you previously learned about produced offspring in a 1:1 ratio?

☐ An individual having a genotype heterozygous for a single trait (*Aa*) crossed with the recessive (*aa*) . . . . page **150C.**

☐ Two individuals having genotypes heterozygous for one trait (*Aa* × *Aa*) . . . . page **136D.**

144C **Incorrect.** Consider two gametes, one containing the genes *ab* and the other containing the genes *ab*. Are these two gametes alike or are they different? _____. If an individual had the genotype *aabb* what kind of gamete other than *ab* could the individual produce? _____. Return to page **154B**.

144D **Incorrect.** Up to this point we have symbolized a heterozygous genotype as *AaBb*, because both pairs of alleles are present in the same individual. However, the genotype written as *AaBb* could apply to either genes on the same chromosome or to genes which assort independently. When two pairs of alleles are on a pair of homologous chromosomes a new method of symbolizing this idea is useful. Return to page **153B**.

From page **139C.**

Correct. In a test cross, the offspring reflect the kinds of gametes **145A**
produced by the individual having the dominant characteristics, since
all of the genes present in the heterozygous parent will be expressed in
the offspring when the other parent has the genotype *aabb*.

In Drosophila (the fruit fly) there is a pair of alleles affecting body
color, gray and black. Gray is dominant to black. Another pair of
alleles affects wing tilt. The normal straight wing is dominant to the
upturned wing. This latter condition is called "jaunty." Use the symbol *B* for the gene for gray body and the symbol *b* for its allele (black
body). Use the symbol *J* for the gene for normal wing and *j* for the
gene for jaunty wing. A fruit fly with gray body and normal wings,
with genotype heterozygous for both traits, was crossed with a black-
bodied and jaunty-winged fly. ON WORKSHEET 4-A RECORD THE GENO-
TYPES OF THESE TWO INDIVIDUALS AND THE TYPES OF GAMETES WHICH
YOU PREDICT WOULD BE PRODUCED BY EACH. Turn to page 147A.

Wrong. You predicted four genotypes: *BbJj*, *Bbjj*, *bbJj*, and *bbjj*. **145B**
Check your worksheet to make sure you have not made a mistake in
these. Of these only *BbJj* and *bbjj* were represented in the 50 offspring.
Which two genotypes were not produced? _____. Therefore
which of the gametes listed on your worksheet for the parent with the
genotype *BbJj* were not produced? _____. Return to page 148D.

From page **142D.**

Correct. We can assume that many genes may be located on a single **145C**
chromosome. With which of the following would you agree? If two or
more genes are located on the same chromosome

☐ they should assort independently of each
   other. . . . . page   **147C.**

☐ they should not assort independently of each
   other. . . . . page   **153B.**

No. Fertilization takes place later. We are now concerned with gamete **145D**
formation. Return to page 141B.

146A **Incorrect.** Since four genes are involved, A, a, B, and b, and since any combination of A and a with B and b is possible there would be more than two possible combinations. The material which follows requires complete understanding of the two-factor cross. If you have answered this question incorrectly you should thoroughly review the material on two-factor crosses, then return to page **133A**.

146B **Wrong.** How can you obtain four different types of gametes from the genotype Aa? Return to page **150C**.

From page **153B**.

146C **Good.** You have recognized that a new symbolization is necessary to differentiate genes of two pairs which are on the same chromosome from genes of two pairs which are on different chromosomes and assort independently of each other. The diagram $\frac{A \quad b}{a \quad B}$ which could also be "diagrammed" as $\frac{A \quad B}{a \quad b}$, represents two homologous chromosomes each of which carries one allele of each pair of genes; that is, in one individual the gene A might be on the same chromosome as the gene B but in some other individual the gene A might be on the same chromosome as the gene b.

If the genes on one pair of homologous chromosomes of an individual having the genotype $AaBb$ were $\frac{A \quad B}{a \quad b}$ what kinds of gametes could this individual produce with respect to these two traits?

☐ One half containing the chromosome $\underline{A \quad B}$ and one half containing the chromosome $\underline{a \quad b}$ ....page **139A**.

☐ One fourth containing the genes AB, one fourth containing the genes Ab, one fourth containing the genes aB, and one fourth containing the genes ab ....page **141C**.

☐ One half containing the chromosome $\underline{A \quad b}$ and one half containing the chromosome $\underline{a \quad B}$ ....page **151C**.

From page **145A**.

You should have recorded the genotypes of the parents as $BbJj$ and **147A**
$bbjj$. For the individual with the heterozygous genotype the gametes
should be BJ, Bj, bJ, bj. For the other parent only one type of gamete
should have been recorded, bj. Correct your worksheet if necessary.
On Worksheet 4-A are recorded in column 1 the four kinds of gametes
that should be produced by the parent with the heterozygous genotype.
IN EACH OF THE FOUR SPACES IN COLUMN 2 OF WORKSHEET 4-A, RECORD
THE GENES CONTAINED IN THE GAMETES PRODUCED BY THE PARENT
WITH THE GENOTYPE $bbjj$. CALCULATE AND RECORD IN COLUMN 3 THE
EXPECTED GENOTYPES OF THE OFFSPRING OF THE UNION OF EACH OF
THE FOUR KINDS OF GAMETES PRODUCED BY THE PARENT WITH THE
GENOTYPE $BbJj$ WITH THE GAMETES (bj) PRODUCED BY THE OTHER
PARENT. IN COLUMN 4 RECORD THE FRACTION REPRESENTING THE
PROBABILITY FOR EACH OF THE FOUR GENOTYPES THAT SHOULD BE
PRODUCED.

Which of the following is the probability equation representing the
expected genotypes of the offspring of the cross $(BbJj \times bbjj)$?

☐ $\frac{9}{16} BbJj + \frac{3}{16} Bbjj + \frac{3}{16} bbJj + \frac{1}{16} bbjj = 1$ .... page   **135D.**

☐ $\frac{1}{4} BbJj + \frac{1}{4} Bbjj + \frac{1}{4} bbJj + \frac{1}{4} bbjj = 1$ .... page   **136C.**

☐ Neither of these............................page   **150B.**

Why not? Only two kinds of offspring in approximately equal num- **147B**
bers appeared as a result of the cross $BbJj \times bbjj$. We have equated
the phenotypic ratio of $1:1$ with the behavior of a single pair of alleles
on a single pair of homologous chromosomes. Could not the alleles Bb
and Jj be on one pair of homologous chromosomes? Return to page
149A.

Incorrect. The concept of independent assortment is the same as **147C**
chance in coin tossing. If a coin falls heads up, this event has no influ-
ence on whether the coin will fall heads or tails on the next toss. That
is, the two events are independent of each other. The same is true of
genes when they are on different chromosomes because it is a matter
of chance whether one chromosome of a pair goes into one or the other
of two daughter cells. However, if two genes are on the same chromosome both genes would go together into one daughter cell; that is,
what happens to one gene is not independent of what happens to the
other. Return to page **145C.**

148A **Incorrect.** All of the offspring were either gray-bodied (B) and normal-winged (J) with the genotype $BbJj$ or they were black-bodied (b) and jaunty-winged (j) with the genotype $bbjj$. Which gene was in the same gamete with the gene B? _____. With the gene b? _____. Therefore, which two genes were on one chromosome of the individual with the heterozygous genotype? _____, and which two genes were on the other chromosome? _____. Return to page **138B**.

148B **Incorrect.** Reexamine the recorded results. Only two types of offspring were produced. Return to page **152C**.

148C **Incorrect.** You have not properly recorded the results of the experiment or you have not filled in your worksheet. Return to page **152C** and correct your worksheet.

From page **135A**.

148D **Correct.** Since only two phenotypes were produced we can assume that only two genotypes were produced. The individuals with the genotype $BbJj$ developed into gray-bodied normal-winged flies, while those with the genotype $bbjj$ developed into black-bodied jaunty-winged flies.

We can also assume that no zygotes were formed with the genotype $Bbjj$ nor with the genotype $bbJj$.

If the absence of offspring reflects absence of zygotes having certain genotypes and if the absence of zygotes with these genotypes reflects absence of gametes of a certain kind, what conclusion can you draw concerning the types of gametes that were *not* formed by the individual having the genotype $BbJj$? (Examine the worksheet for a clue to the answer.)

☐ BJ, bj . . . . .page   **136B.**

☐ BJ, Bj . . . . .page   **145B.**

☐ bJ, bj . . . . .page   **140D.**

☐ Bj, bJ . . . . .page   **150A.**

From page **139A.**

From page **139A.**

Correct. The probability equation ½ $\underline{A \quad b}$ + ½ $\underline{a \quad B}$ = 1 **149A**
would represent the gametes of an individual with the genotype
$\dfrac{A \quad b}{a \quad B}$.

Could a cell of an individual with the genotype heterozygous for
body color and wing tilt (*BbJj*) be represented by diagrams as follows?

$$\frac{B \quad J}{b \quad j}$$

$$\frac{B \quad j}{b \quad J}$$

☐ Yes.......................................page **138B.**

☐ No..page **147B.**

Incorrect. The 9:3:3:1 ratio is a phenotypic ratio and not a ratio of **149B**
gametes. A complete understanding of the two-factor cross is essential
for mastery of the material in this chapter. Thoroughly review the
two-factor cross before proceeding; then return to page **135C.**

From page **151A.**

Correct. Since the characteristics black body and jaunty wing are **149C**
not always found together in a single individual, we must conclude
that at least two pairs of alleles are involved. However, we have also
discovered that these pairs of genes do not assort independently of
each other and at random. In fact they behave in the cross we have
been discussing as if they were a single gene. To help to solve the problem of how two pairs of alleles can behave in some crosses as if they
were one, answer the following question: In the two-factor cross where
there is independent assortment and the formation of four types of
gametes in a 1:1:1:1 ratio, how many pairs of homologous chromosomes did you assume were involved?

☐ One.......................................page **139B.**

☐ Two.......................................page **141D.**

☐ Four......................................page **152A.**

From page 148D.

150A **Correct.** Gametes containing the combinations Bj and bJ apparently were not produced.

The results of the actual cross did not conform with the predictions you made on the basis of the assumption of independent assortment, therefore our next problem is to attempt to find an explanation for the discrepancy between predicted results and actual results.

You had assumed that four different types of offspring would be produced in a $1:1:1:1$ ratio because you had assumed that four types of gametes would be formed in a $1:1:1:1$ ratio by the individual with a genotype heterozygous for both traits ($BbJj$).

Does the lack of two of the four possible kinds of gametes mean that in this case we should question the assumption of independent assortment?

☐ Yes. . . . . .page **144B.**

☐ No. . . . . .page **138C.**

150B **Incorrect.** What are the four gametes produced by an individual with the genotype $BbJj$? _____ _____ _____
_____. Are these not produced in equal number? _____.
Does not the individual with the genotype $bbjj$ produce but one type of gamete, bj? _____. So what would be the ratio of the offspring?
_____. Expressed as a probability equation this would be
_____ $BbJj$ + _____ $Bbjj$ + _____ $bbJj$ +
_____ $bbjj$ = 1. Return to page **145A.**

From page 144B.

150C **Correct.** A $1:1$ ratio of offspring is produced by the cross $Aa \times aa$.

What ratio of gametes did you assume to be produced by the individual with the heterozygous genotype Aa in order to result in a $1:1$ phenotypic ratio of offspring?

☐ $1:1:1:1$. . . . . .page **146B.**

☐ $3:1$. . . . . .page **137D.**

☐ $1:1$. . . . . .page **143B.**

From page 143B.

Correct. No individuals would ever be found which had gray body **151A** and jaunty wings, nor would any individuals ever be found which had black body and normal wings. This, however, is not the case. Wild fruit flies of each of these two types have been found, so we must discard the hypothesis that one gene is responsible for the development of both black body and jaunty wings. Therefore, we must conclude that for the production of body color and wing tilt

☐ one pair of alleles is involved............... page   **140A.**

☐ at least two pairs of alleles are involved ...... page   **149C.**

Although it is possible that with fifty offspring one might obtain a **151B** ratio which was abnormal, it is unlikely. However, further experiments were carried out and even with 500 offspring the ratio of the predicted types was not 1:1:1:1. Return to page **134A.**

Incorrect. If the genotype was $\dfrac{A \qquad B}{a \qquad b}$ and if during meiosis **151C** these homologous chromosomes lined up on the spindle as follows

would not genes A and B go together into one gamete? And would not the genes a and b go together into the other gamete formed at this meiotic division? Return to page **146C.**

Wrong. How many different kinds of gametes can the black-bodied **151D** jaunty-winged individual with the genotype $bbjj$ produce? _____. You have predicted that the heterozygous individuals will produce four kinds of gametes in a ratio of 1:1:1:1. So what will be the predicted ratio for the offspring? _____. A 9:3:3:1 ratio is only obtained when two individuals, heterozygous for two traits, are crossed. Return to page **136C.**

152A **No.** You assumed that four chromosomes would be involved, but how many pairs of homologous chromosomes would the four chromosomes represent? _____. Return to page **149C.**

152B **No.** If each gene were on a separate chromosome, then an individual having 3,000 inheritable traits would have to have 3,000 pairs of chromosomes. How many pairs of chromosomes does the fruit fly have? _____. Return to page **142D.**

From page **136C.**

152C **Correct.** You have predicted that four types of offspring would be produced in a 1:1:1:1 ratio. RECORD THIS EXPECTED PHENOTYPIC RATIO AT THE PROPER PLACE ON WORKSHEET 4-A. When this cross between an individual having a genotype heterozygous for both traits and one having both recessive characteristics ($BbJj \times bbjj$) was actually made, of 50 offspring 26 were gray-bodied and normal-winged and 24 were black-bodied and jaunty-winged. ON WORKSHEET 4-A ON LINE 1 OF COLUMN 7 RECORD 26 GRAY NORMAL TO INDICATE THAT THIS PHENOTYPE ACTUALLY OCCURRED IN THIS NUMBER AMONG THE OFF-SPRING. ON LINE 4 OF COLUMN 7 RECORD 24 BLACK JAUNTY TO INDICATE THAT THIS PHENOTYPE ALSO OCCURRED IN THIS NUMBER AMONG THE OFFSPRING. IN COLUMN 8 RECORD THE FRACTION OF THE TOTAL NUMBER OF OFFSPRING WHICH WERE GRAY-BODIED NORMAL-WINGED, AND THE FRACTION WHICH WERE BLACK-BODIED AND JAUNTY-WINGED. USE SMALL WHOLE NUMBER FRACTIONS SUCH AS $\frac{1}{4}$, $\frac{1}{2}$, $\frac{3}{4}$, ETC.

Which of the following represents an equation that expresses the observed results of the cross?

☐ $\frac{1}{2}$ gray-bodied normal-winged + $\frac{1}{2}$ black-bodied jaunty-winged = 1 .... page **134A.**

☐ $\frac{3}{4}$ gray-bodied normal-winged + $\frac{1}{4}$ black-bodied jaunty-winged = 1 .... page **133C.**

☐ $\frac{1}{4}$ gray normal + $\frac{1}{4}$ gray jaunty + $\frac{1}{4}$ black normal + $\frac{1}{4}$ black jaunty = 1 .... page **148B.**

Incorrect. Consider two gametes, one containing the genes *ab* and **153A** the other containing the genes *ab*. Are these two gametes alike or are they different? _____. If an individual had the genotype *aabb* what kind of gamete other than *ab* could the individual produce? _____. Return to page **154B**.

From page **145C**.

Correct. Independent assortment applies to chromosomes, and applies **153B** to genes only when the genes are on different nonhomologous chromosomes. To illustrate: if during meiosis two pairs of homologous chromosomes line up on the equator of the spindle in one cell as

they may line up on the equator of another cell as

Chance determines how the homologous chromosomes are arranged on the spindle. In the first case diagrammed above, after the reduction division chromosomes *A* and *B* will go into one daughter cell together and chromosomes *a* and *b* will go into the other. In the second case chromosomes *a* and *B* will go together into one cell and chromosomes *A* and *b* into the other cell.

If two pairs of genes are located on homologous chromosomes and thus do not assort independently of each other, which of the following diagrams represents an individual with a genotype heterozygous for two traits? (Let a line stand for a single chromosome. Letters represent genes located on that chromosome, as _A_ .)

☐ $\dfrac{A \quad b}{a \quad B}$ ....page **141A**.

☐ $\dfrac{A \quad B}{a \quad b}$ ....page **143A**.

☐ Both of these ....page **146C**.

☐ Neither of these; the genotype must be written
  AaBb ....page **144D**.

154A **Incorrect.** If the genes A and b are on one chromosome as $\underline{A \quad b}$ and the alleles are on the other chromosome of the homologous pair as $\underline{a \quad B}$,would not A and b go together into one gamete and a and B go together into the other gamete? Return to page **139A.**

From page **135C.**

154B **Correct.** If there is independent assortment of genes, the gametes should be produced in a ratio of $1AB:1Ab:1aB:1ab$.

Now consider an individual with the genotype $aabb$. How many kinds of gametes should this individual produce?

☐ One.....................................page **134C.**

☐ Two.....................................page **153A.**

☐ Four....................................page **144C.**

From page **140B.**

154C **Correct.** The assumption that genes always assort independently must be restricted to the condition where genes are on nonhomologous chromosomes.

The results of the cross $BbJj \times bbjj$ conflicted with predictions made on the basis of the postulate of the gene theory, "Genes assort independently of each other." When predictions from a theory conflict with obtained results, first the correctness of the data may be questioned. However, we have assumed that if independent assortment took place, at least some of the 50 offspring should have been gray-bodied jaunty-winged and some black-bodied normal-winged. Therefore, we accepted the data as correct.

If the data are correct then the postulate of independent assortment must be questioned. Apparently there are some cases in which independent assortment does not occur. These are situations where the genes are on the same chromosomes and as a result go together during gamete formation. Continue with the review of Part I.

REVIEW—Chapter 4, Part I

If a backcross is made between an individual with a genotype heterozygous for two traits and an individual recessive for both traits ($AaBb \times aabb$), when there is independent assortment gametes are produced by the individual with the genotype $AaBb$ in the ratio of (#) _____. Therefore the ratio of the offspring should be (#) _____. In such a cross this random assortment of the two pairs of alleles is explained by assuming that two pairs of alleles are located on (#)_____ pair(s) of homologous chromosomes. If, however, the ratio of the offspring is $1:1$ we assume that only (#) _____ types of gametes were produced. Such a condition is called (wd) _____ and can be explained by assuming that the two pairs of alleles are located on (#) _____ pair(s) of homologous chromosomes.

Check your responses to the review with those on page 358 and continue with the summary of Part I.

SUMMARY—Chapter 4, Part I

On the basis of the assumption that different pairs of genes assort independently in gamete formation we predicted that a dihybrid individual having the genotype $AaBb$ would produce four kinds of gametes: AB, Ab, aB, and ab. Such an individual crossed with a recessive having the genotype $aabb$ would produce four kinds of offspring in equal numbers.

In a particular cross of fruit flies having the contrasting characteristics black and gray body color, and normal and jaunty wing, the expected four kinds of offspring did not appear. Instead only two of the four possible kinds were produced. One possible explanation was that only a single pair of genes was involved where this pair of genes controlled two sets of characteristics. However, if this explanation were true only two of the four possible combinations of characteristics could appear together. That is, the flies could only be gray-bodied normal-winged or black-bodied jaunty-winged. No gray jaunty flies nor black normal-winged flies could be expected. Because all four combinations of these characteristics appeared, it was concluded that two pairs of genes were operating and not just one pair.

If two genes behaved in gamete formation and fertilization as if they were one, then the two genes must be linked together in some fashion so that they did not assort independently. Such linkage would be possible if the two genes were on the same chromosome. This assumption was made.

Continue with Part II.

PART II

156A In Part I, data which conflicted with predictions from the assumption of independent assortment were presented. These data led to the assumption that genes located on the same chromosome did not assort independently. Such association of genes is called linkage. Thus in order to explain the results of the cross $BbJj \times bbjj$, a new assumption must be added to the gene theory, that is, that **genes on the same chromosome go together during gamete formation.**

Now let us consider a cross involving two other pairs of characteristics of the fruit fly. A fruit fly with normal-shaped eyes and normal wings, with a genotype heterozygous for both traits ($KkSs$), was crossed with a fly having kidney-shaped eyes and short wings ($kkss$). What should be the ratio of the offspring?

☐ 1:1:1:1 . . . . page **161A.**

☐ 1:1 . . . . page **164A.**

☐ I have no basis for making a prediction; it might
be either of these . . . . page **159D.**

156B **Correct but incomplete.** Return to page **162A.**

From page **158A.**

156C **Correct.** One of the genotypes was diagrammed as $\frac{K \qquad S}{k \qquad s}$

Which of the following genotypes did you NOT record?

☐ $\frac{K \qquad S}{k \qquad s}$ . . . . page **169B.**

☐ $\frac{k \qquad s}{k \qquad s}$ . . . . page **160A.**

☐ $\frac{K \qquad s}{k \qquad S}$ . . . . page **164B.**

Incorrect. Since crossing-over is due to a break across the width of **157A** the chromosome that separates linked genes, the genes must be arranged in tandem along the length of the chromosome, like beads on a string. Return to page **180A**.

Incorrect. If the genotype of the parent having the two dominant **157B** characteristics is symbolized as $\dfrac{K \quad S}{k \quad s}$ and if chromosomes segregate so that one chromosome goes into one gamete and the other into the other gamete, what should be the ratio of gametes containing the chromosomes $K \quad S$ to those containing the chromosome $k \quad s$? _____. What is the ratio of the genotypes $\dfrac{K \quad S}{k \quad s}$: $\dfrac{k \quad s}{k \quad s}$? _____. Therefore the phenotypic ratio should be _____. Return to page **164B**.

Correct but incomplete. Return to page **173A**.   **157C**

From page **167A**.

Correct. If the gene K was linked with the gene S, the genotype **157D** would be diagrammed as $\dfrac{K \quad S}{k \quad s}$.

On the assumption that the gene for normal eye and the gene for normal wing are linked on the same chromosome, ENTER ON WORK-SHEET 4-B THE TYPES OF GAMETES THAT AN INDIVIDUAL WITH THE GENOTYPE $KkSs$ WOULD PRODUCE, THAT IS, GAMETES $K \quad S$ AND $k \quad s$.

ALSO RECORD THE GAMETES THAT SHOULD BE PRODUCED BY AN INDIVIDUAL HAVING THE GENOTYPE $kkss$. USE A LINE TO REPRESENT A CHROMOSOME.

Which of the following have you recorded for the gametes produced by the individual with the genotype $kkss$?

☐ k and s ....page   **182B.**

☐ $k \quad s$ ....page   **158A.**

From page **157D.**

158A **Correct.** All of the gametes produced by the individual having the genotype *kkss* in which the genes *k* and *s* are assumed to be linked would be   *k s*

USING THE CHROMOSOME AND GENE SYMBOLS COMBINE THE GAMETES. RECORD ON WORKSHEET 4-B THE EXPECTED GENOTYPES AND RATIO OF THE OFFSPRING OF A CROSS BETWEEN *KkSs* × *kkss* WHERE THE GENES ARE ASSUMED TO BE LINKED.

One of the genotypes recorded is

☐ *KkSs* . . . . .page   **160B.**

☐ $\dfrac{K \quad S}{k \quad s}$ . . . . .page   **156C.**

158B **Incorrect.** If the individual had two genes for normal wing (*VV*), then it would be true that the normal allele for the vestigial gene would be at that locus on each chromosome of the pair; but what about the flies in the population that had only genes for vestigial (*vv*)? Would these flies have the normal allele at this locus? _____. Return to page **165D.**

158C **Incorrect.** Linkage was defined as the association of two genes on one chromosome. You were instructed to assume that the genes *K* and *S* were linked. The line with the dots (___•_____•___) is used as a symbol for a single chromosome. Place the genes *K* and *S* on this line. The individual is known to have a genotype heterozygous for both traits. What two genes would be on the other chromosome? _____. Return to page **167A.**

158D **Wrong.** *K* and *S* were linked on the chromosome before the exchange as   *K S* . Then we assume a break between *K* and *S* and a recombination of the genes.

Return to page **171A.**

Why not? "Assortment" means that the various gene combinations, **159A** as KS, Ks, kS and ks, occur in the gametes. The term "independent" means that the assortment is random, that is, due to chance. If the assortment is due to chance the ratio of the gametes should be $1:1:1:1$. The ratio of test cross offspring was not $1:1:1:1$, therefore we assume the gamete ratio was not $1:1:1:1$, and hence assortment was not random. Return to page **179A**.

No. The percentage of crossing-over is the sum of the percents of **159B** individuals who have the phenotypes which would not be expected if linkage were complete. Return to page **160C**.

How come? If the ratio of gametes produced by the dihybrid were **159C** $1:1:1:1$, each of the four types of offspring would have represented 25% of the total number. This is contrary to the data obtained. Return to page **161C**.

From page **156A**.

Good. No data were presented which would enable you to tell whether **159D** pairs of alleles were on two pairs of homologous chromosomes, or whether they were both on a single pair of homologous chromosomes. If the genes were linked you would expect the ratio of the phenotypes of the offspring of the cross $KkSs \times kkss$ to be (#) _____, while if the genes assorted independently you would expect a phenotypic ratio of (#) _____ in the offspring.

FIRST ASSUME THAT THE GENES ASSORTED INDEPENDENTLY. ENTER ON WORKSHEET 4-B THE EXPECTED GENOTYPES AND THE RATIO OF THESE GENOTYPES. ALSO ENTER THE EXPECTED PHENOTYPES AND THEIR RATIO.

What have you recorded for the phenotypic ratio?

☐ 1 normal-eye normal-wing : 1 normal-eye short-wing : 1 kidney-shaped-eye normal-wing : 1 kidney-shaped-eye short-wing..................page **177A**.

☐ 1 normal-eye normal-wing : 1 kidney-shaped-eye short-wing...............................page **181B**.

160A **Incorrect.** What genotype have you recorded as the result of the union of the gamete symbolized as $\underline{\quad k \quad s \quad}$ from the parent with the heterozygous genotype with the gamete produced by the parent having the genotype $\dfrac{k \qquad s}{k \qquad s}$? Return to page **156C**.

160B **Partially incorrect.** The genotype *KkSs* is one of the genotypes that would be produced, but you were instructed to use symbols which would also indicate linkage. Return to page **158A**.

From page **165D**.

160C **Correct.** For any one chromosome of the pair of homologous chromosomes that carry the genes for vestigial or its allele, the gene for normal wing, either the gene for vestigial or its normal allele would be at that locus, but not both.

We assumed linkage and crossing-over to explain the appearance among the offspring of a test cross of four different kinds of offspring in a ratio that deviated from $1:1:1:1$.

The offspring with the two phenotypes that appeared in the largest number were assumed to be due to linkage between two pairs of genes. The offspring with the two phenotypes that appeared in the smaller number were explained by assuming crossing-over. The percentage of such offspring reflected the percentage of crossing-over that must have occurred between the linked genes.

Examine the following data obtained from a cross between a male having the recessive genes for vestigial wings and cinnabar eyes (*vvcc*) and a normal-winged, red-eyed female with a genotype heterozygous for both characteristics (*VvCc*).

Of the offspring produced, 5% were normal-winged and cinnabar-eyed, 5% were vestigial-winged and red-eyed, 45% were normal-winged and red-eyed, and 45% were vestigial-winged and cinnabar-eyed.

What is the percentage of crossing-over between these two pairs of genes?

☐ 5% . . . . .page   **159B.**

☐ 10% . . . . .page   **169C.**

☐ Cannot be determined from the data given . . . page   **165A.**

Wrong. How can you tell whether the genes are located on a single **161A** chromosome or whether they are located on different chromosomes? Return to page **156A**.

Correct but incomplete. Return to page **162A**.   **161B**

From page **166D**.

Correct. Since there were more than seven times as many normal- **161C** eyed normal-winged and kidney-shape-eyed short-winged offspring as there were normal-eyed short-winged and kidney-shape-eyed normal winged offspring, we can conclude that there was some degree of linkage.

The ratio of offspring of the cross between the normal-eyed normal-winged flies with flies having kidney-shaped eyes and short wings ($KkSs \times kkss$) was

> 22 normal-eyed normal-winged:
> 3 normal-eyed short-winged:
> 3 kidney-shape-eyed normal-winged:
> 22 kidney-shape-eyed short-winged.

Since the offspring of a test cross reflect the ratio of the kinds of gametes produced, we can conclude that the ratio of the gametes produced by the individual having a genotype heterozygous for both traits was

☐ $1KS:1Ks:1kS:1ks$ . . . . page   **159C.**

☐ $1KS:1ks$ . . . . page   **166C.**

☐ $22KS:3Ks:3kS:22ks$ . . . . page   **176C.**

Incorrect. Whenever a ratio such as $9:1:1:9$ reflects linkage and **161D** crossing-over, the two larger numbers of the ratio represent the two phenotypes that were linked. If the genotype of the parent with the two dominant characteristics was $\dfrac{V \quad\quad c}{v \quad\quad C}$, this would indicate linkage of normal wing with cinnabar eye and vestigial wing with red eye, and a ratio of 9 normal wing cinnabar-eyed:1 normal wing red-eyed:1 vestigial wing cinnabar-eyed:9 vestigial wing red-eyed. Return to page **163C**.

From page 182A.

162A **Correct.** The crosses leading to concepts of linkage and of crossing-over required that the concept of independent assortment be restricted to chromosomes rather than to genes. The data on crossing-over and observations of chromosome behavior prior to meiosis lead to the hypothesis that occasionally chromosomes break and exchange parts. Such an hypothesis requires certain assumptions about the arrangement of genes on chromosomes. Which of the following are necessary assumptions?

☐ Genes are located on chromosomes in linear order . . . . .page **161B.**

☐ Alleles occupy corresponding loci on homologous chromosomes . . . . .page **156B.**

☐ Both of these are necessary . . . . .page **182C.**

162B **Incorrect.** If we assume linkage, it is true that only two types of gametes would be produced, but how can we tell from the data given whether gene K is linked with gene S or s? Return to page **177A.**

162C **Wrong.** If in 12 of the original immature germ cells there was crossing-over, then 12 cells would have genes as follows and divide.

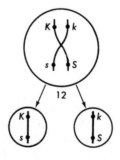

How many cells would be produced as a result of division of these 12 cells? _____. What percent of them would contain the genes K and s? _____. What is 50% of 24? _____. Return to page **167C.**

No. Six individuals out of 1000 were of the types which would not be **163A**
expected if there were complete linkage. Expressed as a fraction this
is 6/1000. What is 6/1000 expressed in percent? _____. Return
to page **178C**.

Wrong. This is the percent of the gametes containing the combination **163B**
K and s; 6% of the gametes would contain the genes k and S. You have
probably not followed the entire argument beginning on page **172A**.
Return to that page.

From page **169C**.

Correct. If the offspring of the cross $VvCv \times vvcc$ are in the ratio **163C**
9 normal-winged red-eyed:1 normal-winged cinnabar-eyed:1 vestigial-
winged red-eyed:9 vestigial-winged cinnabar-eyed, we would conclude
that in the parent with the heterozygous genotype, the genes for cinnabar and vestigial were on one chromosome and the genes for normal
wings and red eyes were on the other chromosome. We knew that
genes V and C were linked, and that genes v and c were linked, because
among the offspring these two gene combinations occurred in greater
numbers. And if genes V and C were linked and genes v and c were
linked, then the genotype of the heterozygous parent could be written
$\dfrac{V \quad C}{v \quad c}$. Now let us reverse the problem. Let us assume that the

heterozygous parent had the genotype $\dfrac{v \quad C}{V \quad c}$; that is, gene v is

linked with gene C and gene V is linked with gene c. If such a fly were
crossed with one having the genotype $\dfrac{v \quad c}{v \quad c}$ what would be the

ratio of the offspring?

☐ 9 normal-winged cinnabar-eyed : 1 normal-
winged red-eyed : 1 vestigial-winged cinnabar-
eyed : 9 vestigial-winged red-eyed . . . . page **180C**.

☐ 9 normal-winged red-eyed : 1 normal-winged
cinnabar-eyed : 1 vestigial-winged red-eyed : 9
vestigial-winged cinnabar-eyed . . . . page **166A**.

☐ Cannot be determined from the data given . . . . page **161D**.

164A **Wrong.** How can you tell whether the genes are located on a single chromosome or whether they are located on different chromosomes? Return to page **156A**.

From page **156C**.

164B **Correct.** If we assume that the genes K and S are linked on one chromosome as $\underline{K\quad S}$ and the genes k and s are linked on the other chromosome of the pair as $\underline{k\quad s}$, when two gametes containing such linked genes unite in fertilization *no* zygote would be found that could be diagrammed as $\dfrac{K\quad s}{k\quad S}$.

Translate the genotypes you have recorded, $\dfrac{K\quad S}{k\quad s}\dfrac{k\quad s}{k\quad s}$

into expected phenotypes. RECORD THESE PHENOTYPES ON WORKSHEET 4-B. ALSO RECORD THE EXPECTED RATIOS. (Remember that normal eye is dominant to kidney-shaped eye and normal wing is dominant to short wing.)

What is the expected phenotypic ratio if the genes for these two traits are linked?

☐ 3:1. . . . . .page **157B**.

☐ 1:1. . . . . .page **183B**.

164C **Incorrect.** Suppose that one chromosome had the genes located as $\underline{K\quad S}$ and the other had the genes located as $\underline{\qquad\qquad}_{ks}$.

When the chromosomes came together in meiosis we would have

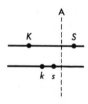

Suppose the break were at the line marked (A). What genes would the resulting gametes contain? _____. Return to page **181C**.

164D **Correct but incomplete.** Return to page **173A**.

No. The percentage of crossing-over is the sum of the percents of **165A** individuals who have the phenotypes which would not be expected if linkage were complete. Return to page **160C**.

Wrong. This would be the distribution if the genes were not on the **165B** same chromosome. Return to page **172A**.

Incorrect. Three gametes out of 50 should contain the genes *Ks*. **165C** What is 3/50 expressed in percent? Return to page **176C**.

From page **180A**.

Correct. The assumption of crossing-over also suggested other new **165D** assumptions to be added to the gene theory. They are:

1. **Genes are located in a linear order on chromosomes**
2. **Alleles occupy corresponding positions on homologous chromosomes**
3. **Alleles line up side by side during meiosis.**

Consider a population of fruit flies some of which have genes for vestigial wing and some of which have its allele, *i.e.*, the gene for normal wing. Also some flies have homozygous genotypes for either of the two characteristics, while others have genotypes heterozygous for the two characteristics.

Let us assume that the locus of the gene for vestigial wing is at the spot diagrammed as

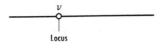

For any *one* chromosome of the pair of homologous chromosomes that carry these genes

☐ the gene for vestigial is at that locus.........page **175A.**

☐ the gene for normal wing, the allele of the vestigial gene, is at that locus...................page **158B.**

☐ either the gene for vestigial or its normal allele
is at that locus, but not both...............page **160C.**

166A **Incorrect.** Whenever a ratio such as 9:1:1:9 reflects linkage and crossing-over, the two larger numbers of the ratio represent the two phenotypes that were linked. If the genotype of the parent with the two dominant characteristics was $\dfrac{V \quad c}{v \quad C}$, this would indicate linkage of normal wing with cinnabar eye and vestigial wing with red eye, and a ratio of 9 normal wing cinnabar-eyed:1 normal wing red-eyed:1 vestigial wing cinnabar-eyed:9 vestigial wing red-eyed. Return to page **163C**.

166B **How come?** If they were completely linked, no individuals with black bodies and normal wings and no individuals with gray bodies and jaunty wings should have been produced. Return to page **180C**.

166C **No.** If the ratio of the gametes produced by the dihybrid were 1:1 (KS and ks) then only two types of individuals would have been produced. This is contrary to the data obtained. Return to page **161C**.

From page **168B**.

166D **Correct.** If there were complete linkage of the gene K with S and of the gene k with s there should have been no flies with normal eyes and short wings nor any with kidney-shaped eyes and normal wings. The fact that these two kinds of flies were produced indicates that there was not complete linkage.

However, there was evidence that some linkage did occur; that is, some genes went together more frequently than would be expected if there had been independent assortment.

What is the evidence?

☐ There was an equal probability of any of the four types of offspring being produced.......page **168A**.

☐ There were more than seven times as many normal-eyed normal-winged and kidney-shape-eyed short-winged offspring as there were normal-eyed short-winged and kidney-shape-eyed normal-winged offspring...............page **161C**.

From page 177A.

Excellent. Even if the genes for eye shape and wing shape were **167A** linked, from the information given it would not be possible to tell whether the gene for normal eye was on the same chromosome with the gene for normal wing or whether the gene for normal eye was linked with the gene for short wing.

If the genes for normal eye K and normal wing S were linked, which of the following diagrams would represent one pair of homologous chromosomes of the parent with the genotype $KkSs$?

☐ $\dfrac{K \quad S}{k \quad s}$ ....page **157D.**

☐ $\dfrac{K \quad s}{k \quad S}$ ....page **158C.**

If there were independent assortment, the ratio of phenotypes of the **167B** offspring should have been 1:1:1:1. Was it? _____. Return to page **183B.**

From page 174A.

Correct. 88 of the cells would contain the genes KS, and 88 would **167C** contain the other linked genes ks.

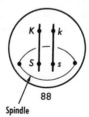 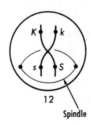

As a result of crossing-over how many of the cells would contain the new combination Ks?

☐ 6 ....page **162C.**

☐ 12 ....page **170C.**

☐ 24 ....page **177C.**

168A **Incorrect.** A ratio of 22:3:3:22 is not a 1:1:1:1 ratio. Equal probability means a 1:1:1:1 ratio in this case. Return to page **166D**.

From page **179A**.

168B **Correct.** The appearance of four kinds of offspring from the cross *KkSs* × *kkss* could only be explained by assuming assortment of genes. Had there been no assortment of genes, then only two kinds of offspring would have been produced, and we would have explained this fact by assuming linkage between the gene *K* and the gene *S* and between the gene *k* and the gene *s*. Because all four possible combinations of characteristics appeared in the offspring we must reason that the four possible combinations of genes, *KS*, *Ks*, *kS*, and *ks*, were produced by the parent with the genotype *KkSs*. These four kinds of gametes could be produced only if assortment had taken place among the four kinds of genes. However, this assortment could not have been independent or random because the ratio of offspring was not 1:1:1:1 but 22:3:3:22.

The results of the cross *KkSs* × *kkss* expressed as a ratio were

> 22 normal-eyed normal-winged:
> 3 normal-eyed short-winged:
> 3 kidney-shape-eyed normal-winged:
> 22 kidney-shape-eyed short-winged.

Compare the above phenotypes and ratio with the phenotypes and ratio predicted on the assumption that there was complete linkage between genes *K* and *S*, and between genes *k* and *s*. Which two phenotypes appeared among the offspring that were *not* predicted on the basis of complete linkage?

☐ Normal-eyed normal-winged and kidney-shape-eyed short-winged . . . . page **173C**.

☐ Normal-eyed short-winged and kidney-shape-eyed normal-winged . . . . page **166D**.

168C **No.** Linkage and crossing-over are concerned with more than one pair of genes; segregation refers to a single pair of genes. Return to page **182A**.

From page 183B.

Correct. There is lack of correspondence between the actual ratio of **169A**
$22:3:3:22$ and the $1:1:1:1$ ratio expected on the basis of assuming
that independent assortment occurred.

EXAMINE WORKSHEET 4-B. Compare the ratio obtained from an actual cross with the ratio expected on the assumption that the genes were linked. Can the results be explained by assuming that there was complete linkage of the genes?

☐ Yes......................................page **170B.**

☐ No.......................................page **179A.**

Incorrect. You must have made a careless error. You have already **169B**
indicated that you recorded the genotype $\frac{K \quad S}{k \quad s}$. Return to

page 156C.

From page 160C.

Correct. The percentage of the total number of individuals resulting **169C**
from crossing-over is the crossover percentage, and is the sum of the
percentages of individuals who have the phenotypes that would not be
expected if linkage were complete. Thus in this case, the crossover
percentage was 10%.

The offspring produced by the test cross were

> 45% normal-winged red-eyed
> 5% normal-winged cinnabar-eyed
> 5% vestigial-winged red-eyed
> 45% vestigial-winged cinnabar-eyed

Which of the following represents the genotype of the parent that had both of the dominant characteristics?

☐ $\frac{V \quad C}{v \quad c}$ ....page **163C.**

☐ $\frac{V \quad c}{v \quad C}$ ....page **179C.**

☐ Either of these...........................page **173B.**

170A **Incorrect.** If 88 of the original immature germ cells have the genes as follows and they divide,

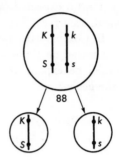

what is the total number of cells that will be produced? _____.
What percent will contain the genes K and S? _____. What is 50% of 176? _____. Return to page **174A**.

170B If there were complete linkage, the ratio for the phenotypes of the offspring should have been 1:1. Was it? _____. Return to page **169A**.

From page **167C**.

170C **Correct.** 12 of the cells would contain the genes Ks, and 12 would contain the genes kS.

Thus out of 100 immature reproductive cells, 200 new cells would be produced.

If crossing-over occurred in 12 of the initial 100 cells, when these 12 cells divided 24 cells would be produced. Half of these 24 cells would contain the gene combination Ks, and the other half would contain the gene combination kS. The 24 cells that would contain the new combination of genes Ks and kS constitute 12% of the total of 200 cells produced by the division of the original 100. Thus the percentage of gametes containing the new gene combinations would be 12%.

If 12% of the gametes produced by the heterozygous parent contained the gene combinations Ks and kS, what percent would contain only one of these combinations, for example Ks?

☐ 12%......................................page **178B.**

☐ 6%.......................................page **175B.**

From page 176C.

Correct. Six percent of the gametes should contain the gene combinations *Ks*. Another 6% should contain the genes *kS*.

Many more offspring appeared with the characteristics normal eye, normal wing combined and with the characteristics kidney-shaped eye, short wing combined than did the other two combinations. We explained the larger number of offspring with these two combinations of characteristics by assuming that the genes for these characteristics (*KS* and *ks*) were linked, and thus were on the same pairs of chromosomes. Thus we assumed some linkage. However, linkage could not have been complete, because a few flies appeared that required that the genes *K* and *S* and the genes *k* and *s* separated and recombined as *Ks* and *kS* to produce gametes containing *Ks* and *kS*.

If the genes *K* and *S* were linked on the same chromosome as ___K___ ___S___ , and the genes *k* and *s* were linked on the homologous chromosome as ___k___ ___s___ , then in order to obtain gametes with the gene combinations *Ks* and *kS* the homologous chromosomes $\frac{K \quad S}{k \quad s}$

would have had to break and exchange ends to produce the new combination $\frac{K \quad s}{k \quad S}$. Could this be possible?

Observations of chromosomes revealed that during the stage of meiosis when homologous chromosomes are paired, the paired chromosomes coil about each other (✕✕✕✕✕✕) . Such coiling could lead to breaks and the exchange of parts.

Let us assume that coiling, breakage, and exchange of parts occurred in some cells having the homologous chromosomes $\frac{K \quad S}{k \quad s}$. If the

break occurred between the genes *K* and *S* and *k* and *s* as follows

then after the break and exchange two chromosomes would be formed with new gene combination as

In these new chromosomes what gene would be linked with gene *K*?

☐ *s* . . . . page 172A.

☐ *S* . . . . page 158D.

From page **171A**.

172A **Correct.** The new chromosome would have the gene K linked with the gene s.

Chromosome breakage and exchange of pieces such as this is called **crossing-over.** By assuming that crossing-over occurs among a certain percentage of the cells during gamete formation, it is possible to explain the appearance of four kinds of offspring rather than the two kinds expected if linkage were complete. Such coiling and exchange of parts of chromosomes has actually been observed.

Because the offspring of the cross between heterozygous normal-eyed normal-winged flies ($KkSs$) with kidney-shape-eyed short-winged flies ($kkss$) was in the ratio of

22 normal-eyed normal-winged ($KkSs$):

3 normal-eyed short-winged ($Kkss$):

3 kidney-shape eyed normal-winged ($kkSs$):

22 kidney-shape eyed short-winged ($kkss$),

we reasoned that the heterozygous parent ($KkSs$) had produced gametes in the following proportion.

$$22KS:3Ks:3kS:22ks$$

In what percent of the germ cells produced by the parent with the heterozygous genotype must crossing-over have taken place?

In order to clarify the answer to this question let us assume that the heterozygous parent started with 100 immature reproductive cells and that each of these divided to produce 200 cells. To simplify the problem we will consider only the first meiotic division, since it is assumed that crossing-over takes place prior to this division. (While crossing-over does not take place in the reproductive cells of the male fruit fly, we will ignore this fact, since it is known that crossing-over does take place in the males of some other species.)

Let us assume that in all 100 immature cells the genes K and S were linked on the same chromosome and the genes k and s were linked on the homologous chromosome. Thus,

Spindle

If no crossing-over took place prior to the first meiotic division among any of the 100 cells, what would be the number and kind of cells produced after the first meiotic division?

☐ 50KS, 50ks . . . . page **176B.**

☐ 100KS, 100ks . . . . page **174A.**

☐ 50KS, 50Ks, 50kS, 50ks . . . . page **165B.**

From page **174C.**

Correct. The crossover percentage between any two linked genes, such **173A**
as vestigial wing and cinnabar eye, is the same for all individuals.

We have found that in a test cross the ratio of gametes is reflected
in the phenotypic ratio of the offspring. We have explained a ratio
such as 3:1:1:3 by assuming that during gamete formation genes
originally on the same chromosome can be separated and recombined
by crossing-over. One criterion by which one can recognize that crossing-over takes place is the greater number of two types and a lesser
number of the other two types. A second criterion is

☐ that the percent of the two types in the greatest
number should be approximately the same . . . . page   **164D.**

☐ that the percent of the two types in the lesser
number should be approximately the same . . . . page   **157C.**

☐ that both of these could be true . . . . page   **182A.**

☐ that neither of these could be true . . . . page   **177B.**

Incorrect. If the genotype of the parent having normal wings and red **173B**
eyes were $\dfrac{V \qquad c}{v \qquad C}$, which kinds of offspring should be produced in
greater number: those having normal wings and red eyes or those hav-
ing normal wings and cinnabar eyes? _____. This is contrary
to the data. Return to page **169C.**

Incorrect. It was assumed that the gene K for normal eye was linked **173C**
with the gene S for normal wing, and the gene k for kidney-shaped eye
was linked with the gene s for short wing. If these genes, K and S, and
the genes k and s had remained together during gamete formation,
then no gametes could have been produced containing either the gene
combination Ks or the combination kS; therefore the phenotypes
resulting from genotypes $Kkss$ and $kkSs$ would not be expected.
Return to page **168B.**

From page 172A.

174A **Correct.** 100 cells containing the genes *KS* and 100 containing the genes *ks* would be produced.

Now assume that in 12 of the original cells crossing-over occurred, while in the remaining 88 the genes *KS* and *ks* remained linked.

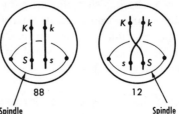

How many of the cells produced by the first meiotic division would contain both the genes *K* and *S*?

☐ 88. . . . . .page   **167C.**

☐ 176. . . . . .page   **170A.**

174B **Incorrect.** Three gametes out of 50 should contain the genes *Ks*. What is 3/50 expressed in percent? Return to page **176C.**

From page 178C.

174C **Correct.** The crossover percentage would be .6%.

We have discovered that the crossover percentage between black body and jaunty wing was .6%, while the crossover percentage between vestigial wings and cinnabar eyes was 10%, and the crossover percentage between kidney-shaped eyes and short wings was 12%. Thus different sets of alleles can have different crossover percentages.

The crossover percentage between different genes, as short wing with kidney-shaped eyes or vestigial wing with cinnabar eye, is different. The crossover percentage for any two linked genes, such as vestigial wing and cinnabar eye is always

☐ the same. . . . . .page   **173A.**

☐ different. . . . . .page   **181A.**

Incorrect. If the individual had two genes for vestigial (*vv*), then it   **175A**
would be true that the gene for vestigial would be at that locus, on
each chromosome of the pair; but what about the flies in the population that were homozygous for the normal allele *VV*? Would these
flies have the genes for vestigial at that locus? _____. Return
to page **165D**.

From page **170C**.

Correct. 6% would contain the genes *Ks*, and 6% would contain the   **175B**
genes *kS*.

If in 12% of the immature reproductive cells crossing-over occurred,
6% of the gametes would contain one of the gene combinations (*Ks*)
resulting from the crossing over, and 6% of the gametes would contain
the other combination (*kS*).

Because the kinds of gametes produced by a parent with a heterozygous genotype are reflected in the offspring of a test cross, in what
percentage of the immature reproductive cells of this parent must
crossing-over have occurred to produce offspring as follows?

> 44% normal-eyed normal-winged
> 6% normal-eyed short-winged
> 6% kidney-shape-eyed normal-winged
> 44% kidney-shape-eyed short-winged

☐ 6%.......................................page   **163B.**

☐ 12%.......................................page   **181C.**

☐ 44%.......................................page   **179B.**

No. Six individuals out of 1000 were of the types which would not be   **175C**
expected if there were complete linkage. Expressed as a fraction this
is 6/1000. What is 6/1000 expressed in percent? _____. Return
to page **178C**.

Incorrect. If we assume linkage, it is true that only two types of   **175D**
gametes would be produced, but how can we tell from the data given
whether gene *K* is linked with gene *S* or *s*? Return to page **177A**.

176A **Correct** but there is a better answer. Return to page **178A**.

176B **Wrong.** We started with 100 cells; each divided. How many cells would there be after division? _____. Return to page **172A**.

From page **161C**.

176C **Correct.** Since the ratio of phenotypes of the offspring is assumed to reflect the ratio of gametes produced by the parent with the heterozygous genotype $KkSs$, the ratio of gametes should be $22KS:3Ks:3kS:22ks$.

If there were complete linkage, the ratio of gametes should be $1KS:1ks$. If there were no linkage and independent assortment operated, the ratio of gametes should be $1KS:1Ks:1kS:1ks$.

Somehow the four kinds of gametes were produced that one would expect on the basis of independent assortment, but there were many more gametes containing the genes S and S combined, and others containing the genes k and s combined, than gametes containing the combinations Ks and kS. In other words the genes K and S and the genes k and s went together more frequently than the genes K and s and the genes k and S.

It would be possible to explain the high incidence of gametes containing the gene combinations KS and ks if we assume that the gene K for normal eye was linked on the same chromosome with the gene S for normal wing, while the gene k for kidney-shaped eye was linked on the homologous chromosome with the gene s for short wing. However, if we make this assumption how can we explain the germ cells having the combinations Ks and kS? They presumably were formed even though in smaller numbers.

Remember that we have assumed that the ratio of gametes produced by the individual having the heterozygous genotype was $22KS : 3Ks : 3kS : 22ks$. These numbers represent a ratio and not percentages. What percent of the germ cells should contain the genes Ks?

☐ 3 . . . . page   **174B.**

☐ 6 . . . . page   **171A.**

☐ 12 . . . . page   **165C.**

From page **159D.**

Correct. The phenotypic ratio expected if there were independent **177A** assortment would be 1 normal-winged normal-eyed : 1 normal-eyed short-winged : 1 kidney-shaped-eye normal-wing : 1 kidney-shaped-eye short-wing.

Now assume that there was linkage between the genes for wing shape and eye shape. The ratio of offspring from the cross $KkSs \times kkss$ should be $1:1$.

If there were linkage between wing shape and eye shape, what kinds of gametes would be produced by an individual with the genotype $KkSs$?

☐ KS and ks ....page **175D.**

☐ Ks and kS ....page **162B.**

☐ Either 1 or 2 above but not both 1 and 2 above . page **167A.**

☐ The individual should produce four different
kinds of gametes ....page **183A.**

Incorrect. If a ratio is $5:1:1:5$, does it not mean that the number of **177B** individuals represented by the first "5" is approximately equal to the number represented by the second "5"? _____. Return to page **173A.**

Wrong. If in 12 of the original immature germ cells there was crossing- **177C** over, then 12 cells would have genes as follows and divide.

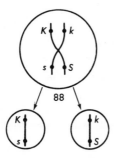

How many cells would be produced as a result of division of these 12 cells? _____. What percent of them would contain the genes K and s? _____. What is 50% of 24? _____. Return to page **167C.**

From page 181C.

178A **Correct.** If crossing-over is the correct explanation for the production of new gene combinations we must also assume that alleles on homologous chromosomes occupy corresponding positions on these chromosomes. Such positions are referred to as **loci** (singular **locus**).

If crossing-over occurs, genes can be exchanged as diagrammed:

Another assumption implicit in this explanation is that when homologous chromosomes pair during meiosis, paired genes as K and k and S and s lie side by side.

If this were *not* the case then

☐ two genes for one trait, such as K and k, might
end up in one gamete......................page **176A.**

☐ some gametes might not have any genes for
some traits.............................page **183C.**

☐ both of these might be true................page **180A.**

178B **Wrong.** If both kinds of gametes, Ks and kS, make up 12% of the total how could only one of the kinds (Ks) also make up 12%? Return to page **170C.**

From page 180C.

178C **Correct.** Presumably there was some crossing-over between the alleles for body color and wing tilt.

What was the percent of crossover in this case when of 1000 flies three had gray bodies, jaunty wings; and three had black bodies, normal wings?

☐ 6%.......................................page **175C.**

☐ 3%.......................................page **180B.**

☐ .6%......................................page **174C.**

☐ .3%......................................page **163A.**

From page **169A.**

From page **169A.**

Correct. The results of this cross cannot be explained either by **179A** assuming independent assortment of the genes or by assuming complete linkage.

The results of the actual cross did not correspond to prediction from either of the postulates of the gene theory which we have developed so far; namely,

1. pairs of genes on nonhomologous chromosomes assort independently of each other.
2. genes on the same chromosome remain together during gamete formation.

Since new problems in science arise out of the lack of correspondence between prediction and observation, we are now confronted with the problem of explaining the unexpected ratio of offspring of this cross.

On the basis of the assumption that the genes for the two traits assorted independently, we predicted that four kinds of offspring would be produced in the ratio of $1:1:1:1$. Actually the four kinds of offspring were produced as expected. However, their ratio was $22:3:3:22$ instead of $1:1:1:1$.

If the four kinds of offspring predicted on the basis of independent assortment did appear, can we assume that assortment of the two pairs of genes did occur but that the assortment was not random?

☐ Yes.....................................page **168B.**

☐ No......................................page **159A.**

Wrong. This is the percent of the gametes containing the combina- **179B** tion K and S. You have probably not followed the entire argument beginning on page **172A.** Return to that page.

Incorrect. If the genotype of the parent having normal wings and **179C** red eyes were $\dfrac{V \quad c}{v \quad C}$,which kinds of offspring should be produced in greater number: those having normal wings and red eyes or those having normal wings and cinnabar eyes? _____. This is contrary to the data. Return to page **169C.**

From page **178A**.

180A **Correct.** Unless the alleles paired side by side when homologous chromosomes paired during meiosis, it would be possible for gametes to be produced following crossing-over with two genes such as K and k for one trait on the same chromosome and for some gametes to have certain genes missing. Normally this does not happen.

We have assumed that genes occupy specific loci on chromosomes and that during pairing in meiosis the loci for any two genes for a particular trait are side by side.

Crossing-over can occur between the loci of any two pairs of genes on homologous chromosomes. Does this require that we assume that the loci of genes are arranged on a chromosome in a linear order, somewhat like beads on a string?

☐ Yes.....................................page **165D.**

☐ No......................................page **157A.**

180B **No.** Six individuals out of 1000 were of the types which would not be expected if there were complete linkage. Expressed as a fraction this is 6/1000. What is 6/1000 expressed in percent? _____. Return to page **178C.**

From page **163C**.

180C **Good.** Since the genotype $\dfrac{V \qquad c}{v \qquad C}$ shows linkage between the gene V for normal wing and the gene c for cinnabar eye and also linkage of the genes v for vestigial wing and C for red eye, the phenotypes that should appear in the larger number among the offspring would have the phenotypes normal-winged cinnabar-eyed and vestigial-winged red-eyed.

On Worksheet 4-A you have recorded the actual results obtained from the cross of gray-bodied normal-winged flies and black-bodied jaunty-winged flies. Of 50 offspring 26 were gray normal; 24 were black jaunty. When further data were obtained on 1000 flies, it was found that 3 flies had gray bodies and jaunty wings and 3 had black bodies and normal wings. RECORD THESE DATA IN COLUMN 9 ON WORKSHEET 4-A. Were the genes for gray and normal and those for black and jaunty completely linked?

☐ Yes.....................................page **166B.**

☐ No......................................page **178C.**

181A

Incorrect. The evidence from crosses involving crossing-over indicates that the crossover percentage between any two alleles is always the same. If the crossover percentage between linked genes differed in different individuals, we could not talk about a crossing-over percentage between two genes. We assume that the percent of gametes with the exchanged genes is about the same for all individuals. The whole idea of linkage and crossing-over is based on the assumption that genes are fixed at certain permanent positions on chromosomes. The chromosomes can break and exchange parts, but the genes do not change their relative positions on the chromosomes. Return to page **174C.**

181B

Incorrect. If there is independent assortment, how many kinds of gametes should be produced by the individual with the genotype *KkSs*? _____. How many different kinds of genotypes would these produce? _____. Is not each of the genotypes expressed as a different phenotype? _____. Return to page **159D.**

From page **175B.**

181C

Correct. The percentage of crossing-over was 12%. The initial question with which we were concerned was, "In what percentage of the germ cells did crossing-over take place?" We have discovered an answer to this question. We have also discovered that the crossover percentage is the sum of the percentages of the offspring who would not have been produced had linkage been complete.

We have accepted the assumption that chromosomes become coiled and exchange parts as

In order for crossover to occur and for genes to be exchanged, would it be necessary to assume that alleles on homologous chromosomes occupy corresponding places on these chromosomes? *i.e.*, does gene *K* on one chromosome occupy the same position on that chromosome as the gene *k* occupies on its chromosome?

☐ Yes..page **178A.**

☐ No...page **164C.**

From page 173A.

182A **Correct.** The concepts of linkage and crossing-over, introduced in this chapter, necessitate the modification of one of the assumptions of the gene theory which has been previously accepted. Which assumption of gene theory requires modification in the light of linkage and cross-over data?

☐ Genes of a pair segregate during gamete forma-
tion . . . . .page   **168C.**

☐ Genes of different pairs assort independently of
each other during gamete formation . . . . .page   **162A.**

182B **Incorrect.** You have already assumed that genes k and s are on the same chromosome. How, then, could they appear in gametes on separate chromosomes? Correct your worksheet. Return to page **157D.**

From page 162A.

182C **Correct.** Below the key are a number of ratios. In each case determine the type of cross which could have produced offspring in this ratio. Use the key.

    Key A. *AaBb* × *aabb* (complete linkage)
        B. *AaBb* × *aabb* (linkage and crossing-over)
        C. *AaBb* × *aabb* (independent assortment)
        D. *AaBb* × *AaBb* (independent assortment)
        E. None of these

☐ 1:1:1:1

☐ 1:5:5:1

☐ 9:3:3:1

☐ 1:1

☐ 6:1:1:6

☐ 7:4:6:1

Turn to page **184** for answers.

Incorrect. We have assumed that the alleles are linked and hence on the same pair of homologous chromosomes. Under these conditions only two kinds of gametes would be produced. What relation of genes and chromosomes is necessary for an individual with a heterozygous genotype such as *AaBb* to produce four kinds of gametes? Return to page **177A.**

183A

From page **164B.**

Correct. If there were linkage the phenotypic ratio should be 1 normal-eye normal-wing:1 kidney-shaped-eye short-wing. If this is not what you have recorded, correct your worksheet. Recall that you have already predicted and recorded on Worksheet 4-B that if there were independent assortment, the phenotypic ratio should be 1 normal-eye normal-wing:1 normal-eye short-wing:1 kidney-shaped-eye normal-wing:1 kidney-shaped-eye short-wing. If there is linkage, the phenotypic ratio should be 1 normal-eye normal-wing:1 kidney-shaped-eye short-wing.

183B

An experimenter not knowing whether the two traits were linked would expect among the offspring of the cross *KkSs* × *kkss* either a 1:1 ratio or a 1:1:1:1 ratio. If the genes were linked, then the ratio should be 1:1. If the genes assorted independently, the ratio should be 1:1:1:1. However, the results of an actual cross (*KkSs* × *kkss*) involving a large number of offspring (about 1000) were

44% normal-eyed normal-winged,
6% normal-eyed short-winged,
6% kidney-shape-eyed normal-winged,
44% kidney-shape-eyed short-winged.

The above numbers reduced to the smallest whole number ratio is 22:3:3:22. RECORD THESE OBSERVED PHENOTYPES AND THEIR RATIO IN THE PROPER COLUMNS ON WORKSHEET 4-B. COMPARE THIS RATIO WITH THE RATIO EXPECTED ON THE BASIS OF THE ASSUMPTION THAT THERE WAS INDEPENDENT ASSORTMENT.

Can these results be explained by assuming that there was complete independent (random) assortment?

☐ Yes . . . . page   **167B.**

☐ No . . . . page   **169A.**

Correct but there is a better answer. Return to page **178A.**

183C

From page **182C**.

1.C; 2.B; 3.D; 4.A; 5.B; 6.E

Continue with the review.

REVIEW—Chapter 4, Part II

If an individual with the genotype *AaBb* is crossed with one having the genotype *aabb*, the ratio of offspring should be (#) _____ if the alleles are on two pairs of homologous chromosomes, but should be (#) _____ if there is complete linkage. If instead of a ratio of 1:1:1:1 or 1:1 we obtained a ratio of 4:1:1:4, we could assume that the two pairs of alleles were located on (#) _____ pair(s) of homologous chromosomes but that there had been a break and recombination of the (*wd*) _____ between the (#)_____ pair(s) of alleles. This type of recombination of genes is called _____. The crossover percent is the (*sum of, difference between*) _____ the percents of the types which would not occur if there were complete linkage. Thus if the ratio of offspring were 4:1:1:4 the crossover percentage would be _____. The percent of crossover was found to be (*the same, different*) _____ for different pairs of alleles, such as vestigial cinnabar and kidney-shaped short.

As a result of the discovery of linkage and crossing-over, one of the assumptions of gene theory had to be modified. The assumption which was modified was that of (*wds*) _____. It was assumed that (*wd*) _____ rather than (*wd*) _____ assort independently.

Also as a result of the discovery of linkage and crossing-over three new assumptions were added to the gene theory. They were (1) that genes are located in a (*wd*) _____ order on the chromosomes (2) alleles occupy corresponding positions (loci) on (*wd*) _____ chromosomes and (3) alleles line up side by side when homologous chromosomes (*wd*) _____ during meiosis.

Check your responses to the review with those on page 358 and continue with the summary of Part II.

SUMMARY—Chapter 4, Part II

The assumption of independent assortment explained ratios of 1:1:1:1 as a result of a test cross (*AaBb* × *aabb*) while complete linkage of two genes on a single chromosome explained 1:1 ratios.

A complication arose when it was discovered that some characteristics seemed to be partly but not completely linked. For example, the offspring of the cross *KkSs* × *kkss* produced

44% normal-eyed normal-winged

6% normal-eyed short-winged

6% kidney-shape-eyed normal-winged

44% kidney-shape-eyed short-winged

The absence of the 1:1:1:1 ratio indicated linkage, but the presence of all four combinations of characteristics indicated some assortment.

The solution to this problem was that linkage had occurred between genes *K* and *S* and between genes *k* and *s*, but that crossing-over of the homologous chromosomes had occurred in 12% of the immature reproductive cells. This crossing-over produced breakage and exchange of chromosome ends so that the linked genes were separated and recombined with the other member of the pair. Thus through crossing-over there was assortment in 12% of the cells and linkage in 88% of the cells.

The assumption of independent assortment was limited to chromosomes. New assumptions added to the gene theory were that

1. genes are located on chromosomes in a linear order, somewhat like beads on a string

2. alleles occupy corresponding loci on homologous chromosomes, and consequently

3. alleles line up side by side when homologous chromosomes pair during meiosis.

Continue with Part III of this chapter.

PART III

Chromosome Mapping

186A We have discovered that crossover percentages between genes are not always the same. For example we found that the crossover percentage for the genes for vestigial wing and cinnabar eye was 10%, while the crossover percentage for the genes for black body and jaunty wing was .6%. Our next problem is to explain the variation in crossover percentages.

We have assumed that genes are located at specific fixed loci on chromosomes and that they are arranged in a linear order like beads on a string. We have also assumed that any one chromosome carries many genes. Recall that in the fruit fly there are approximately 3000 genes but only four pairs of chromosomes. Thus on any one chromosome one gene could be at one end, the next one farther from that end, and so on until the last gene could be at the other end of the chromosome. Any two genes along this chromosome would have a certain fixed distance between them.

Examine the following diagram of three pairs of genes on two homologous chromosomes.

Crossing-over is assumed to be due to coiling of homologous chromosomes, breakage, and exchange of parts at some point between genes. The exact point on a chromosome where breakage occurs is assumed to be due to chance. Under these conditions it is reasonable to assume that the chance of breakage and exchange is

□ greater if the genes are far apart . . . . page **194B.**

□ greater if the genes are close together . . . . page **192B.**

186B **Incorrect.** If Podunk is nine miles from Goonville, and Smithtown is two miles from Podunk away from Goonville, how far is it from Smithtown to Goonville? Return to page **198C.**

186C **Incorrect.** If gene *g* were 15 units to the right of the gene for bristle, would not the crossover percentage between gene *g* and the gene for pink eye be 24%? It was 6%. Return to page **188A.**

Incorrect. We have assumed that the genes which are farther apart **187A** would have a greater chance of breakage and crossing and that this would be reflected in the crossover percentage. Thus those genes having the greatest crossover percentage would be the farthest apart. Return to page **194B**.

Incorrect. There were 212 individuals in all; 11 were of the types **187B** which would not have been predicted if there were complete linkage. Expressed as a percent $\frac{11}{212}$ is approximately _____. Return to page **190C**.

From page **192C**.

Correct. Evidence of linkage and crossing-over between pairs of **187C** genes is evidence that the two pairs of genes are located on the same pair of homologous chromosomes.

Three pairs of contrasting characteristics of the fruit fly are (a) red eye — pink eye (b) nonbristled — bristled (c) normal body-size — dwarf. The genes for red eye, nonbristle, and normal body-size are all dominant to their alleles, pink eyes, bristle and dwarf.

The two following crosses were made.

(a) Red eye, nonbristle $(PpBb)$ × pink eye, bristle $(ppbb)$. The crossover percentage was 9%

(b) Red eye, normal body-size $(PpDd)$ × pink eye, dwarf $(ppdd)$. The crossover percentage was 2%

Are the loci of these three genes (pink eye, dwarfism, bristles) and their alleles located on the same chromosome pair?

☐ Yes......................................page **195C.**

☐ No.......................................page **193C.**

☐ Cannot de determined......................page **188B.**

Incorrect. If you are looking for the crossover percentage between **187D** dwarf and clipped wing, why would you make a cross that did not include the gene for dwarf? Return to page **202A**.

From page **193D.**

188A **Correct.** The gene for dwarfism would be located between the gene for pink and the gene for bristle. By assuming that each percentage of crossover equals one unit distance on a chromosome map, the gene for dwarfism would be two units away from the gene for pink eye and seven units away from the gene for bristle as

Now let us assume that there is a gene *g* having a crossover percentage with the gene for bristle of 15%. If gene *g* also had a crossover percentage of 6% with the gene for pink eye, where would you place gene *g* on the chromosome?

☐ 15 units to the right of the gene for bristle......page **186C.**

☐ 6 units to the left of the gene for dwarfism......page **195D.**

☐ 6 units to the left of the gene for pink.........page **201D.**

188B **Incorrect.** Any evidence of linkage and crossing-over between pairs of genes is evidence that the pairs of genes are on the same pair of homologous chromosomes. There is crossover between pink and bristles, so they would be on the same chromosome pair, would they not? _____. There is also a crossover between pink and dwarf, so they must be on the same chromosome pair, must they not? _____. Then what about dwarf and bristles? _____.
Return to page **187C.**

188C **Incorrect.** The crossover percentage between pink eye and dwarf is 2%; therefore these genes are two map units apart. The crossover percentage between pink eye and clipped wing is 3%; therefore clipped wing is three map units from pink eye. However, we have no information concerning the direction the gene for clipped wing is away from the gene for pink eye. Return to page **191B.**

188D **Incorrect.** There is information. What is the relation of any gene and its alleles to a locus on homologous chromosomes? Return to page **199B.**

Incorrect. We have assumed that the genes which are farther apart **189A**
would have a greater chance of breakage and crossing and that this
would be reflected in the crossover percentage. Thus those genes having the greatest crossover percentage would be the farthest apart.
Return to page **194B.**

From page **203A.**

Correct. The parent having the genotype *ccPPDDbb* would produce   **189B**
gametes of but one kind:

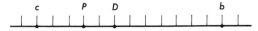

The parent with the genotype *CCppddBB* would also produce but
one kind of gamete, as

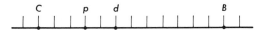

The union of such gametes would produce an individual with the
chromosome makeup

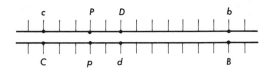

Two other characteristics in the fruit fly that are linked are lobe
eye and fringed wing. These characteristics are recessive to normal
eye and normal wing. The crossover percentage is 8%. In a test cross
a normal-eyed, normal-winged fly with the genotype *LlFf* was
crossed with a lobe-eyed, fringe-winged fly with the genotype *llff*.

The two parents of the fly with the heterozygous genotype *LlFf*
used in the test cross had the genotypes *LLFF* and *llff*. Which of the
following would be the ratio of the offspring of the test cross?

☐ 23 Normal-eyed fringe-winged:

   2 Normal-eyed normal-winged:

   2 Lobe-eyed fringe-winged:

  23 Lobe-eyed normal-winged . . . . page   **197A.**

☐ 23 Normal-eyed normal-winged:

   2 Normal-eyed fringe-winged:

   2 Lobe-eyed normal-winged:

  23 Lobe-eyed fringe-winged . . . . page   **200A.**

190A **Incorrect.** The P_1 parents were both pure line and hence their genotypes were (homozygous, heterozygous) _____. The genotype

$$\frac{D \quad C}{d \quad c}$$

represents an individual with a (homozygous, heterozygous) _____ genotype. Return to page **200A**.

190B **Incorrect.** We have previously established that two pairs of genes on
nonhomologous chromosomes assort independently and therefore the
four kinds of offspring should all be in approximately equal numbers.
Return to page **192C**.

From page **202A**.

190C **Correct.** Since the problem was to determine how far the locus of
the gene for clipped wing was from the locus of the gene for dwarf, the
information needed is the crossover percentage between dwarf and
clipped wing. Therefore the proper cross was normal body-size, normal
wing (heterozygous for both traits) $\times$ dwarf, clipped wing.

When this cross was made, the offspring occurred in the following
numbers.

104 normal body-size, normal wings

5 normal body-size, clipped wings

6 dwarf, normal wings

97 dwarf, clipped wings.

What is the crossover percentage?

☐ 1%....................................page   **193B.**

☐ 5%....................................page   **196B.**

☐ 10%...................................page   **187B.**

190D **Incorrect.** If the locus of the gene for red eye were three map units
from the gene for pink eye and five map units from the locus of the
gene for dwarf, it would be at the same locus as the gene for clipped
wing. This locus is the locus of the gene for clipped wing and its alleles.
What is the relation of any gene and its alleles to a locus on homologous chromosomes? Return to page **199B**.

Incorrect. Although it is conceivable that some individual fruit fly **191A** might have a chromosome with all of the "abnormal" genes possessed by the species, it is most unlikely. A chromosome map is the product of human minds and is not meant to be a reflection of the chromosomes of any one individual fruit fly. When thinking of the locus for the gene for vestigial wings on a map, one should also think of the normal allele at the same locus. This means that one or the other, but not both, genes (V and v) will be at that spot on each chromosome of any and every fruit fly. Return to page **195C.**

From page **201D.**

Correct. Since the crossover percentage equals the sum of the kinds **191B** of individuals which would not be expected if linkage were complete, 2% crossover includes 1% having the phenotype red eye and dwarf and 1% having the phenotype pink eye and normal size.

Now consider another pair of alleles in the fruit fly; normal wing (C) and clipped wing (c).

The crossover percentage between clipped wing and pink eye is 3%. On a chromosome map how far would the gene for clipped wing be from the gene for dwarf? The crossover percentage between pink eye and dwarf is 2%.

☐ One unit . . . . page   **201C.**

☐ Five units . . . . page   **188C.**

☐ Either one or five units . . . . page   **202A.**

Incorrect. The chromosome arrangement   **191C**

is one of the many that an individual having the genotype *CcPpDdBb* might have. However, to have this chromosome makeup one parent of the individual would have contributed a chromosome having the genes

One of the parents had the genotype *ccPPDDbb*; the other had the genotype *CCppddBB*. Neither parent could have produced a gamete containing a chromosome having all recessive genes. Return to page **203A.**

192A **Incorrect.** While it is true that the assumption that genes are arranged in a linear order is essential for the idea of mapping chromosomes, the assumption that permits us to use only one allele to determine the locus of both is the assumption that pertains to the relative position of alleles on homologous chromosomes. Return to page **202C**.

192B **No.** Consider the following diagram of two chromosomes.

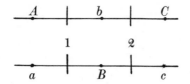

Assume that there is a breaking and rejoining of these two chromosomes but that there is no way to know where the break will occur. Which two would be more likely to be separated from each other, A and C or A and b? _____. If the break were at point 1, both b and C would be separated from A; but if it were at point 2, only C would be separated from A. Return to page **186A**.

From page **194B**.

192C **Good.** Two pairs of genes having a crossover percentage of 10% should be farther apart than genes having a smaller crossover percentage.

The assumption that the crossover percentage reflects distance between genes on a chromosome led to the idea of locating the loci of genes on the chromosomes of the fruit fly.

In order to do this it was first necessary to know which pairs of genes were on the same homologous chromosomes. This information was available on the basis of observation of the offspring of a test cross of an individual with a heterozygous genotype such as $AaBb$ with one having the genotype $aabb$. If the ratio of phenotypes of the offspring showed evidence of linkage and crossing-over, in that two of the four possible phenotypes were in large numbers and approximately equal to each other while the other two were in small numbers and also approximately equal to each other, the two pairs of genes were assumed to be

☐ on the same homologous chromosomes....... page **187C**.

☐ on different, nonhomologous chromosomes.... page **190B**.

Incorrect. Alleles, as Cc, occupy the same locus on homologous **193A** chromosomes. You have indicated the genes c and p at the same locus. Are c and p alleles? _____. Return to page **203A**.

Incorrect. There were 212 individuals in all; 11 were of the types **193B** which would not have been predicted if there were complete linkage. Expressed as a percent $\frac{11}{212}$ is approximately_____. Return to page **190C**.

Incorrect. Any evidence of linkage and crossing-over between pairs **193C** of genes is evidence that the pairs of genes are on the same pair of homologous chromosomes. There is crossover between pink and bristles, so they would be on the same chromosome pair, would they not? _____. There is also a crossover between pink and dwarf, so they must be on the same chromosome pair, must they not? _____. Then what about dwarf and bristles? _____. Return to page **187C**.

From page **198C**.

Correct. The crossover percentage between bristles and dwarf would **193D** be either 7% or 11%, depending on which side of the gene for pink the gene for dwarf is. It could be

A.

    d p b

or it could be

B.

    p d b

    Crosses to determine the crossover percentage between bristle and dwarf determined the crossover value to be 7%. If we equate one arbitrary unit of distance on a chromosome with 1% of crossover, which of the above chromosome maps is the correct one?

☐ A...page **203B.**

☐ B...page **188A.**

From page 197B.

194A **Correct.** Keep in mind that the crossover percent between pink eye and bristle is 9%, that between pink eye and dwarfism is 2%. The locus of the gene for dwarfism could be two units away from the gene for pink eye on the other side, as follows.

    Dwarfism Pink eye   Bristle

If the locus of the gene for dwarfism were between the genes for pink eye and bristle as

    Pink eye Dwarfism   Bristle

what should be the crossover percentage of the genes for dwarfism and bristle?

☐ 9% . . . . .page **200B.**

☐ 7% . . . . .page **198C.**

☐ 11% . . . . .page **196A.**

From page 186A.

194B **Good.** On the basis of the assumption that crossing-over will occur more frequently between pairs of genes that are far apart, it is possible to explain the different crossover percentages that have been observed.

Which of the following pairs of genes would you expect to be the farthest apart?

☐ Two pairs of genes having a crossover percentage of 1% . . . . .page **187A.**

☐ Two pairs of genes having a crossover percentage of 5% . . . . .page **189A.**

☐ Two pairs of genes having a crossover percentage of 10% . . . . .page **192C.**

Incorrect. If the locus of the gene for red eye were two map units **195A** from the gene for pink eye and five map units from the gene for clipped wing, it would be at the same locus as the gene for dwarf. This is the locus for the gene for dwarf and its alleles. What is the relation of any gene and its alleles to a locus on homologous chromosomes? Return to page **199B**.

Incorrect. The crossover percentages were: **195B**

$$\text{dwarf — clipped, } 5\%$$
$$\text{dwarf — pink, } 2\%$$
$$\text{pink — clipped, } 3\%$$

If the genes were located as ⊦⊦⊦⊦⊦⊦⊦⊦⊦⊦⊦⊦⊦⊦⊦ what

p   *d*   *c*

would be the crossover percent between pink and clipped? _____. Does this correspond to the data? _____. Return to page **196B**.

From page **187C**.

Correct. The loci of the three genes and their alleles are on the same **195C** pair of chromosomes.

When it has been discovered that three specific pairs of genes are located on a single pair of homologous chromosomes, as P and p, D and d, B and b, it is possible to calculate the location of the loci of these alleles in relation to each other. Such location of loci of genes is called "mapping."

It is customary when building a chromosome map to locate the allele which is *not* possessed by the normal fruit fly with a homozygous genotype. That is, those characteristics such as pink eye, bristle, dwarf, etc. are used for mapping of the locus of the alleles. The chromosome map represents an abstraction and probably no one individual would ever have a chromosome with all of the genes as represented on a chromosome map. Thus a chromosome map represents

☐ an actual chromosome of an individual . . . . page   **191A**.

☐ a generalized chromosome of the species . . . . . . page   **202C**.

Incorrect. The gene for dwarfism was not mentioned in this experi- **195D** ment. The three genes involved were pink eye, bristle, and *g*. Return to page **188A**.

196A **Incorrect.** The crossover percentage between the locus of pink and the locus of bristle is 9%; therefore the loci of these two genes are 9 map units apart. If the locus of the gene for pink were two map units toward bristle from pink, how many map units from bristle would it be? _____. Therefore the percent crossover should be _____. Return to page **194A**.

From page **190C**.

196B **Correct.** The crossover percentage between dwarf and clipped wing is 5%.

 We have established that the crossover percentage between dwarf and pink eye was 2% and between clipped wing and pink eye was 3%.

 Which of the following would represent a section of a chromosome map showing the loci of these three recessive genes?

☐   p   d   c   page   **202B.**

☐   p   d   c   page   **195B.**

☐   c   p   d   page   **199B.**

196C **Incorrect.** The crossover percentage between pink and bristles was given as 2%. Crossover percentage is defined as the sum of the percent of types produced that would not have been produced if there were complete linkage. In the cross $\dfrac{P \quad D}{p \quad d} \times \dfrac{p \quad d}{p \quad d}$ one of the crossover genotypes would be $\dfrac{P \quad d}{p \quad d}$. What would the other crossover genotype be? _____. What percent of the individuals should have each of these genotypes? _____. Return to page **201D**.

196D **Impractical.** It would be possible to obtain the crossover percentage between dwarf and clipped wing from a cross involving pink eye as well as clipped wing and dwarf. However, you could obtain it only by ignoring the eye color of the offspring. Thus adding the eye color alleles to the cross adds an unnecessary complication. Return to page **202A**.

Incorrect. We were given the information that the genotypes of the parents of the individual with the heterozygous genotype used in the test cross were *LLFF* and *llff*. Thus the individual with the heterozygous genotype *LlFf* received genes *L* and *F* from one parent and genes *l* and *f* from the other parent. Because the ratio of offspring of the test cross was 22:3:3:22 we could conclude that linkage and crossover had occurred. Therefore if the genes *L* and *F* came from one parent, these genes presumably were linked. Therefore the genes *l* and *f* were also linked. The linked characteristics are always reflected as the greater number among the offspring of a test cross. Return to page **189B**.

From page **204A**.

Correct. The locus of the gene for bristle would be farther away from the locus of the gene for pink eye than would the locus of the gene for dwarfism.

Let us arbitrarily assume that 1% of crossing-over equals 1 unit distance on a chromosome map. At this point we do not know the locus of either the gene for pink eye, the gene for bristle, or the gene for dwarfism. Also we do not know in terms of microns, centimeters, or any other scale, how far apart the genes are. However, if our assumption concerning the relation of percentage of crossing-over to distance apart is correct, then we do know that the locus of the gene for bristle is farther away from the locus of the gene for pink eye than is the locus of the gene for dwarfism; that is, the distance between the loci of the genes for pink eye and bristle is 9 units, while the distance between the loci of the genes for pink eye and dwarfism is 2 units.

Assuming that all three recessive genes *p*, *d*, and *b* were on a single chromosome, we could diagram this as follows:

In this diagram we have placed the locus for the gene for dwarfism two units away from the gene for pink eye. On the basis of the information we have so far (that the percentage of crossover between the genes for pink eye and dwarfism is 2%), would it be possible for the gene for dwarfism to have a locus at some other point on the chromosome?

☐ Yes . . . . page   **194A.**

☐ No . . . . page   **201A.**

198A **Incorrect.** If the P_1 parents had had the genotypes $\dfrac{D \quad C}{D \quad C}$ and $\dfrac{d \quad c}{d \quad c}$, then which genes should have been linked, dwarf with normal leaf or dwarf with crinkly leaf? _____. If the genes dwarf and crinkly leaf were linked, which type of offspring should have appeared in the larger number: dwarf with crinkly leaf or dwarf with normal leaf? _____. This does not correspond with the data. Return to page **200A**.

198B **Incorrect.** You either misunderstood the assumption we made concerning crossover percentage and map distance or you made a careless error. We have assumed that crossover percentage is directly related to distance apart on a chromosome map. If in comparing two crossover percentages one is larger than the other, then the two pairs of genes having the larger crossover percentage are farther apart on the chromosome map than are those with the smaller crossover percentage. Return to page **204A**.

From page **194A**.

198C **Correct.** The crossover percentage of the genes for dwarfism and bristle should be 7%, if we assume that the locus of the gene for dwarfism is between the loci of the genes for pink eye and bristle.

However, if the locus of the gene for dwarfism were on the other side of the locus of the gene for pink eye as

Dwarfism Pink eye   Bristle

what would be the crossover percentage of the genes for dwarfism and bristle?

☐ 9% . . . . page **186B.**

☐ 7% . . . . page **201B.**

☐ 11% . . . . page **193D.**

Partially correct. You have neglected to take into account the alleles 199A
of the genes c, p, d, and b. Return to page **203A**.

From page **196B**.

Correct. The correct chromosome map would be 199B

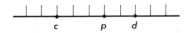

If the locus of the gene for pink eye is between the loci of the genes
for clipped wing and dwarf and is three map units from the locus
of clipped wing and two map units from the locus of dwarf, the locus
of the gene for red eye, the normal allele for the gene for pink eye
would be

☐ two map units from the locus of the gene for
pink eye and five map units from the locus of
the gene for clipped wing.................page   **195A.**

☐ three map units from the locus of the gene for
pink eye and five map units from the locus of
the gene for dwarf........................page   **190D.**

☐ three map units from the locus of the gene for
clipped wing and two map units from the locus
of the gene for dwarf.....................page   **203A.**

☐ the question cannot be answered on the basis of
the information given.....................page   **188D.**

Incorrect. The crossover percentage between pink and bristles was 199C
given as 2%. Crossover percentage is defined as the sum of the percent
of types produced that would not have been produced if there were
complete linkage. In the cross $\dfrac{P \quad D}{p \quad d} \times \dfrac{p \quad d}{p \quad d}$ one of the

crossover genotypes would be $\dfrac{P \quad d}{p \quad d}$. What would the other

crossover genotype be? _____. What percent of the individuals
should have each of these genotypes? _____. Return to
page **201D**.

From page **189B**.

200A **Correct.** The ratio of offspring in the cross *LlFf* × *llff* should be

23 normal-eyed normal-winged:

2 normal-eyed fringe-winged:

2 lobe-eyed normal-winged:

23 lobe-eyed fringe-winged

if the original parents of the heterozygous parent were *LLFF* and *llff*. Because we knew the genotype of the parents which produced the individual with the genotype *LlFf* used in the test cross, and because we know the crossover percent, we could predict which genes should remain together and the proportion of crossover individuals to be expected.

Two pure lines of corn (P₁) were crossed producing F₁ individuals heterozygous for two traits. When these F₁ individuals which were normal height and were normal leafed were crossed with plants which were dwarf plants with crinkly leaves (*ddcc*) four kinds of offspring were produced in the following ratio.

9 normal-height normal leaf:

41 normal-height crinkly-leaf:

41 dwarf normal-leaf:

9 dwarf crinkly-leaf

What were the genotypes of the P₁ parents?

☐ $\dfrac{D \quad C}{D \quad C}$ and $\dfrac{d \quad c}{d \quad c}$ ....page **198A.**

☐ $\dfrac{D \quad c}{D \quad c}$ and $\dfrac{d \quad C}{d \quad C}$ ....page **204B.**

☐ Both were $\dfrac{D \quad C}{d \quad c}$ ....page **190A.**

200B **Incorrect.** The crossover percentage between the locus of pink and the locus of bristle is 9%; therefore the loci of these two genes are 9 map units apart. If the locus of the gene for pink were two map units toward bristle from pink, how many map units from bristle would it be? _____. Therefore the percent crossover should be _____. Return to page **194A.**

Why not? If you live on Main Street, a street which runs all the way through the city and the only direction you give someone for finding your house is that you live in the pink house exactly two miles from the center of town, wouldn't it be possible for someone to go to the wrong side of the town? Return to page **197B**.

Return to page **197B**.

201A

Incorrect. If Podunk is nine miles from Goonville, and Smithtown is two miles from Podunk away from Goonville, how far is it from Smithtown to Goonville? Return to page **198C**.

201B

Incorrect. The crossover percentage between pink eye and dwarf is 2%; therefore these genes are two map units apart. The crossover percentage between pink eye and clipped wing is 3%; therefore clipped wing is three map units from pink eye. However, we have no information concerning the direction the gene for clipped wing is away from the gene for pink eye. Return to page **191B**.

201C

From page **188A**.

201D

Correct. The locus of the gene g would be 6 units to the left of the locus of the gene for pink eye.

On a chromosome map the gene for pink eye and the gene for dwarfism were two map units apart. Assume that you are crossing an individual having the genotype $\dfrac{P \quad D}{p \quad d}$ with an individual having the genotype $\dfrac{p \quad d}{p \quad d}$. What percent of the offspring should have the genotype $\dfrac{P \quad d}{p \quad d}$ and thus have the phenotype red eyed and dwarf?

☐ 1% . . . . page   **191B.**

☐ 2% . . . . page   **199C.**

☐ 4% . . . . page   **196C.**

☐ None of the offspring should have this genotype . . . . page   **203C.**

From page **191B**.

202A **Correct.** From the data given, it cannot be determined whether the locus of the gene for clipped wing is one unit or five units from the locus of the gene for dwarf, as

Which of the following crosses would you make in order to discover the locus for the gene for clipped wing and its allele normal wing?

☐ Normal body-size, red eye, normal wing (heterozygous for all three traits) × dwarf, pink eye,
clipped wing. . . . . .page **196D.**

☐ Normal body-size, normal wing (heterozygous
for both traits) × dwarf, clipped wing. . . . . . .page **190C.**

☐ Normal body-size, normal wing (heterozygous
for both traits) × pink eye, clipped wing. . . . .page **187D.**

202B **Incorrect.** The crossover percentages were:

$$\text{dwarf — clipped, } 5\%$$
$$\text{dwarf — pink,} \quad 2\%$$
$$\text{pink — clipped, } 3\%$$

If the genes were located as _____ what would
the crossover percent between dwarf and clipped be? _____.
Does this correspond to the data? _____. Return to
page **196B.**

From page **195C**.

202C **Correct.** A chromosome map represents a generalized chromosome for the species. We stated that it is customary when building a chromosome map to locate the allele which is **not** possessed by a normal fruit fly with a homozygous genotype. Which of the following assumptions about genes permits us to do this?

☐ Genes are located on chromosomes in linear
order. . . . . .page **192A.**

☐ Alleles occupy corresponding loci on homolo-
gous chromosomes. . . . . .page **204A.**

From page **199B.**

Correct. The locus of red eye, the normal allele of the gene for pink   **203A**
eye, is the same as the locus of the gene for pink eye. Any gene and its
allele occupy the same locus.
    We have discovered that the genes for clipped wing, pink eye,
dwarfism, and bristle and their alleles are on a single pair of homologous chromosomes. Let us assume that an individual fruit fly had a
genotype heterozygous for all four of these traits (*CcPpDdBb*). One of
the parents of this fruit fly had a genotype homozygous for clipped
wing, red eyes, normal size, and bristles (*ccPPDDbb*) and the other
parent had the genotype (*CCppddBB*). Which of the following could
represent the paired chromosomes of the heterozygous offspring of
these two parents, that is, the individual having the genotype
CcPpDdBb?

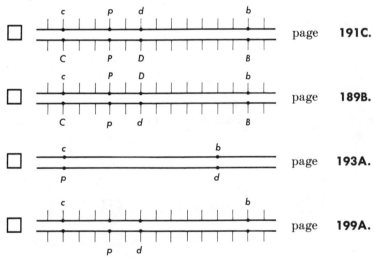

□   page   **191C.**

□   page   **189B.**

□   page   **193A.**

□   page   **199A.**

No. If the gene for dwarf were 2 units to the left of pink, it would be   **203B**
farther from bristle than pink is, and the crossover percent between
bristle and dwarf should have been 11%. It was not 11%, it was 7%.
Return to page **193D.**

Incorrect. If none of the offspring of the cross $\dfrac{P \quad D}{p \quad d} \times \dfrac{p \quad d}{p \quad d}$ **203C**

would have the genotype $\dfrac{P \quad d}{p \quad d}$ it would mean there was com-

plete linkage. There wasn't; there was a 2% crossing-over. Return to
page **201D.**

From page 202C.

204A **Correct.** The assumption that alleles occupy corresponding loci on homologous chromosomes permits us to use the allele **not** possessed by a normal fruit fly with a homozygous genotype, when constructing a chromosome map. To construct a chromosome map it is essential to know the relative distance between genes on the same chromosome.

On the basis of the assumption that genes having the higher percentage of crossing-over are farther apart on a chromosome, plus the information that pink-eye — bristle crossover percentage is 9%, while pink-eye — dwarfism crossover percentage is 2%, the locus of which gene is farther away on the chromosome from the locus of the gene for pink eye? The locus of the

☐ gene for bristle..............................page **197B.**

☐ gene for dwarfism.........................page **198B.**

From page 200A.

204B **Correct.** This is the end of this chapter. Continue with the review.

REVIEW—Chapter 4, Part III

The discovery of linkage and crossing-over led to the concept of genes as being located in linear order on a chromosome. The closer two alleles are to each other on a chromosome the (*larger, smaller*) _____ will be the crossover percentage. If the crossover percent between genes a and b is 5%, and between genes b and c is 3%, the crossover percent between genes a and c might be _____% or it might be _____%. To discover which of these is correct we would have to make the actual cross. If it is 8% it means that c is (*closer to, farther from*) _____ a than b is. On the basis of crossover percents it has been possible to construct chromosome maps. If the crossover percentage between gene a and gene b is known, and between gene b and gene c is known, it (*is, is not*) _____ necessary to know the crossover percent between gene a and gene c in order to construct a section of a chromosome map.

To check your responses to the review, turn to page 359 and then continue with the summary of Part III.

SUMMARY—Chapter 4, Part III

Examination of linkage and crossing-over among a number of different characteristics revealed that the crossover percentage was constant for any two linked genes; it differed between different linked genes. The difference in crossing-over percentage among linked genes was assumed to be due to different distances between linked genes on a chromosome. Presumably genes farther apart would have a greater chance of crossing-over than those closer together.

By comparing the crossing-over percentages of three genes on the same chromosome it was possible to determine their relative positions on the chromosomes. With the accumulation of crossover data on a large number of genes on the same chromosome, maps could be made of the chromosome with respect to the relative positions of the genes on the chromosomes.

The discovery of linkage and crossing-over made it necessary to limit the assumption of the gene theory concerning independent assortment. The assumption applied only to those gene pairs that were on nonhomologous chromosomes.

Continue with the self test for Chapter 4.

SELF TEST—Chapter 4

Indicate your choice of answers by placing a check ($\checkmark$) in the spaces provided.

1. There is assumed to be a total of 46 chromosomes in each somatic cell of a human. How many different linkage groups should there be?

    __A. 2

    __B. 23

    __C. 46

    __D. 92

    __E. Cannot be determined from the data given.

After the map distance has been determined for a large number of genes on the basis of data obtained from crossover percentages, specific chromosome maps can be constructed. One end of the chromosome is arbitrarily indicated as the zero (0) point and other loci are designated.

Questions 2–19 are concerned with the following chromosome map:

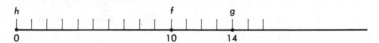

2. The crossover percentage between a fourth gene d and gene g is 6%. In order to determine the position of d, it is necessary to know the crossover percent between d and (#) _____ additional gene(s) on the map.
    _A. One
    _B. Two
    _C. Three
    _D. Four
    _E. No particular number.

3. On the basis of the information presented thus far, the gene d could be predicted to be at one of how many loci?
    _A. One
    _B. Two
    _C. Three
    _D. Four
    _E. No locus can be predicted.

4. If the gene d were between the gene g and the gene h, how many map units would it be from gene f?
    _A. Two
    _B. Four
    _C. Six
    _D. Eight
    _E. Ten

5. If the gene d were not between gene g and gene h how many map units would it be from gene f?
    _A. Two
    _B. Four
    _C. Six
    _D. Eight
    _E. Ten

6. If a cross between individuals with the genotypes *FfDd* and *ffdd* (these genes are the same as on the chromosome map for questions 2–19) is made (*FfDd* × *ffdd*) and if the offspring are in the ratio of 49:1:1:49 what is the percent crossover between genes *d* and *f*?

   __A. 1%
   __B. 2%
   __C. 4.9%
   __D. 6%
   __E. None of these.

7. On the basis of all of the information given about gene *d*, its locus on the chromosome can be determined as being at

   __A. 2
   __B. 8
   __C. 12
   __D. 20
   __E. None of these.

8. What percent of the offspring of the cross *HhFf* × *hhff* should have the genotype *Hhff* (assume that the genes *H* and *F* are on one chromosome and *h* and *f* are on the homologous chromosome of the individual having the genotype *HhFf*)?

   __A. 0%
   __B. 5%
   __C. 10%
   __D. 25%
   __E. None of these.

9. In the cross *FfGg* × *ffgg* what should be the phenotypic ratio of the offspring?

   __A. 1:1:1:1
   __B. 4:1:1:4
   __C. 14:1:1:14
   __D. 24:1:1:24
   __E. None of these.

To solve the problem *What is the locus of gene d?* certain information which has been given in the introductory material and in Questions 2–9 must be used and certain calculations must be made. Evaluate items 10–19 according to the following key:

KEY: A.   Given and necessary to solve the problem.
       B.   Given but not necessary to solve the problem.
       C.   Not given; can be determined and is necessary.
       D.   Not given; can be determined but is not necessary.
       E.   Not given; cannot be determined.

__10. The locus of gene *f*.

__11. The locus of gene *h*.

__12. The percent crossover between gene *f* and gene *d*.

__13. The approximate percent crossover between gene *h* and gene *f*.

__14. The locus of gene *g*.

__15. The ratio of offspring of the cross *HhGg* × *hhgg*.

__16. The ratio of offspring of the cross *FfDd* × *ffdd*.

__17. The approximate percent of offspring with the genotype *Hhff* from the cross *HhFf* × *hhff* (as Question 8 above).

__18. The approximate percent crossover between genes *f* and *g*.

__19. The ratio of the F_2 generation of a cross *FfGg* × *FfGg* if the genes *F* and *G* are both on the same chromosome in both F_1 individuals.

For items 20–25 use the following key:

KEY: A.   The two traits are controlled by a single pair of genes, or the loci are less than one map unit apart.
       B.   The loci of the genes are on the same chromosome pair but are more than one map unit apart.
       C.   The two pairs of genes are located on two pairs of homologous chromosomes.
       D.   No decision can be made concerning the loci of the genes.

__20. In the fruit fly normal body is dominant to short, fat body and normal eye is dominant to rough eye. A normal-bodied and normal-eyed fruit fly with genotype heterozygous for both traits was crossed with one having a short, fat body and rough eyes. Of 50 offspring 27 had normal body shape and normal eyes; 23 had fat bodies and rough eyes.

__21. In corn the gene for dwarf plant is recessive to the gene for normal, and the gene for sugary seed is recessive to the gene for starchy seed. The cross *DdSs* × *ddss* produced 39 offspring having starchy seeds which developed into dwarf plants, 43 having starchy seeds which developed into normal-height plants, 37 having sugary seeds which developed into dwarf plants, and 40 having sugary seeds which developed into normal-size plants.

__22. In corn the gene for crumpled leaves is recessive. A cross of a dwarf plant with crumpled leaves with one of normal height and normal leaves produced 36 plants which were normal height but had crumpled leaves, 10 plants of normal height and normal leaves, 7 dwarf plants with crumpled leaves, and 40 dwarf plants with normal leaves.

__23. In mice the gene for pigmy is recessive; so also is the gene for rough coat. A rough-coated pigmy was crossed with a smooth-coated normal-size mouse. In the litter were two pigmy mice having rough coats, one normal-size mouse with rough coat, and two normal-size mice with smooth coat.

__24. A fat, jaunty-winged fruit fly *ffjj* was crossed with a normal fruit fly. Of the offspring 44 were normal, 38 were fat and jaunty-winged, 14 were fat and normal-winged, 16 were normal body-shaped but jaunty-winged.

__25. In tomato the gene for round fruit is dominant to the gene for elongated fruit and the gene for simple inflorescence is dominant to the gene for compound inflorescence. Two round-fruited plants with simple inflorescence were crossed. Of the offspring 69 had round fruit and simple inflorescence, 8 had round fruit and compound inflorescence, 9 had elongated fruit and simple inflorescence, and 15 had elongated fruit and compound inflorescence.

On the basis of the following information construct a chromosome map and then answer the next two questions which follow.

Gene *a* to *b*, 4 units.
Gene *b* to *c*, 6 units.
Gene *c* to *a*, 2 units.
Gene *d* to *b*, 14 units.
Gene *d* to *a*, 10 units.

26. How many units from *d* to *c*?
__A. 2
__B. 4
__C. 6
__D. 8
__E. 10

27. In what order are the genes on the chromosome?
__A. *a, b, c, d*
__B. *d, c, a, b*
__C. *a, c, d, b*
__D. *c, b, a, d*

Use the Key which follows the two crosses to respond to items 28–37 which are concerned with the following two crosses of chickens.

Cross I.   Pure-line colored with curly feathers × pure-line white, straight feathers

Offspring: All white, straight-feathered.

Cross II. F_1 offspring × recessive for both traits

Offspring: 11 white, curly; 41 white, straight;
                     38 colored, curly; 10 colored, straight.

KEY: A.   Cross I gives evidence for the statement.
          B.   Cross I gives evidence against the statement.
          C.   Cross II gives evidence for the statement.
          D.   Cross II gives evidence against the statement.
          E.   Neither of these crosses gives evidence for or against the statement.

__28.   Curly is dominant.

__29.   Colored is dominant.

__30.   The F_2 generation would have the ratio 9:3:3:1.

__31.   The genes for curly and for colored were on the same chromosome in the F_1 individuals.

__32.   In a dihybrid backcross the ratio of offspring is always 1:1:1:1.

__33.   Curly and colored are two effects produced by the same gene.

__34.   Genes always assort independently at gamete formation.

__35.   The crossover percentage between the genes for curly and colored is about 20%.

__36.   The genes for feather structure and for feather color are on two pairs of homologous chromosomes.

__37.   The genes for feather structure and for feather color assort independently.

For items 38–41 use the following Key.

KEY: A.   Genes occur in pairs in all body cells.
          B.   Paired genes separate (segregate) during gamete formation.
          C.   Genes are located in linear order on chromosomes.
          D.   Separate pairs of genes assort independently at gamete formation.
          E.   None of these.

__38.   Accounts for the 9:3:3:1 phenotypic ratio of F_2 in dihybrid cross.

__39.   Accounts for linkage of two different traits.

__40.   Must be modified to account for crossover percentages.

__41.   Must be modified to account for linkage.

Correct answers to the self test for Chapter 4 are on page 365.

P_1 gray $\times$ black, $BB \times bb$

	Phenotypic ratio	Genotypic ratio	Gene ratio	Gene frequencies
F_1	All gray	All Bb	_____	_____
F_2	_____	_____	_____	_____
F_3	_____	_____	_____	_____
F_4	_____	_____	_____	_____
F_5	_____	_____	_____	_____
F_6	_____	_____	_____	_____
N_1	All gray	_____	_____	_____
N_2	_____	_____	_____	_____
N_3	_____	_____	_____	_____
M_1	Yellow	Both Yy	$1Y:1y$	
M_2	2 yellow:1 normal	_____	_____	
M_3		_____	_____	
M_4		_____	_____	
M_5		_____	_____	
M_6		_____	_____	
M_7			_____	
M_8			_____	
M_9			_____	
M_{10}			_____	
M_{11}		_____		

chapter 5

POPULATION GENETICS

PART I

The application of the theory of the gene to the study of inheritance **213A**
in populations of organisms introduces another method of investigating inheritance. You have studied the pedigree method, the controlled breeding method, and the family method. We now introduce the **population method.**

A human population has been defined as the total number of persons inhabiting a country, a city, or any district or area. In biology the concept of population applies to other organisms as well as to man and usually refers to an assemblage of interbreeding organisms of one kind that lives in a particular area, such as a pond, lake, or forest. An essential feature of the biological concept of population is the reproduction among members of the population that produces sequences of generations. In this book the term "population" will be used in the biological sense of the word.

A few fruit flies, males and females, were placed in a pint milk bottle containing food. A specially constructed stopper placed in the neck of the bottle permitted air to pass in and out of the bottle but prevented the enclosed flies from leaving and other flies from entering. The young flies which were produced grew up and reproduced in turn. This continued for several generations. Would such a collection of flies constitute a population?

☐ Yes..page **220B.**

☐ No...page **225C.**

From page **220B.**

214A **You are right.** None of the situations described illustrated the method used in population genetics. In the population method particular matings are ignored. Instead the entire population is analyzed. The proportion of individuals possessing each phenotypic expression of a trait is determined. Suppose that there is a population of human beings where 70% are tasters and 30% are nontasters; 45% are blood Type O, 40% are Type A, 11% are Type B, and 4% are Type AB. Many members of this population are of marriageable age and many will marry. Then in a few years they will produce another generation. What will be the percentages of tasters and nontasters and of the various blood types in this generation? And when this generation grows up and produces the next generation what will be the proportion of tasters, nontasters and various blood types in it? What is the ratio of one allele to the other for each of the above inherited traits? It would be very difficult if not absolutely impossible to answer such questions on the basis of the methods of investigating inheritance examined so far. If we were to use these methods we would have to know exactly what matings had occurred and the number and kinds of offspring. We would have to know what proportion of the population was composed of children and of old people who do not contribute to the next generation. We would have to know if there was a tendency for persons with one characteristic to marry persons with the same or some other characteristic. All of these and other factors could affect the relative proportion of characteristics in the population from one generation to the next.

While information of this sort is important in the study of heredity of populations, sometimes it is virtually impossible to obtain such information. Therefore, the geneticist makes use of a method which reduces the problem to its simplest form. Such a method is called a **simple model method.** The principles of this method are to ignore all the complications that cannot be handled, and to mentally devise an ideal or model experiment which can be performed and where the results will have some bearing on the original problem.

The basic idea in relation to the model is that attention is shifted from individual crosses and their offspring to combined crosses and their offspring. For example, let us imagine a group of 20 fish, 10 males and 10 females, living in an aquarium. When these fish reproduce the females expel their unfertilized eggs into the water. At the same time all the males expel their sperm into the water. Thus all the eggs from all the females and all the sperm from all the males are mixed together. Which sperm will unite with which egg is a matter of chance, so that using the rules of probability it is possible to calculate what combinations of sperm and egg will occur. *Continue on next page.*

When you used the checkerboard to calculate the ratio of offspring expected from a single cross such as $Aa \times Aa$, you used the rules of probability for a single cross of one male with one female. In the case of the population model, that is, the fish in the aquarium, you use the same rules. The only difference is that in the population model you treat the combined sperm from many males as though they came from a single male and you treat the combined eggs from many females as though they came from one female.

To begin a study of populations we will use this idea and choose a simple situation and a simple population. Fruit flies have been used extensively in the study of heredity and have also been used to study populations. Let us assume that we placed two fruit flies, male and female, in a milk bottle. The genotype of one of the fruit flies was homozygous for gray body and of the other homozygous for black body. After the flies had mated and laid the eggs for the next generation they were removed. Let us assume that only 20 offspring were produced and that half were male and half female. All of the F_1 individuals were gray-bodied and had the heterozygous genotype Bb. Therefore the gene for gray is dominant to the gene for black. When these flies matured each of them would produce gametes in the ratio

☐ $1B:1b$ . . . . page **219D.**

☐ $3B:1b$ . . . . page **217C.**

Incorrect. We had to make the assumption of random production of gametes in the population in order to predict the ratio of $1B:1b$ which you have recorded on your worksheet. But when we predict the genotypic or phenotypic ratio we are concerned with union, not production of gametes. Return to page **229A.**

Incorrect. We assumed that the gametes are in a ratio of $1B:1b$ and that gametes unite at random at fertilization because we assumed random mating. What will be the genotypic ratio of the individuals of the F_3? _____. So the phenotypic ratio would be _____. Return to page **221A.**

Incorrect. To answer this question you must translate a ratio into its decimal equivalent. For example, a $1:1$ ratio indicates that each type represents $\frac{1}{2}$, or 50% of the whole. What is 50% expressed as a decimal fraction? _____. Return to page **222C.**

216A **Incorrect.** You have not followed the line of reasoning we have been developing. Return to page **224B** and start from there.

From page **226D.**

216B **Correct.** The expected phenotypic ratio for the total F_2 generation should be 3 gray:1 black.

We will follow this population through several generations removing the parents after the eggs for each new generation have been laid. The questions that we will attempt to answer as we follow this population through a number of generations are: *What will be the phenotypic ratios at the end of ten generations? What will be the ratio of one allele to the other after ten generations? Will the recessive allele gradually be lost in the population?*

Recall that we have mentioned that the expected phenotypic ratio would be 3 gray:1 black in the F_2 generation, and the genotypic ratio for the F_2 would be $1BB:2Bb:1bb$. RECORD BOTH OF THESE ON WORK-SHEET 5-A.

Now consider this population as a unit. When reproduction takes place to produce the next generation what will be the genotypic ratio and the phenotypic ratio of this generation? We can predict this by again using the simple model method. For example, assume that there are 400 individuals. How many of them will have each of the following genotypes for body color, *BB*, *Bb*, and *bb*? Record the expected numbers in the proper place below.

No. of Individuals

BB _____

Bb _____

bb _____

What do you have recorded above?

☐ 100, 200, 100 . . . . page   **223A.**

☐ 133, 133, 133 . . . . page   **219A.**

☐ 200, 100, 100 . . . . page   **227B.**

Incorrect. Did you make a mistake in arithmetic? The total number **217A** of gametes containing gene *B* should equal the number containing gene *b*. What ratio reflects equality? _____. Return to page **225A**.

Incorrect. If the genotypic ratio of all of the individuals of the F_2 is **217B** $1BB:2Bb:1bb$ and if these individuals collectively produce gametes in the ratio of $1B:1b$, then what will be the ratio of gametes produced by the F_3 where the genotypic ratio is also $1BB:2Bb:1bb$? _____. Return to page **224B**.

No. You have forgotten one of the assumptions of the gene theory. **217C** The genotype of each individual is *Bb*. How many kinds of gametes can be produced by each individual with respect to this trait? _____, and in what ratio? _____. Have you confused the 3:1 ratio of the offspring of hybrids with the ratio of gametes produced by hybrids? _____. Return to page **214A**.

From page **222A**.

You are correct. The recessive allele will not gradually be lost no **217D** matter how many generations are produced.

Since the ratio of genes in the gametes and the genotypic ratio do not change from generation to generation under the conditions of this experiment we can make a generalization about randomly mating populations. **Populations remain constant generation after generation; that is, there is a stability of the proportion of alleles in a population.** This generalization is called the **Hardy-Weinberg Law.** In this particular example the ratio of the allele *B* to the allele *b* was 1:1. Such ratios of alleles represent a gene frequency of .5 for each of the alleles. Since all of the gametes produced by this population are in the ratio of $1B:1b$ we can write a probability equation for the gametes of the entire population. It would be

☐ $\frac{1}{4}BB + \frac{1}{2}Bb + \frac{1}{4}bb = 1$ . . . . page **218C.**

☐ $\frac{1}{2}B + \frac{1}{2}b = 1$ . . . . page **228D.**

☐ $\frac{3}{4}B + \frac{1}{4}b = 1$ . . . . page **225B.**

218A **How come?** EXAMINE YOUR WORKSHEET. Was the ratio of genes in the population the same in the F_6 generation as it was in the F_3? _____. Was it the same in the F_3 as in the F_1? _____.
If the ratio of the alleles is the same is one allele decreasing? _____.
If the recessive is not decreasing how can it "get lost"? Return to page **222A**.

218B **Incorrect.** Genes in both sperm and eggs are in a 1:1 ratio. We can use a checkerboard to make a prediction concerning the genotypic ratio in the next generation as follows:

Eggs \ Sperm	B	b
B		
b		

What would the genotypic ratio be? _____. Return to page **226A**.

218C **Incorrect.** This is the equation for the genotypes of this population. The question asked for the probability equation for the gametes. Return to page **217D**.

From page **224B**.

218D **Correct.** The ratio of gametes produced by the F_3 generation collectively should be $1B:1b$. RECORD THIS RATIO ON YOUR WORKSHEET. COMPLETE THE GENOTYPIC RATIOS, PHENOTYPIC RATIOS AND RATIOS OF GENES IN GAMETES FOR THE F_4, F_5, F_6 AS INDICATED ON WORKSHEET 5-A. If we continued the experiment with gray and black bodied flies, what prediction would you make concerning the ratio of phenotypes in the 10th generation of this population?

☐ The phenotypic ratio would be the same, *i.e.*,
3 gray to 1 black . . . . page   **229A**.

☐ The phenotypic ratio would be different, but I
don't know exactly what it would be . . . . page   **223B**.

No. Since the genotypic ratio is $1BB:2Bb:1bb$ and since we assumed **219A**
400 individuals, what fraction of these individuals would have the
genotype BB? _____. What is $\frac{1}{4}$ of 400? _____. Return to page **216B**.

From page **222C**.

Correct. The frequency of the allele B in such a population would be **219B**
.5. ENTER THIS VALUE ON THE WORKSHEET IN COLUMN "GENE FRE-
QUENCIES." Now consider a different population having all black flies.
Remember that the gene for gray is dominant to the gene for black.
In such a population the frequency of the allele b would be

☐ 1. . . . . .page   **226D.**

☐ .75. . . . . .page   **228B.**

☐ .5. . . . . .page   **222B.**

☐ 0. . . . . .page   **224A.**

Incorrect. This would be an example of the pedigree method. In the **219C**
population method of studying heredity, no particular family is
studied; all of the individuals in the population are equally important.
Return to page **220B**.

From page **214A**.

Correct. Any one male of this generation having the genotype Bb **219D**
would produce sperm in the ratio $1B:1b$. Because all the males are
alike, if we pooled together all of the sperm produced by all of the
males the ratio of gametes of all of the males would reflect the ratio
of the genes in these males. This ratio would be

☐ $1B:1b$. . . . . .page   **222C.**

☐ $3B:1b$. . . . . .page   **221D.**

220A **Incorrect.** You know that gray, not black, is dominant. If the off-spring of each pair of flies is in a ratio of 3 gray:1 black, what will be the ratio of offspring of all 10 pairs of flies? _____. Return to page **226D.**

From page 213A.

220B **Correct.** The fruit flies in the bottle would be a population as previously defined because they are one kind of organism inhabiting a restricted area and they interbreed to produce generation after generation.

Partial answers to such questions as *What will be the percentage of people with various blood types ten generations from now? Will blue eye color increase or decrease in the population? What will be the effect on the population of increased fallout of radioactive material?* are to be found in the study of population genetics.

Recall that in the pedigree method we examined a single family through three generations with respect to a single inherited trait. When we discussed the controlled breeding method we described the results of selected and controlled matings. In the family method we selected particular kinds of marriages and grouped these in classes on the basis of the kinds of offspring produced. In all three of the above methods attention was paid to particular matings or to particular kinds of matings and the kinds of offspring produced by each.

In the population method particular matings are ignored. Instead the entire population is analyzed. The proportion of individuals in the population possessing each phenotypic expression of a trait is determined. From these kinds of data the ratio of the alleles is determined. Factors influencing changes in these ratios are also studied in that branch of genetics known as population genetics.

In the study of the genetics of populations one is primarily concerned with

☐ histories of families exhibiting a particular
characteristic............................page **219C.**

☐ results of matings of individuals of pure lines,
and of F_1 hybrids........................ page **224D.**

☐ kinds of offspring produced by particular kinds
of matings................................page **223C.**

☐ none of these............................page **214A.**

From page **226A.**

Correct. The genotypic ratio of the F$_3$ generation should be 1*BB* :   **221A**
2*Bb* : 1*bb*. What will be the phenotypic ratio of the individuals of the
F$_3$ generation? Keep in mind that the gene for gray is dominant to the
gene for black.

☐ 3 gray:1 black............................page   **224B.**

☐ 1 gray:1 black...........................page   **227C.**

☐ All gray.................................page   **215C.**

☐ Since the parents were of all three genotypes I
   cannot predict what the next generation
   will be...................................page   **229B.**

Incorrect. To answer this question you must translate a ratio into   **221B**
its decimal equivalent. For example, a 1:1 ratio indicates that each
type represents ½, or 50% of the whole. What is 50% expressed as a
decimal fraction? _____. Return to page 222C.

From page **225A.**

Correct. The ratio of the genes in the gametes for the entire popula-   **221C**
tion would be 1*B*:1*b*. RECORD THIS RATIO ON WORKSHEET 5-A UNDER
GENE RATIO FOR THE F$_2$ GENERATION.
    Gene frequencies are normally expressed as decimal fractions. What
would be the frequency of each of the two genes?

☐ .75*B* + .25*b*.............................page   **228C.**

☐ .5*B* + .5*b*...............................page   **226A.**

☐ .25*B* + .25*b*.............................page   **224C.**

Incorrect. If every male had the genotype, *Bb*, so that the ratio of   **221D**
gene *B* to gene *b* in any one male was 1:1, how could the ratio of gene
B to gene *b* in all the males be 3*B*:1*b*? Where would the extra genes *B*
come from? Return to page **219D.**

From page 227A.

222A **Correct.** The ratio of types of gametes as well as the phenotypic and genotypic ratios should remain constant.

The third question regarding the population of fruit flies we were following through a number of generations was: Will the recessive allele gradually be lost in the population? Will it?

☐ Yes . . . . page **218A.**

☐ No . . . . page **217D.**

222B **Incorrect.** If all of the individuals are black, their genotypes would be bb. What would be the percent of gametes produced with the gene b? _____. Return to page **219B.**

From page 219D.

222C **Correct.** If each male produced sperm in the ratio $1B:1b$, the ratio of the alleles for all of the sperm would be $1B:1b$. If we also collected all of the eggs produced by the females each of which has the genotype Bb in a composite pool the ratio of their gametes would also be $1B:1b$. Therefore, the ratio of genes in the gametes of this population is $1B:1b$. RECORD THIS ON WORKSHEET 5-A AS THE GENE RATIO FOR THE F_1 GENERATION.

In any population the ratio of the genes in all the gametes reflects the ratio of the two alleles in all the individuals. The proportion of any one allele is referred to as the **gene frequency** of that allele.

Gene frequencies are usually expressed as decimal fractions. The frequency of the allele B in a population where all of the individuals have heterozygous genotypes would be

☐ .75 . . . . page **215D.**

☐ .5 . . . . page **219B.**

☐ .25 . . . . page **221B.**

222D **Incorrect.** Some of the individuals would be heterozygous with the genotype Bb. You have neglected to include these individuals. Return to page **228D.**

From page **216B.**

Correct. Your completed table for 400 individuals would be: **223A**

No. of Individuals

BB 100

Bb 200

bb 100

Our next step is to determine the ratios of different kinds of gametes produced by these fruit flies. Gametes of fruit flies are produced in enormous numbers but because we are interested only in the ratio of the different kinds of gametes produced we can simplify the arithmetic by assuming that each fly produces 10 gametes. Therefore if we assume that each fly produces 10 gametes how many gametes containing the gene *B* and how many containing the gene *b*, would be produced by the individuals listed in the table below?

Genotype	No. of Individuals	Gametes Containing	
		Gene *B*	Gene *b*
BB	100	————	————
Bb	200	————	————
bb	100	————	————

Turn to page **225A.**

Did you follow directions? If not, COMPLETE THE WORKSHEET. If so, **223B** you may have made some error. Or did you fail to translate the genotypic ratio into the proper phenotypic ratio? All the gene ratios should be 1*B*:1*b*; all the genotypic ratios should be 1*BB*:2*Bb*:1*bb*; and all the phenotypic ratios should be 3 gray :1 black. Return to page **218D.**

Incorrect. Although this method utilizes masses of data on various **223C** kinds of individuals, the emphasis of the family method is on the kind of matings in the population and not on the proportions of the kinds of individuals in a population. Return to page **220B.**

224A Incorrect. If all of the individuals are black, their genotypes would be bb. What would be the percent of gametes produced with the gene b? _____. Return to page **219B**.

From page **221A**.

224B Correct. You have predicted that in the F_3 generation the phenotypic ratio would be 3 gray:1 black. Experimental data confirm this prediction. RECORD THIS PHENOTYPIC RATIO ON WORKSHEET 5-A.

Note that the ratio of gray-bodied flies to black-bodied flies is the same in both the F_2 and F_3 generations. The F_1 generation that produced the F_2 generation consisted of only one genotype, Bb, while the F_2 generation that produced the F_3 generation consisted of three genotypes, BB, Bb, and bb. However, because the ratio of B and b gametes produced by both the F_1 and F_2 generations was the same, that is $1B:1b$, the ratio of genotypes of the offspring (F_2 and F_3) produced by the entire population was $1BB:2Bb:1bb$ for both generations. So long as gametes combine at random the ratio of offspring, as determined by the ratio of gametes, will be the same regardless of whether the gametes come from a single pair of organisms or from hundreds of pairs. RECORD THE GENOTYPIC RATIO FOR THE F_3 GENERATION ON WORKSHEET 5-A.

What will be the ratio of gametes produced by the F_3 generation to produce the F_4 generation?

☐ $1B:1b$...................................page **218D.**

☐ $2B:1b$...................................page **217B.**

☐ $3B:1b$...................................page **226C.**

☐ Cannot be predicted......................page **229C.**

224C Incorrect. If the ratio is $1B:1b$ the two genes must be equal in numbers in the population. If the total number of genes equals 100%, and both genes are equal in number what decimal fraction added to itself would equal 1 or 100%? Return to page **221C**.

224D Incorrect. This is an example of the controlled breeding method and is not typical of what happens in a population. Return to page **220B**.

From page **223A**.

The table should have been filled out as follows:

Genotype	No. of Individuals	Gametes Containing	
		Gene B	Gene b
BB	100	1000	0
Bb	200	1000	1000
bb	100	0	1000

If your answer does not correspond to the one given above you probably made one or both of two possible errors. One is that you forgot to multiply the number of individuals by 10 (the number of gametes produced by each). The other is that you failed to recognize that individuals having the genotype Bb would produce gametes one-half of which would contain gene B and one-half of which would contain the gene b. If you made an error make sure that you know the reason for it before proceeding.

Now add the total number of gametes containing gene B and the total number containing gene b. What is the ratio of alleles in the gametes for the entire population?

☐ 3:1 . . . . page **217A.**

☐ 1:1 . . . . page **221C.**

☐ 1:0 . . . . page **226B.**

Incorrect. We have established that the ratio is $1B\!:\!1b$. What
fraction of the gametes would contain the gene B? _____.
What fraction would contain the gene b? _____. So the probability equation would be _____B + _____b = 1. Return to page **217D**.

Why not? Are not the flies interbreeding organisms of one kind?
_____. Are they living together in a particular place? _____.
A population is defined here as an interbreeding group of organisms living in a particular place. Perhaps you were using a different definition of population. This is permissible in other fields, but we have adopted the above definition for this text. Return to page **213A**.

From page 221C.

226A **Correct.** The frequency of each gene would be .5. RECORD THIS ON WORKSHEET 5-A UNDER "GENE FREQUENCIES."

If the F_2 generation has a gene frequency of .5 for gene B and .5 for gene b, then these genes would occur in a 1:1 ratio in the gametes produced by the F_2 generation. If we assume that the sperm and eggs combine at fertilization by chance then the genotypic ratio of the F_3 generation would be

☐ $1BB : 2Bb : 1bb$ . . . . .page **221A.**

☐ $1BB : 1Bb : 1bb$ . . . . .page **218B.**

226B **Incorrect.** Did you make a mistake in arithmetic? The total number of gametes containing gene B should equal the number containing gene b. What ratio reflects equality? _____. Return to page 225A.

226C **Incorrect.** If the genotypic ratio of all of the individuals of the F_2 is $1BB:2Bb:1bb$ and if these individuals collectively produce gametes in the ratio of $1B:1b$, then what will be the ratio of gametes produced by the F_3 where the genotypic ratio is also $1BB:2Bb:1bb$? _____. Return to page 224B.

From page 219B.

226D **Correct.** In a population of all black fruit flies the frequency of the allele b would be 1, and, since there would be no gray flies, the frequency of the allele B would be 0.

Going back to the F_1 gray flies, we know that the expected ratio of offspring produced by two individuals having the heterozygous genotype Bb should be 3 gray:1 black, because the gametes would be produced in a $1B:1b$ ratio and gray is dominant to black. Inasmuch as all of the F_1 individuals comprising the population of flies have genotypes that are heterozygous, Bb, and all sperm and all eggs are produced in a $1B:1b$ ratio, the expected ratio of phenotypes in the F_2 generation (the entire population) would be

☐ 3 gray:1 black . . . . .page **216B.**

☐ 3 black:1 gray . . . . .page **220A.**

☐ 1 gray:1 black . . . . .page **228A.**

From page **229A.**

Correct. Initially we posed three questions. One of these was: **227A**
What will be the phenotypic ratio at the end of 10 generations? We
answered this question by mentally combining all of the gametes produced by all of the females of one generation into one group or "pool"
and determined the ratio of one kind of gamete to the other. We did the
same for the sperm produced by all of the males. Thus we could deal
with this situation in the same manner as we did when we considered
the kinds of gametes produced by one individual only.

The concept of **gene pool** relates to the total collection of genes
available in a population. Were we to count and tabulate all of the
alleles of all of the genes in a population, and pool them, we would
have some measure of the population's net genetic make-up. This is
what we did mentally in relation to the alleles for gray and black body
in our model population. We pooled the alleles produced in the gametes
of both males and females, determined their ratios, and predicted the
consequences of random mating in the next generation.

We found that by pooling the alleles in gametes the ratio of these
alleles remained $1B:1b$. Thus we also have answered a second of the
original questions posed, namely: What will be the ratio of one allele
to the other after 10 generations? It will be

☐ $3B:1b$ . . . . page   **216A.**

☐ $1B:1b$ . . . . page   **222A.**

Incorrect. Since the genotypic ratio is $1BB:2Bb:1bb$ and since we   **227B**
assumed 400 individuals, what fraction of these individuals would
have the genotype BB? _____. What is $\frac{1}{4}$ of 400? _____.
Return to page **216B.**

Incorrect. We assumed that the gametes are in a ratio of $1B:1b$ and   **227C**
that gametes unite at random at fertilization because we assumed
random mating. What will be the genotypic ratio of the individuals of
the F_3? _____. So the phenotypic ratio would be _____.
Return to page **221A.**

Incorrect. Some of the individuals would be heterozygous with the   **227D**
genotype Bb. You have neglected to include these individuals. Return
to page **228D.**

228A **Incorrect.** If each pair of flies produces offspring in the ratio of 3 gray:1 black, what will be the ratio of gray:black for the combined offspring? _____. Have you forgotten that the individuals of the F_2 that have heterozygous genotypes will be gray, since gray is dominant? Return to page **226D.**

228B **No.** You must have forgotten that the gene for gray is dominant. The black flies would all have the genotype *bb*. Return to page **219B.**

228C **Incorrect.** If the ratio is $1B:1b$ the two genes must be equal in numbers in the population. What decimal fraction indicates equality? Return to page **221C.**

From page **217D.**

228D **Correct.** The probability equation for the gametes of the population, $\frac{1}{2}B + \frac{1}{2}b = 1$, can be expressed in decimal form as $.5B + .5b = 1$. These decimal fractions can be included in the checkerboard to develop the equation $\frac{1}{4}BB + \frac{1}{2}Bb + \frac{1}{4}bb = 1$ as follows:

	.5B	.5b
.5B	BB .25	Bb .25
.5b	Bb .25	bb .25

The probability equation, $\frac{1}{4}BB + \frac{1}{2}Bb + \frac{1}{4}bb = 1$ can also be expressed as

☐ $.25BB + .50Bb + .25bb = 1$............. page **230A.**

☐ $.75BB + .25bb = 1$........................ page **227D.**

☐ Either of these............................ page **222D.**

From page **218D.**

Correct. The phenotypic ratio would be the same, and the fre- **229A**
quency of each gene is .5.

When we used the controlled breeding method of investigating inheritance we assumed that for any trait if two F_1 individuals with
heterozygous genotypes Aa mated the gametes would be in a $1A:1a$
ratio. We also assumed that the random combination of these gametes
would produce a $1AA:2Aa:1aa$ genotypic ratio in the next generation.
Inasmuch as we have reasoned that our model population of F_2 individuals would collectively produce gametes in a $1B:1b$ ratio, a prediction could be made concerning the ratio of phenotypes in the F_3
generation of the entire population.

In order to make a prediction concerning the ratio of the individuals
in any generation it would be necessary to assume

A. **that mating is random, that is, that the choice of mate will
not depend on the phenotype or genotype of the mate.**
B. **that the number of offspring produced by any one type of
cross would be on the average the same as that produced
by any other cross.**

The first assumption concerning a population, namely, that the
mating of individuals is random with respect to the phenotypes or
genotypes is equivalent to which of the following assumptions of the
gene theory?

☐ Random production of gametes by one indi-
vidual. . . . . .page   **215B.**

☐ Random union of gametes produced by a single
male and single female. .page   **227A.**

Incorrect. You apparently do not understand the basis on which pre- **229B**
dictions are made in a model population. Return to page **216B.**

It can be predicted. If the genotypic ratio of all of the individuals of **229C**
the F_2 is $1BB:2Bb:1bb$ and if these individuals collectively produce
gametes in the ratio of $1B:1b$, then what will be the ratio of gametes
produced by the F_3 where the genotypic ratio is also $1BB:2Bb:1bb$?
_____. Return to page **224B.**

From page **228D.**

230A **Correct.** The probability equation $\tfrac{1}{4}BB + \tfrac{1}{2}Bb + \tfrac{1}{4}bb = 1$ can also be expressed as $.25BB + .50Bb + .25bb = 1$. Continue with the review.

REVIEW—Chapter 5, Part I

A population of fruit flies in a bottle was studied for several generations. Of the two original flies of this population one had a homozygous genotype for black body (*bb*) the other had a homozygous genotype for gray body, (*lt*) _____. All of the F_1 individuals had the genotype, (*lt*) _____ and were (*wd*) _____ bodied. These F_1 individuals would produce gametes in the ratio of 1 (*lt*) _____ : (#) _____ *b*. Thus the ratio of the alleles in the individuals of the F_1 generation was _____ : _____. Expressed as a decimal fraction the frequency of the gene *B* was (#) _____, and the frequency of the gene *b* was also (#) _____. In a population of gray flies all with homozygous genotypes the frequency of the gene *B* would be (#) _____ and in the same population the frequency of the gene *b* would be (#) _____. When the F_1 individuals, considered as a population, mated, they produced offspring in the ratio of (#) _____ gray : (#) _____ black; the genotypic ratio would be (# and *lt*) _____ : _____ : _____. If a total of 4000 gametes were produced by the individuals of this generation (#) _____ should contain the gene *B* and (#) _____ should contain the gene *b*. Thus the ratio of the gametes and hence the ratio of the genes in this generation would be _____ : _____. Hence again the frequency of the gene *B* and the gene *b* would be (#) _____; therefore the ratio of genotypes for the F_3 generation should be _____ : _____ : _____, which would yield a phenotypic ratio of (#) _____ gray : (#) _____ black. This ratio of alleles would remain constant generation after generation providing mating (*is, is not*) _____ random; thus the recessive allele (*will, will not*) _____ be reduced in frequency. If the ratio of two alleles (*A* and *a*) in a population is 1:1, this ratio can be expressed as the probability equation (#) _____ $A + \tfrac{1}{2}$ (*lt*) _____ = (#) _____.

Since gene frequencies are usually written as decimal fractions this equation can be expressed as (#) _____A + (#) _____a = 1. The equation for the genotypes of the population can be developed from this equation by multiplication of the binomials of two such equations to give the genotypic ratio for the population; this equation, expressed in decimal fractions is (#) _____AA + (#) _____Aa + .25 (lt) _____ = 1.

Check your responses to the review with those on page 359 and continue with the summary of Part I.

SUMMARY—Chapter 5, Part I

The pedigree method, controlled breeding method, and family method of studying heredity cannot be applied to populations of organisms because of the impossibility of knowing and keeping track of all the factors that would be effective. For populations the method used involves the creation of a model population, the concepts of the gene pool and gene frequencies, and the calculation and prediction of gene frequencies from generation to generation.

To make the calculations of the history of gene frequencies over a number of generations it is necessary to assume that in the model population, (1) mating is at random, and (2) the number of offspring produced by any one mating is the same as that produced by any other mating.

In the first example of a model population we started with two alleles, B and b, having the same frequency. We discovered that the genotypes having the ratio $1BB:2Bb:1bb$ produced in each generation a ratio of gametes $1B:1b$. Because this same ratio of gametes was produced each generation and because each member of the population mated, mating was random, and each mating produced the same number of offspring, the frequency of genes B and b did not change. This stability of gene frequencies from generation to generation is known as the Hardy-Weinberg Law.

Continue with Part II of this chapter.

232A   In building the model population we arbitrarily made the alleles B and b of equal numbers because this ratio corresponded with ratios with which you were familiar, and thus made it easier to develop the concept of gene frequency in a population as being related to the ratio of one allele to another. However, not all alleles are of equal frequency in all populations.

To illustrate what happens when two alleles have a different frequency let us imagine a different population. We will start by selecting all the gray-bodied flies from a population like the F_2 generation of our first population. We will designate this first generation as N_1 and the subsequent generations as N_2, N_3, etc.

One-third of the gray-bodied flies would have homozygous genotypes, BB, and two-thirds would have heterozygous genotypes, Bb. RECORD THE GENOTYPIC RATIO $1BB:2Bb$, FOR THE N_1 GENERATION ON WORKSHEET 5-A.

Now consider the individuals with the genotype BB. Assume that there are 20 of them, and 40 with the genotype Bb, and that each individual produces 10 gametes.

Complete the table below.

Genotypes	Number of Individuals	Number of Gametes	
		B	b
BB	20	_____	_____
Bb	40	_____	_____
		Sum_____	Sum_____

What is the ratio of the gametes produced by the 60 individuals?

☐ $1B:1b$ . . . . page   **238C.**

☐ $2B:1b$ . . . . page   **237D.**

232B   Incorrect. You have recorded the genotypic ratio as $4BB:4Bb:1bb$. What color would those having the genotype bb be? _____. Return to page **234B.**

232C   Incorrect. Four spaces might be used to represent a ratio of gametes, but it would be used to represent a $3:1$ ratio, not a $2:1$. Return to page **242C.**

Incorrect. The 1:2:1 genotype ratio is obtained only when the **233A** gametes of both sexes are produced in a 1:1 ratio. We have discovered that the ratio of gametes produced by the gray F_2 flies of the N_1 population was $2B:1b$. Go back and recount the various genotypes represented in the checkerboard. Return to page **241A**.

Incorrect.
$$\begin{array}{r} p + q \\ \underline{p + q} \\ pq + q^2 \\ \underline{p^2 + \quad pq} \\ p^2 + 2pq + q^2 \end{array}$$

233B

Return to page **243D**.

From page **235C**.

Correct. You predicted that the ratio of gray-bodied to black- **233C** bodied flies would be 8:1. Experiments have demonstrated that this is the actual ratio obtained generation after generation, for a population where the original parents were the gray-bodied flies having a genotypic ratio of $1BB:2Bb$.

We have found that when we know the genotypic ratio and the gene frequencies in a population it is possible to demonstrate that the gene frequencies will remain constant, if the only factors operating are the normal processes of heredity.

Can we do more than this and discover the actual frequency of two alleles in a population from the proportion of phenotypes in the population? We have expressed gene frequencies as decimal fractions such as $.5B + .5b = 1$ and as $.67B + .33b = 1$. If we let p stand for the frequency of the dominant allele and q stand for the frequency of the recessive allele and if there are only two alleles, the sum of the two decimal fractions, $p + q$, would have to be _____. Which of the following equations would represent the generalized relationship of the frequencies of two alleles in a population?

☐ $pA + qa = 1$ . . . . page **243D**.

☐ $.5p + .5q = 1$ . . . . page **236A**.

☐ Either of these . . . . page **239D**.

234A **You are incorrect.** The expression $\frac{1}{2}B + \frac{1}{2}b = 1$ is the probability equation for a 1:1 ratio. Remember the denominator represents the sum of the events. Return to page **240D.**

From page **241A.**

234B **Correct.** RECORD THE GENOTYPIC RATIO $4BB:4Bb:1bb$ FOR GENERATION N₂ ON YOUR WORKSHEET. What fraction of these would be gray? (Remember gray is dominant) _____. What fraction would be black? _____.

What would be the ratio of gray to black fruit flies in this generation?

☐ They would all be gray.....................page **232B.**

☐ 8 gray:1 black.............................page **240D.**

☐ 3 gray:1 black.............................page **254A.**

234C **Incorrect.**

$$\begin{array}{r} pA \;+\; qa \\ pA \;+\; qa \\ \hline p^2AA \;+\; pqAa \\ pqAa + q^2aa \\ \hline p^2AA + 2pqAa + q^2aa \end{array}$$

Return to page **246C.**

From page **239B.**

234D **Correct.** The probability equation $4/9BB + 4/9Bb + 1/9bb = 1$ corresponds with the results obtained from the checkerboard.

We have mentioned that gene frequencies are usually expressed as decimal fractions. Therefore, the probability equation for gametes produced by each sex, $2/3B + 1/3b = 1$, can be expressed as

☐ $.5B + .5b = 1$...........................page **236C.**

☐ $.67B + .33b = 1$.........................page **244A.**

From page **240B**.

Correct. The proportion of individuals in a population that have the **235A** heterozygous genotype is represented by the symbol 2pq.

What symbols represent the proportion of individuals having the dominant characteristic?

☐ $p^2 + 2pq + q^2$ . . . . .page **238A.**

☐ $p^2 + 2pq$ . . . . .page **248B.**

☐ p^2 . . . . .page **241D.**

Incorrect. Keep the following expression in mind: $p^2AA + 2pqAa +$ **235B** q^2aa. Also remember that p^2, 2pq and q^2 represent the proportion of each of these genotypes in a population. What proportion of the population has the genotype aa? The answer is q^2; and what proportion has the genotype AA? _____ . Return to page **236D.**

From page **236B**.

Correct. In order to discover whether the gene frequency remains **235C** constant over several generations it is necessary to translate the expected genotypic ratios into observable phenotypic ratios and then to observe the particular generation. What would you expect the genotypic ratio would be for the N_6 generation? _____ . This genotypic ratio would be expressed as a phenotypic ratio of

☐ 3 gray:1 black . . . . .page **258C.**

☐ 8 gray:1 black . . . . .page **233C.**

☐ Neither of these . . . . .page **239C.**

Incorrect. While it is true that at least two spaces were necessary **235D** because there were two kinds of gametes, the relative number of spaces actually reflects the ratio of the kinds of gametes. The ratio of gametes was $1B:1b$. Start again on page **237D.**

236A **Incorrect.** The symbols p and q are generalized symbols which stand for decimal fractions. They, the symbols p and q, do *not* stand for genes. What you have said, in effect, in selecting the answer .5p + .5q = 1, is that $(.5 \times .5) + (.5 \times .5) = 1$. Return to page **233C**.

From page **238D**.

236B **Correct.** The genotypic ratio would be $4BB:4Bb:1bb$. RECORD THIS RATIO AND THE PHENOTYPIC RATIO FOR THE N₃ GENERATION ON YOUR WORKSHEET. Do these calculations support the Hardy-Weinberg Law? (The gene frequency remains stable unless some factor other than normal genetic mechanism is in operation.)

☐ Yes. . . . . .page   **235C.**

☐ No. . . . . .page   **246A.**

236C **You have made an error.** .5 is the fraction ½. What is the decimal fraction which is equivalent to 2/3? _____. Return to page **234D**.

From page **241C**.

236D **Right.** The equation $p^2 + 2pq + q^2 = 1$ represents the relative proportions of the various genotypes in a population for two alleles.

The proportion of individuals in a population having the homozygous recessive genotype, such as bb, is represented in this equation by the symbol _____, while the proportion of individuals of this same population having the homozygous dominant genotype, such as BB, is represented by the symbol _____. What do you have recorded in the above two blanks and in what order?

☐ p^2 and q^2. . . . . .page   **235B.**

☐ q^2 and p^2. . . . . .page   **240B.**

☐ q^2 and $2pq$. . . . . .page   **242A.**

☐ $2pq$ and q^2. . . . . .page   **259C.**

Incorrect. If p = .45 what is p²? What is .45 × .45? _____. **237A**
Return to page **257C**.

Incorrect. .09 is the frequency of the recessive phenotype; therefore, **237B**
.09 is the value for q². Return to page **259B**.

Incorrect. The problem was to find the value for q. The square root **237C**
of q is not q itself, unless q is 1. Return to page **253D**.

From page **232A**.

Correct. The ratio of gametes would be $2B:1b$. RECORD THIS RATIO **237D**
ON WORKSHEET 5-A FOR THE GENE RATIO OF THIS N_1 GENERATION.
Again assume that each individual mates and that matings between
males and females are random, and that an equal number of offspring
is produced by each pair.

In calculating the genotypic and phenotypic ratios for the whole
population when the ratio of alleles was $1B:1b$ we used a checkerboard
with but one each of these two alleles on each side as follows:

	B	b
B		
b		

Why did we use only two spaces per side for the gametes?

☐ Because there are only two kinds of gametes
produced, with respect to this trait..........page **235D**.

☐ Because there was an equal number of the two
kinds of gamete produced, with respect to this
trait.....................................page **242C**.

☐ Because the gametes and hence the genes unite
at random...............................page **239A**.

238A **Incorrect.** $p^2 + 2pq + q^2$ represents *all* of the individuals in the population, those with the dominant characteristic and those with the recessive. Return to page **235A**.

From page **253D**.

238B **Correct.** To find the value of q you would extract the square root of q^2. You have already equated q^2 with .30 for nontasters in the population. The square root of .30 is approximately .55. Thus the gene frequency for the gene *t* is .55.

Can the frequency of the dominant allele be determined by extracting the square root of the per cent of individuals having the phenotype of the dominant characteristic?

☐ Yes.....................................page **243C.**

☐ No......................................page **250B.**

238C **Incorrect.** Did you fail to follow directions? If 40 individuals with genotype *Bb* each produced 10 gametes, how many of the 400 gametes would contain the gene *B*? _____. How many the gene *b*? _____. How many gametes containing the gene *B* would 20 individuals having the genotype *BB* produce? _____. Return to page **232A**.

From page **244A**.

238D **Correct.** The ratio of gametes was $2B:1b$ and therefore did not change in this generation. RECORD THIS RATIO OF GENES IN GAMETES FOR GENERATION N_2 ON THE WORKSHEET. Therefore the genotypic ratio of the next generation (N_3) would be

☐ $4BB:4Bb:1bb$............................page **236B.**

☐ $9BB:9Bb:1bb$............................page **248D.**

☐ It cannot be determined from the information given......................................page **242B.**

Incorrect. Random union of gametes is symbolized by the placing of **239A**
the letters in the squares, not by placing the letters at the side and top.
Return to page **237D**.

From page **240D**.

Correct. The probability equation for the ratio $2B:1b$ would be   **239B**
$2/3B + 1/3b = 1$. Since it is possible to equate fertilization with the
multiplication of the binomials of the probability equations of the
gametes, we can check the checkerboard results on page 241A, 'as
follows:

$$
\begin{array}{l}
2/3B + 1/3b \\
2/3B + 1/3b \\
\hline
4/9BB + 2/9Bb \\
\qquad\qquad 2/9Bb + 1/9bb \\
\hline
4/9BB + 4/9Bb + 1/9bb
\end{array}
$$

Thus, the probability equation at fertilization would be $4/9BB +
4/9Bb + 1/9bb = 1$.

Does this correspond with the results obtained by using the checkerboard on page 241A, that is, with the ratio $4BB:4Bb:1bb$?

☐ Yes...................................page   **234D.**

☐ No....................................page   **242D.**

Incorrect. You should have $4BB:4Bb:1bb$ recorded as the geno-   **239C**
typic ratio. Remember that gray is dominant. What color would the individuals with the genotype BB be? _____; with the genotype
Bb? _____; with the genotype bb? _____. Return to
page **235C**.

Incorrect. The symbols p and q are generalized symbols which stand   **239D**
for decimal fractions. They, the symbols p and q, do *not* stand for
genes. What you have said, in effect, in selecting the answer .5p +
.5q = 1, is that $(.5 \times .5) + (.5 \times .5) = 1$. Return to page **233C**.

240A **No.** Did you make the calculation or did you guess? If you guessed, go back and make the calculations. Or did you make some error in addition? Or did you make an error in reducing the ratio to small whole numbers? Return to page **244A.**

From page **236D.**

240B **Correct.** The proportion of the population having the genotype *bb* is q^2 and the proportion having the genotype *BB* is p^2. Which of the following symbols represents the proportion of the individuals in the population which have the heterozygous genotype *Bb*?

☐ pq . . . . .page   **246B.**

☐ 2pq . . . . .page   **235A.**

☐ Either of these . . . . .page   **249C.**

240C **Incorrect.** p^2 represents only a part of that fraction of the population which exhibits the dominant characteristic. Which part of the equation represents those individuals exhibiting the dominant characteristic, but having the heterozygous genotype? _____. Return to page **250B.**

From page **234B.**

240D **Correct.** The phenotypic ratio would be 8 gray : 1 black. RECORD THIS PHENOTYPIC RATIO FOR THE N_2 GENERATION. EXAMINE YOUR WORKSHEET. You will observe that you have recorded $2B:1b$ as the ratio of gametes produced by the N_1 generation.

    Which of the following probability equations expresses the ratio $2B:1b$?

☐ $\frac{1}{2}B + \frac{1}{2}b = 1$ . . . . .page   **234A.**

☐ $\frac{2}{3}B + \frac{1}{3}b = 1$ . . . . .page   **239B.**

☐ $\frac{3}{4}B + \frac{1}{4}b = 1$ . . . . .page   **245B.**

From page **242C.**

Correct. We could use the symbols as follows: **241A**

	B	B	b
B			
B			
b			

Fill in the above checkerboard to produce the genotypic and phenotypic ratios for the next generation. The genotypic ratio would be

☐ 1*BB*:2*Bb*:1*bb* . . . . .page   **233A.**

☐ 4*BB*:4*Bb*:1*bb* . . . . .page   **234B.**

☐ neither of these . . . . .page   **245C.**

Incorrect. If you subtract q from 2q you would know the value of q,   **241B**
but how could you obtain a value for 2q? You do know the value of q^2.
How can you determine q from this? Return to page **253D.**

From page **246C.**

Correct. For two alleles the general equation $p^2 + 2pq + q^2 = 1$ **241C**
always represents

☐ the relative proportions of the various geno-
types of the population .page   **236D.**

☐ the relative proportions of the phenotypes of
the population . . . . .page   **248A.**

Incorrect. p^2 represents only a portion of the individuals having the   **241D**
dominant characteristic, namely those with *two* genes for the dominant
characteristic. Return to page **235A.**

242A Incorrect. Keep the following expression in mind: $p^2AA + 2pqAa + q^2aa$. Also remember that p^2, $2pq$ and q^2 represent the proportion of each of these genotypes in a population. What proportion of the population has the genotype aa? The answer is q^2; and what proportion has the genotype AA? _____. Return to page **236D**.

242B Incorrect. If the ratio of gametes is $2B:1b$, the probability equation is $2/3B + 1/3b = 1$. Calculate the genotypic ratio of the N_3 generation by multiplication of the probability equation or by a checkerboard with three spaces per side. Now return to page **238D** and answer the question.

From page **237D**.

242C Correct. The number of spaces needed on each side of a checkerboard is determined by the total of the numbers in the ratio. For a $1B:1b$ ratio, two spaces on each side would be needed. For a $3B:1b$ ratio four spaces on each side would be needed. Keep in mind that the checkerboard as used here does not represent gametes produced by a single individual. It represents the gene pool, that is, the gametes produced by all of the males and all of the females of the generation under consideration.

In the N_1 population that produced gametes in the ratio $2B:1b$, how many spaces on each side of the checkerboard would you need to represent this ratio of gametes containing the two alleles?

☐ Two . . . . page   **247A.**

☐ Three . . . . page   **241A.**

☐ Four . . . . page   **232C.**

242D Incorrect. Have you forgotten that the denominator for the fractions of the probability equation for any ratio is the sum of the numbers in the ratio? For example, what would be the denominator in a ratio of $3:2:1$? _____. What would the three numerators be? _____. Return to page **239B**.

Incorrect. $.03 \times .03 = .0009$ or $.09\%$; 9%, not $.09\%$, of the popula- **243A** tion are left handed. Return to page **259B**.

No. This is contrary to the data presented. Go back to page **258D** **243B** and start the sequence from there.

Incorrect. Individuals having the dominant phenotype are repre- **243C** sented by $p^2TT + 2pqTt$. Return to page **238B**.

From page **233C**.

Correct. The symbol p represents the frequency of the dominant **243D** allele and q represents the frequency of the recessive allele. Because both alleles added together make up 100% of all the alleles for any one trait in a population, $pA + qa$ would equal 100% (1). Thus the equation $pA + qa = 1$ states in general terms the relationship of the frequencies of two alleles. Writing this equation for a particular trait such as gray body and black body we would have $pB + qb = 1$. This equation also reflects the ratio of gametes for the entire popula- tion.

We have stated that the equation $pA + qa = 1$ is a generalization for all gene frequency equations for two alleles. We demonstrated that by multiplying the binomials of two equations representing gametes $(.5B + .5b)(.5B + .5b)$ we could produce an equation for the propor- tion of genotypes in the population. Can we also multiply $(pA + qa)$ by $(pA + qa)$ and produce a general equation for the proportion of genotypes? In order to simplify the calculation of frequencies of geno- types we can abbreviate the expression $pA + qa = 1$ to $p + q = 1$. To illustrate: $.67A + .33a = 1$ can be abbreviated to $.67 + .33 = 1$. Multiply $(p + q)$ by $(p + q)$. Which of the following equations would represent the relative proportions of genotypes in the population produced by the union of gametes containing the alleles in the fre- quency of $p + q = 1$?

☐ $p^2 + pq + q^2 = 1$ . . . . page **233B**.

☐ $p^2 + 2pq + q^2 = 1$ . . . . page **246C**.

From page **234D**.

244A **Correct.** The probability equation $2/3B + 1/3b = 1$ can be written $.67B + .33b = 1$. RECORD THESE GENE FREQUENCIES ON THE WORK-SHEET. Recall that in the population where the alleles were in a 1:1 ratio we used a checkerboard to express this ratio in decimals as follows:

	.5B	.5b
.5B	BB .25	Bb .25
.5b	Bb .25	bb .25

Using this same kind of checkerboard but substituting the decimals that apply in this population, i.e., $.67B + .33b = 1$, we will have the following checkerboard.

	.67B	.33b
.67B	BB .45	Bb .22
.33b	Bb .22	bb .11

Rounded off to the nearest hundredth this produces a genotypic ratio of $.45BB:.44Bb:.11bb$. This ratio corresponds to the $4BB:4Bb:1bb$ that we obtained by using the checkerboard with three spaces for the gametes produced by each sex. The ratio in decimal fractions is the form in which this information is usually expressed.

Recall that we showed that when the gene frequencies of two alleles were $.5B$ and $.5b$, the frequencies of the genes remained constant generation after generation. The next problem is to discover whether the Hardy-Weinberg Law (gene frequencies remain stable unless factors other than those of the genetic mechanism are in operation) holds for populations where the ratio of the genes is not 1:1. Examine the worksheet. You have recorded the genotypic ratio for the N_2 generation. This ratio was $4BB:4Bb:1bb$. *Continue on next page.*

Assume that there are 40 gray-bodied individuals, *BB*, 40 gray- **245A** bodied individuals, *Bb*, and 10 black-bodied individuals, *bb*. Assume that each produced 10 gametes.

Complete the following table.

Genotypes	Number of Individuals	Number of Gametes	
		B	*b*
BB	40	_____	_____
Bb	40	_____	_____
bb	10	_____	_____
		Sum_____	Sum_____

The ratio of the gametes can be expressed as

☐ 1*B*:1*b*......................................page **250A.**

☐ 2*B*:1*b*......................................page **238D.**

☐ 3*B*:1*b*......................................page **257B.**

☐ None of these............................page **240A.**

Incorrect. The expression $\frac{3}{4}B + \frac{1}{4}b = 1$ is the probability equation **245B** for the ratio 3:1. This says 3 out of 4 of the gametes would contain the gene *B*. The ratio 2:1 means 2 out of _____ gametes will contain the gene *B*. Return to page **240D.**

No. You have probably made some error in transposing the letters **245C** into the squares, or you have made some error in adding up the various combinations. Check your work and re-answer the question on page **241A.**

Incorrect. The fraction q represents the frequency of the recessive **245D** gene in the population; p^2 and q^2 represent the proportion of individuals with homozygous genotypes. What symbol represents the proportion of individuals with the homozygous recessive genotype? _____. Return to page **247B.**

246A **Why not?** Did the gene frequency change? _____. Wasn't the genotypic ratio the same in the N_3 as in the N_2? _____. Return to page **236B**.

246B **Incorrect.** The equation $p^2AA + 2pqAa + q^2aa = 1$ represents the proportion of the various genotypes in the population. The proportion of the individuals having the recessive genotype aa is represented by q^2 and not just q. The proportion of individuals having the homozygous genotype AA is p^2 and not just p. Therefore the proportion of individuals with the heterozygous genotype is represented by the total term 2pq and not just pq. 2pq is twice as great as pq and is important in stating the correct proportion. Consider the following:

$$
\begin{array}{l}
.5A \quad + .5a \\
.5A \quad + .5a \\
\hline
.25AA + .25Aa \\
\quad\quad\quad .25Aa + .25aa \\
\hline
.25AA + .50Aa + .25aa = 1
\end{array}
$$

pq = .25 \qquad 2pq = .50

The expression $.25AA + .25Aa + .25aa$ does not equal 1 and does not represent the proper arithmetic operation. Return to page **240B**.

From page **243D**.

246C **Correct.** The product of $(p + q)$ times $(p + q)$ is $p^2 + 2pq + q^2$. Therefore the equation stating the frequencies of the genotypes is

☐ $pAA + pqAa + qaa = 1$.................page **234C**.

☐ $p^2AA + 2pqAa + q^2aa = 1$...............page **241C**.

246D **Incorrect.** If 25% of the population had the phenotype due to the recessive gene, the value for q^2 would be .25. The square root of .25 is .5, so the value of q would be .5 and since $p + q = 1$, p would be _____. Wouldn't the frequency of the genes be equal? _____. Doesn't .5 = .5? Return to page **255A**.

You are in error. Two spaces were used to represent a 1:1 ratio of 247 A gametes. Return to page **242C.**

Correct. The value .11 corresponds to q^2.   **247B**
   In human populations it is impossible to determine the genotypes of very many people for traits having dominance, but we can discover the percentages of different phenotypes. For example, we know that in the United States approximately 70% of the population are tasters of PTC and 30% are nontasters. On the basis of this information can we determine the gene frequencies of these two alleles?
   Knowing that the gene for lack of ability to taste PTC is recessive and that 30% of the population are nontasters, .30 nontasters is represented by

☐ q.................................page   **256C.**

☐ p.................................page   **245D.**

☐ q^2................................page   **253D.**

☐ p^2................................page   **258B.**

Incorrect. The gene frequencies were $T = .45$, $t = .55$. Which is   **247C** greater? Return to page **249A.**

Correct. $p^2 + 2pq$ would be equal to 70%. We cannot take the square   **247D** root of $p^2 + 2pq$ to find the value of p. We have determined that the value of q is .55.
   Which of the following equations will give the value for p providing we know the value of q?

☐ $p + q = 1$................................page   **254D.**

☐ $p^2 + 2pq + q^2 = 1$........................page   **251A.**

248A **Incorrect.** The equation $p^2 + 2pq + q^2 = 1$ would only represent proportions of the various phenotypes when there is lack of dominance. It cannot be used as a general equation for the proportion of phenotypes. Return to page **241C**.

From page **235A**.

248B **Correct.** Those individuals having the phenotype of the dominant characteristic may have the genotype AA or the genotype Aa and the proportions of these are represented by $p^2 + 2pq$. However since all of these have the dominant characteristic we cannot tell by data on the proportion of individuals who have the dominant characteristic how many have homozygous genotypes and how many have heterozygous genotypes. p^2 represents the proportion of homozygous dominant genotypes such as BB; $2pq$ represents the proportion of the heterozygous genotypes, such as Bb, and q^2 represents the proportion of the recessive genotypes, bb.

Since any individual with a phenotype due to a recessive gene has the homozygous genotype aa we can determine the value of one part of the equation $p^2 + 2pq + q^2 = 1$ by finding the percent of such individuals in a population. Which of the following parts of this equation would represent the proportion of individuals who have the recessive characteristic, such as black body?

☐ p^2 . . . . page **255B.**

☐ $2pq$ . . . . page **252B.**

☐ q^2 . . . . page **251B.**

248C **Incorrect.** We have established that .55 is the value for q, and $p + q = 1$. Therefore $p + .55 = 1$. What is the value for p? _____. Return to page **254D**.

248D **Incorrect.** If the ratio of gametes is $2B:1b$, the probability equation is $2/3B + 1/3b = 1$. Calculate the genotypic ratio of the N_3 generation by multiplication of the probability equation or by a checkerboard with three spaces per side. Now return to page **238D** and answer the question.

From page 252C.

Correct. Whenever the dominant characteristic is present in 75% of **249A** the population and the recessive characteristic is 25%, then the gene frequencies of the two alleles are the same (.5).

   In the taster-nontaster population the per cent of nontasters (recessive) was 30%, *i.e.*, more than 25%, and the frequency of the recessive allele was

☐ greater than that of the dominant allele......page   **256B.**

☐ less than that of the dominant allele........page   **247C.**

Incorrect. If 50% of the population had the phenotype due to the **249B** recessive gene the value for q^2 would be .50. The square root of .50 is .71, so the value of q would be .71. Since $p + q = 1$, $p + .71 = 1$. What would be the value of p? _____. Which is larger, .29 or .71 (29% or 71%)? Which gene is more frequent? _____.
Return to page **255A.**

Incorrect. The equation $p^2AA + 2pqAa + q^2aa = 1$ represents the **249C** proportion of the various genotypes in the population. The proportion of the individuals having the recessive genotype *aa* is represented by q^2 and not just q. The proportion of individuals having the homozygous genotype *AA* is p^2 and not just p. Therefore the proportion of individuals with the heterozygous genotype is represented by the total term 2pq and not just pq. 2pq is twice as great as pq and is important in stating the correct proportion. Consider the following:

$$
\begin{array}{r}
.5A + .5a \\
.5A + .5a \\
\hline
.25AA + .25Aa \\
.25Aa + .25aa \\
\hline
.25AA + .50Aa + .25aa = 1
\end{array}
$$

pq = .25   2pq = .50

The expression $.25AA + .25Aa + .25aa$ does not equal 1 and does not represent the proper arithmetic operation. Return to page **240B.**

250A No. Did you make the calculation or did you guess? If you guessed, go back and make the calculations. Or did you make some error in addition? Or did you make an error in reducing the ratio to small whole numbers? Return to page **244A.**

From page **238B.**

250B **Correct.** It would be impossible to determine the frequency of the dominant allele by extracting the square root of the per cent of individuals having the dominant characteristic. Keep in mind that up to this point we have the equation

$$p^2 TT + 2pq\,Tt + .30tt = 1$$

and in abbreviated form

$$p^2 + 2pq + .30 = 1$$

Which parts of this equation would be equal to 70%?

☐ p^2 . . . . .page **240C.**

☐ $p^2 + 2pq$ . . . . .page **247D.**

250C **Incorrect.** If 50% of the population has the dominant characteristic then about 50% has the recessive characteristic and therefore $q^2 = .5$. What is the approximate value of q? _____; and $p + q = 1$. What is the approximate value for p? _____. The frequency of the dominant gene is represented by the symbol p. Return to page **257A.**

From page **258D.**

250D **Correct.** If $q^2 = .64$, what would be the value of q?

☐ .36 . . . . .page **257D.**

☐ .50 . . . . .page **253C.**

☐ .80 . . . . .page **255C.**

While the equation $p^2 + 2pq + q^2 = 1$ could be used you would **251A**
have to extract its square root to produce the equation $p + q = 1$ before you could obtain the value of p. Return to page **247D.**

From page **248B.**

Correct. The symbol q^2 equals the proportion of individuals in a popu-   **251B**
lation having the recessive characteristic.

On the checkerboard where decimal fractions were used to express the proportions of individuals with the genotypes of the gray and black flies in the generations N_2 and N_3 as follows:

	.67B	.33b
.67B	BB .45	Bb .22
.33B	Bb .22	bb .11

the individuals with homozygous recessive genotypes were expected to make up .11 or 11% of the population. This value corresponds to

☐ q . . . . page   **259D.**

☐ 2pq . . . . page   **255D.**

☐ q^2 . . . . page   **247B.**

No. This is contrary to the data presented. Go back to page **258D**   **251C**
and start the sequence from there.

Incorrect. We have established that .55 is the value for q, and p   **251D**
+ q = 1. Therefore p + .55 = 1. What is the value for p? _____.
Return to page **254D.**

252A **Incorrect.** It is true that the gene frequencies were $T = .45$ and $t = .55$ in the taster-nontaster population where tasters occurred in 70% of the population and nontasters in 30%. However, in this population the relative percentages are different. In this one 75% are tasters and 25% are nontasters. Would this not indicate a different gene frequency? Return to page **256B**.

252B **Incorrect.** Since we arbitrarily let p represent the frequency of the dominant gene, p^2 and $2pq$ would represent those individuals in the population who had the characteristic due to the (*dominant, recessive*) _____ gene. Start again on page **248B**.

From page **257C**.

252C **Correct.** In the population in which 70% are able to taste PTC and 30% are unable to taste it about 20% have the genotype TT and about 50% have the genotype Tt.

    The equation for the frequencies of the genotypes is $.20TT + .50Tt + .30tt = 1$. The equation for the frequencies of alleles is $.45T + .55t = 1$. We have shown in the case of taster and nontaster genes, that while the dominant taster phenotype is present in a higher per cent (70%) of the population than the nontaster recessive phenotype (30%) the nontaster gene is more frequent than the taster gene. For some students this comes as a surprise because they inadvertently assume that if a given phenotype appears more often than another the gene for that phenotype must be more frequent.

    To clarify this misunderstanding recall that in the population of gray and black bodied flies the gray bodied flies made up 75% of the population and the black bodied flies made up the remaining 25%. However, the gene frequencies were

☐ equal . . . . page   **249A.**

☐ unequal . . . . page   **259A.**

252D **Incorrect.** We have let p stand for the frequency of the dominant allele and q stand for the frequency of the recessive allele. Therefore q^2 is the frequency of the individuals in the population with the characteristic due to the (*dominant, recessive*) _____ gene. If $q^2 = 64\%$, what decimal fraction is equivalent to 64%? _____. Return to page **258D**.

Incorrect. You extracted the square root of .91 and subtracted this **253A** from 1. Can the frequency of the dominant gene be obtained by extracting the square root of the frequency of the dominant phenotype? _____. The frequency of the dominant phenotype includes both p^2 and $2pq$. Return to page **259B**.

From page **254D**.

Correct. The value for p would be .45. This means that $.45T + .55t$ **253B** $= 1$. From this equation we can calculate the per cent of individuals in the population having the genotype homozygous for the dominant characteristic and those having the heterozygous genotype.

We know that the equation, $p^2TT + 2pqTt + q^2tt = 1$, states the proportions of individuals having the three different genotypes. We also know that the generalized equation $p^2 + 2pq + q^2 = 1$ can be obtained by multiplying $(p + q)$ by $(p + q)$.

We have calculated values for both p and q. How, then, can we calculate the value p^2 and for $2pq$?

☐ $(.45 + .55)^2 = 1$. . . . . .page   **257C.**

☐ $2(.45 + .55) = 1$. . . . . .page   **254C.**

Incorrect. What number multiplied by itself is .64? $.5 \times .5 = .25$. **253C** Return to page **250D**.

From page **247B**.

Correct. Since 30% of the population are nontasters and since the **253D** gene for lack of ability to taste PTC is recessive, the value for q^2 in the equation $p^2 + 2pq + q^2 = 1$ is .30. Thus the entire equation is $p^2TT + 2pqTt + .30tt = 1$. Having the value q^2 how could you obtain the value for q?

☐ Subtract q from 2q. . . . . .page   **241B.**

☐ Extract the square root of q. . . . . .page   **237C.**

☐ Extract the square root of q^2. . . . . .page   **238B.**

254A **Incorrect.** Those individuals with the genotypes *BB* and *Bb* would be gray; 4/9 + 4/9 equals how many ninths? _____, and 1/9 would be black. What is the probability equation 8/9 + 1/9 = 1 expressed as a ratio? _____. Return to page **234B**.

254B **Incorrect.** You extracted the square root of .50 which is approximately .7. But do not forget that the expression is $p^2AA + 2pqAa + q^2aa$. And p^2 *plus* 2pq = .5. What is the value for q^2? _____. What is the approximate square root of .5? _____. What is the approximate value for q? _____. p + q = 1. What is the approximate value for p? _____. Then what is the approximate frequency of the *dominant* allele? _____. Return to page **257A**.

254C **Incorrect.** If the equation $p^2 + 2pq + q^2 = 1$ can be obtained by multiplying (p + q) by (p + q) and if p = .45, and q = .55 could we not substitute as follows

$$(p + q) \quad (p + q)$$
$$(.45 + .55) \quad (.45 + .55)$$

and thus by multiplying

$$.45 + .55$$
$$\underline{.45 + .55}$$

obtain the values for $p^2 + 2pq$? Return to page **253B**.

From page **247D**.

254D **Correct.** The equation p + q = 1 represents the gene frequencies of two alleles. If q = .55, what would be the value of p, that is, what would be the frequency of the gene *T* in the human population?

☐ .55 . . . . page **248C.**

☐ .50 . . . . page **251D.**

☐ .45 . . . . page **253B.**

From page 255C.

Correct. 80% of the genes for eye color in the population would be **257A**
the gene for blue eyes.

If about 50% of a population has the dominant characteristic what is
the approximate frequency of the dominant allele?

☐ .7 . . . . .page   **254B.**

☐ .5 . . . . page   **250C.**

☐ .3 . . . . .page   **259B.**

No. Did you make the calculation or did you guess? If you guessed,   **257B**
go back and make the calculations. Or did you make some error in
addition? Or did you make an error in reducing the ratio to small
whole numbers? Return to page **244A**.

From page 253B.

Correct. By squaring $(.45 + .55)$ we can obtain the value for p^2 and   **257C**
for $2pq$ as well as the value for q^2 which we already knew to be .30.
Make this calculation and enter the value for p^2 and for $2pq$ here:

$$p^2 = \underline{\hspace{2cm}}$$

$$2pq = \underline{\hspace{2cm}}$$

From this calculation we can conclude that in this population
approximately

☐ 20% have the genotype TT and 50% have the
genotype Tt. . . . . .page   **252C.**

☐ 25% have the genotype TT and 50% have the
genotype Tt . . . . .page   **237A.**

Incorrect. What number multiplied by itself is .64? $.36 \times .36 =$ **257D**
.1296. Return to page **250D**.

258A **Incorrect.** If the frequencies of the genes were p = .75 and q = .25 the per cent of individuals who are nontasters would be $(.25)^2$ or .0625, that is 6.25%. You are confusing the frequencies of phenotypes with gene frequencies. p + q = 1 is the equation representing gene frequencies. $p^2 + 2pq + q^2 = 1$ is the equation representing the genotypes. $p^2 + 2pq = 75\%$ and $q^2 = 25\%$. Return to page **256B**.

258B **Incorrect.** The fraction q represents the frequency of the recessive gene in the population; p^2 and q^2 represent the proportion of individuals with homozygous genotypes. What symbol represents the proportion of individuals with the homozygous recessive genotype? _____. Return to page **247B**.

258C **Incorrect.** You should have $4BB:4Bb:1bb$ recorded as the genotypic ratio. Remember that gray is dominant. What color would the individuals with the genotype BB be? _____; with the genotype Bb? _____; with the genotype bb? _____. Return to page **235C**.

From page **255A**.

258D **You are correct.** If the characteristic due to the recessive gene is found in 25% of the population, the frequencies of the two alleles are the same since the ratio $1A:1a$ of genes produces a phenotypic ratio of 75% due to the dominant gene to 25% due to the recessive gene. If any characteristic due to the recessive gene is found in over 25% of the population, the recessive allele must be the more frequent.

Suppose that 64% of the population of an island had blue eyes and 36% had brown eyes. While eye color inheritance is complex, for the purpose of this problem assume that the gene for brown eyes (B) is dominant to the gene for blue eyes (b).

If q^2 equaled the percent of individuals with the genotype bb, what would be the value of q^2 with respect to the proportions of blue and brown eyes in the population?

☐ .36. . . . . .page   **256D.**

☐ .50. . . . . .page   **252D.**

☐ .64. . . . . .page   **250D.**

Incorrect. In an F_2 generation, when there is dominance the ratio of **259A** phenotypes is $3:1$ or 75% to 25%. This generation is produced by a cross of hybrids. What is the ratio of the genes in the gametes of the hybrids? _____. What does a $1:1$ ratio mean, equality or inequality? Return to page **252C**.

From page 257A.

Correct. If 50% of a population has a certain dominant characteristic **259B** the frequency to the dominant gene is about .3.

Assume that in a certain population 91% of the people are right handed and that right handedness is due to a dominant gene. What is the frequency of the gene for left handedness?

☐ .03 . . . . page **243A.**

☐ .04 . . . . page **253A.**

☐ .09 . . . . page **237B.**

☐ .3 . . . . page **260A.**

Incorrect. Keep the following expression in mind: $p^2AA + 2pqAa$ **259C** $+ q^2aa$. Also remember that p^2, $2pq$ and q^2 represent the proportion of each of these genotypes in a population. What proportion of the population has the genotype aa? The answer is q^2; and what proportion has the genotype AA? _____. Return to page **236D**.

Incorrect. The general equations are $pB + qb = 1$ and p^2BB **259D** $+ 2pqBb + q^2bb = 1$. The first equation refers to the proportion of genes, the second equation refers to the proportion of individuals with each genotype. Does the .11 refer to the frequency of the genes or to the proportion of individuals with the genotype bb? _____. Go back to page **251B**.

From page **259B.**

260A **Correct.** **Continue with review.**

REVIEW—Chapter 5, Part II

Population genetics is concerned with the entire "pool" of genes in a population and not with specific crosses or with selected families. The proportion of any one allele in a population is referred to as the (*wds*) _____ of that allele, and is expressed as a (*wds*) _____. The ratio of the genes in the gametes reflects the (*wds*) _____ of the alleles in the entire population. When the gene frequencies of two alleles are both .5 and there is dominance the phenotype ratio of the entire population will be _____; therefore if any characteristic due to a recessive gene is present in more than 25% of the population, the recessive allele must be (*more, less*) _____ frequent than the dominant allele.

In any population, if the only factors in operation are those of heredity, the frequency of any allele (*will, will not*) _____ change; therefore a recessive allele (*would, would not*) _____ decrease in successive generations.

Since the general equation for gene frequencies in a population is p + q = (#) _____, the equation $p^2 + 2pq +$ _____ $= 1$ expresses the proportion of the various genotypes in the population. The p^2 represents individuals who are (*homozygous, heterozygous*) _____ for the dominant gene. The proportion of individuals having the characteristic due to the recessive gene is represented by _____ of the equation. If 19% of a population has a particular characteristic due to a dominant gene, the value of q^2 would be (#) _____. The gene frequency of the recessive allele can be calculated by taking the square root of _____; therefore for the above mentioned trait in which 19% of the population had the characteristic due to the dominant gene, the frequency of the recessive allele would be (#) _____, while the frequency of the dominant allele would be (#) _____.

Check your responses to this review with those on page 360 and then continue with the summary of Part II.

SUMMARY—Chapter 5, Part II

The Hardy-Weinberg Law states that the gene frequency of alleles in a population does not change from generation to generation if the only factors operating are the normal processes of heredity. In Part I of this chapter you discovered that gene frequencies did not change if the alleles had an equal frequency in the population. In Part II we followed the history of two alleles with different frequencies, one being .67 and the other .33. In this case, also, the Hardy-Weinberg Law applied.

The ability to state gene frequencies in terms of the equation $p + q = 1$ offered a method of calculating gene frequencies if the percentages of dominant and recessive phenotypes in the population are known. $(p + q)(p + q) = 1$ is $p^2 + 2pq + q^2 = 1$. The equation $p^2 + 2pq + q^2 = 1$ represents the proportion of genotypes in a population. In this equation q^2 represents the proportion of recessive genotypes and hence also the phenotypes. By applying this equation to the characteristics taster and nontaster of PTC, we equated q^2 with the 30% of nontasters in a population.

If $q^2 = 30\%$ nontasters, then q equals the square root of .30 or .55. By substituting .55 for q in the equation $p + q = 1$ we have $p + .55 = 1$. Therefore $p = .45$. Thus the frequencies of the two alleles for taster and nontaster were calculated as .45 and .55.

Continue with Part III of this chapter.

262A   We have seen that under circumstances where only the normal genetic mechanism is in operation the gene frequencies remain constant in a population generation after generation. The dominant gene does not increase in frequency at the expense of the recessive gene as some people might have expected. However, there are forces and factors which do change gene frequencies. Part III of this chapter will deal with some but not all of these factors.

Imagine an island on which there were no mice until two mice with yellow coats reached its shores. Assume that one of the mice was male and the other was female. In mice the gene for yellow coat is dominant to the gene for normal coat. Since some of the offspring had normal coats, the genotypes of both parents must have been heterozygous. We would predict a 3:1 phenotypic ratio from such parents. However their offspring were in the ratio of 2 yellow:1 normal coat color. The deviation from the expected 3:1 ratio was due to the fact that embryos having a genotype homozygous for yellow coat stop development before birth. Homozygous yellow genotypes are lethal. Mice with heterozygous genotypes are yellow and those with genotypes homozygous for the other allele have normal coat color.

Assume, as we did in the model population, that mating is random and that each mating produces the same number of offspring. However, in this case we must add the special condition that all mice having genotypes homozygous for yellow coat never develop and never produce offspring. Assume that the two original mice had several litters of mice in rapid succession, and then both of the original parent mice died. What would be the genotypic ratio of all of the living offspring of the two original yellow mice? (We will call these mice generation M_2. Use Y for the allele for yellow coat and y for the gene for normal coat color.)

☐ $1YY:2Yy:1yy$ . . . . .page   **266A.**

☐ $2Yy:1yy$ . . . . .page   **264D.**

☐ $1Yy:2yy$ . . . . .page   **274A.**

262B   Correct but incomplete. Go back to page **266B**.

262C   Incorrect. What about the individuals with heterozygous genotypes? Return to **269D**.

From page 271C.

Correct. The genotypic ratio for the M_4 generation would be $2Yy:3yy$. **263A** RECORD THIS RATIO ON WORKSHEET 5-A AT M_4. An easy way to calculate the gene frequency for this generation and hence the ratio of types of gametes is to write each genotype as many times as it appears in the ratio, as $Yy - Yy - yy - yy - yy$, and then count the genes, as $2Y$ and $8y$. Thus the gamete ratio for the M_4 generation would be $1Y:4y$. RECORD THIS RATIO ON THE WORKSHEET. The genotypic ratio for the M_5 generation can be calculated by multiplying $(1/5Y + 4/5y)$ by $(1/5Y + 4/5y)$. Since individuals with genotypes homozygous for the gene Y die, the ratio for the M_5 is $1Yy + 2yy$. RECORD THIS ON THE WORKSHEET. What would be the gamete ratio for the M_5 generation? _____. Turn to page 265A.

Incorrect. You have discovered that the frequency of the allele for **263B** total colorblindness should increase. The frequency of an allele is expressed as a fraction and the sum of the frequencies of all the alleles must be 1. Therefore if the allele for total colorblindness increases in frequency the frequency of the allele for normal color vision must _____. Return to page 271A.

From page 270B.

Correct. The genotypic ratio would be $1Yy:1yy$. RECORD THIS FOR **263C** GENERATION M_3 ON YOUR WORKSHEET. Calculate the ratio of different gametes produced by this generation. It is

- [ ] $1Y:2y$ . . . . page **264C.**

- [ ] $1Y:3y$ . . . . page **271C.**

- [ ] $3Y:1y$ . . . . page **268D.**

Incorrect. Since gene frequency of one allele is expressed as the **263D** fraction of the genes for a particular trait the sum of the frequencies must be 1. Thus if one allele increased in frequency the other allele would have to _____. However, if the opposite process is occurring at the same rate, what would be the net effect? Return to page 273C.

264A **Incorrect.** Suppose a certain disease that lasted for a year started in a community and that each week 10% of the people who had not had the disease came down with it. Would the percent of people with the disease decrease, increase, or remain unchanged? _____
Return to page **274C**.

264B **Right.** The recessive gene would not be completely removed if you destroyed all of the individuals having characteristics due to the recessive gene because the individuals having heterozygous genotypes would carry the gene. If you eliminated all individuals with the characteristic due to the dominant gene would this eliminate the dominant gene? _____. Now return to page **273A**.

264C Your calculations are incorrect. Did you take into account the fact that one-half of the individuals have the genotype Yy and one-half the genotype yy? _____. Did you assume equal numbers of gametes formed by each type? _____. Return to page **263C**.

From page **262A**.

264D **Correct.** RECORD THE GENOTYPIC RATIO $2Yy:1yy$ ON WORKSHEET 5-A FOR GENERATION M_2.

Assume that this generation consisted of 20 yellow mice (Yy) and 10 normal colored mice (yy), that mating was random, and that each mouse produced 10 gametes only. To determine the ratio of gametes complete the following table:

Genotypes	Number of Individuals	Number of Gametes Containing	
		Y	y
Yy	20	_____	_____
yy	10	_____	_____
		Sum_____	Sum_____

The gametes containing Y and y would be in the ratio of

☐ $1Y:1y$ . . . . .page **266C**.

☐ $2Y:1y$ . . . . .page **268B**.

☐ $1Y:2y$ . . . . .page **270B**.

From page 263A.

The gamete ratio for the M_5 would be $1Y:5y$ and the genotypic ratio **265A**
for the M_6 generation would be $2Yy:5yy$. RECORD THESE TWO RATIOS
ON WORKSHEET 5-A.

EXAMINE THE GENOTYPIC RATIOS AND THE GAMETE RATIOS ON THE
WORKSHEET. Notice the pattern of change in gene frequency. On the
basis of this pattern, predict the ratio of gametes produced by the
M_{10} generation, and then calculate the genotypic ratio for the 11th
generation. RECORD YOUR PREDICTIONS ON THE WORKSHEET. Turn to
page **267A**.

Incorrect. Complete the following checkerboard: **265B**

	Y	y	y
Y	YY dies		
y			
y			

What ratio did you obtain? _____. Return to page **270B**.

From page 272C.

Good. You will notice that where a lethal factor is involved the gene **265C**
frequencies of the two alleles change in a regular pattern; the normal
allele gradually increases in frequency over the lethal allele.

Would the lethal allele ever disappear completely from the population if the only factors operating were the normal processes of
heredity?

☐ Yes . . . . page **272A**.

☐ No . . . . page **266B**.

Correct but incomplete. Go back to page **266B**. **265D**

266A **Incorrect.** How could any of the living mice have the genotype YY? Would these not have genotypes homozygous for yellow? Mice with the YY genotype do not develop. Return to page **262A**.

From page **265C**.

266B **Correct.** Although a gene might become so infrequent in a population that it is lost, the loss from the population would be due to the operation of other factors, such as death before reproduction, and not due to the operations of heredity. In theory at least, it would diminish in frequency but never be completely lost.

Which of the following factors might also alter the gene frequencies in a population?

☐ Intentional destruction in each generation by plant or animal breeders of organisms with undesirable characteristics..................page **262B**.

☐ Immigration of individuals with only one of the pair of contrasting phenotypic characteristics..page **265D**.

☐ Both of these............................page **273A**.

☐ Neither of these..........................page **270C**.

266C **Incorrect.** Did you fail to complete the calculations? If so do them. Did you forget that the individuals Yy would produce the two types of gametes in equal numbers? _____. Check your numbers and reanswer the question on page **264D**.

266D **Incorrect.** If you were to destroy all of the individuals having a characteristic due to a recessive gene (such as yellow color of tomatoes) would this necessarily remove all of the recessive genes from the population?

☐ Yes..page **269A**.

☐ No...page **271B**.

From page **265A.**

The gamete ratio for the 10th generation would be $1Y:10y$. The **267A**
genotypic ratio for the 11th generation would be $1Yy:5yy$. Compare
these with your predictions.

Are they the same as yours?

☐ Yes.......................................page   **272C.**

☐ No..page   **268C.**

Incorrect. The genotypic ratio for the gametes produced by the   **267B**
M_3 generation was $1Y:3y$, or $\frac{1}{4}Y + \frac{3}{4}y = 1$.

$$\begin{array}{c} \frac{1}{4}Y \ + \ \frac{3}{4}y \\ \underline{\frac{1}{4}Y \ + \ \frac{3}{4}y} \\ 3/16Yy + 9/16yy \end{array}$$

(dies)
$$\underline{\boxed{1/16YY} + 3/16Yy}$$
$$6/16Yy + 9/16yy = \text{ratio } 6:9 \text{ or } 2:3.$$

Return to page **271C.**

Incorrect. Suppose a certain disease that lasted for a year started   **267C**
in a community and that each week 10% of the people who had not
had the disease came down with it. Would the percent of people with
the disease decrease, increase, or remain unchanged? _____.
Return to page **274C.**

From page **269B.**

Correct. The gene having the greater mutation rate should increase   **267D**
in frequency at a more rapid rate than the gene of lower rate of mutation, provided all other factors were equal.

It is known that radiation greatly increases mutation rates. One
of the problems posed at the beginning of this chapter was: What
will be the effect on the population of increased fall-out of radioactive
material? The answer is

☐ it should change gene frequencies............page   **275C.**

☐ it should not change gene frequencies........page   **270A.**

268A **Incorrect.** Since gene frequency of one allele is expressed as the fraction of the genes for a particular trait the sum of the frequencies must be 1. Thus if one allele increased in frequency the other allele would have to _____. However, if the opposite process is occurring at the same rate, what would be the net effect? Return to page **273C**.

268B **Incorrect.** Did you fail to complete the calculations? If so do them. Did you forget that the individuals Yy would produce the two types of gametes in equal numbers? _____. Check your numbers and reanswer the question on page **264D**.

268C Your prediction is **not** correct. The pattern that appeared in the gamete ratios from generation to generation was that the number of gametes containing gene Y remained 1, while the number of gametes containing gene y increased by 1 each generation. Thus

Generation	Gene or gamete ratio	Probability equation
M_2	$1Y:2y$	$\frac{1}{3}Y + \frac{2}{3}y = 1$
M_3	$1Y:3y$	$\frac{1}{4}Y + \frac{3}{4}y = 1$
M_4	$1Y:4y$	$1/5Y + 4/5y = 1$
M_5	$1Y:5y$	$1/6Y + 5/6y = 1$

By continuing to add $1y$ to each generation what would the gamete ratio be in the 10th generation? _____. What would be the probability equation? _____.

    To determine the genotypic ratio for the 11th generation multiply $(1/11Y + 10/11y)$ by $(1/11Y + 10/11y)$ and reduce the numbers to the smallest whole numbers. Go back to page **267A**.

268D Your calculations are incorrect. Did you take into account the fact that one-half of the individuals have the genotype Yy and one-half yy? _____. Did you assume equal numbers of gametes formed by each type? _____. Return to page **263C**.

Incorrect. What about the individuals with heterozygous genotypes? **269A**
Return to page **266D.**

From page **270D.**

Correct. There would be a net increase in the gene frequency of the **269B**
gene for total colorblindness if the back-mutation rate were less than
the rate of mutation from normal to colorblindness.

The rate of mutation of the gene for normal vision to that of total
colorblindness was given as 28 per million gametes. A mutation causing
lack of iris of the eye occurs at the rate of approximately 10 per
million gametes. Ignoring the back-mutation rate and ignoring the
fact that there might be differential selection against these two genes,
which gene should have the greater increase in frequency in a population?

☐ The gene for total colorblindness . . . . page **267D.**

☐ The gene for lack of iris . . . . page **272D.**

☐ Both would increase at the same rate . . . . page **271D.**

Incorrect. Suppose a certain disease that lasted for a year started **269C**
in a community and that each week 10% of the people who had not
had the disease came down with it. Would the percent of people with
the disease decrease, increase, or remain unchanged? _____.
Return to page **274C.**

Incorrect. If you were to destroy all of the individuals having a **269D**
characteristic due to a recessive gene (such as yellow color of tomatoes)
would this necessarily remove all of the recessive genes from the
population?

☐ Yes . . . . page **262C.**

☐ No . . . . page **264B.**

270A **Incorrect.** Any factor which causes an increase or a decrease in mutation rate would change gene frequencies unless back-mutation balanced the mutation rate. Return to page **267D**.

From page **264D**.

270B **Right.** The ratio of gametes of the second generation would be $1Y:2y$. RECORD ON WORKSHEET 5-A THE RATIO OF THE GENES OF THE GAMETES OF GENERATION M$_2$.

Keeping in mind that YY individuals die before birth, what would be the genotypic ratio of the 3rd generation? (Hint: Use a checkerboard with 3 spaces per side, or use the frequency of the genes as p and q. Do not forget that YY individuals do not develop.)

☐ $1Yy:1yy$ . . . . .page **263C**.

☐ $2Yy:1yy$ . . . . .page **272B**.

☐ $3Yy:1yy$ . . . . .page **265B**.

270C **Incorrect.** Shifts in gene frequency are caused by removing genes from the gene pool or adding genes to the gene pool. Reexamine the choices. Will either (or both) of these methods remove genes or add genes to the gene pool? _____. Return to page **266B**.

From page **273C**.

270D **Correct.** If the rate of mutation and the rate of back mutation were the same, the frequencies of the two alleles would not vary. However, these two rates are seldom the same. If the rate of back mutation of the gene for total colorblindness is less than the mutation rate of the normal gene to the gene for total colorblindness

☐ the gene frequency for total colorblindness would increase in the population . . . . .page **269B**.

☐ the gene frequency of the gene for total colorblindness would remain constant . . . . .page **273B**.

From page 274C.

Correct. The frequency of the gene for total colorblindness would **271A** increase.

If the frequency of the gene for total colorblindness increases through mutations, what would happen to the frequency of the gene for normal color vision?

The frequency of the gene for normal color vision would

☐ remain the same . . . . .page **263B.**

☐ increase . . . . .page **275B.**

☐ decrease . . . . .page **273C.**

Right. The recessive gene would not be completely removed if you **271B** destroyed all of the individuals having characteristics due to the recessive gene because the individuals having heterozygous genotypes would carry the gene. If you eliminated all individuals with the characteristic due to the dominant gene would this eliminate the dominant gene? _____. Go back to page **273A.**

From page 263C.

Correct. The gene (or gamete) ratio of the M_3 generation would be **271C** $1Y:3y$. RECORD THIS RATIO ON THE WORKSHEET. Using either the equation $\frac{1}{4}Y + \frac{3}{4}y = 1$ or an appropriate checkerboard calculate the expected genotypic ratio for the M_4 generation. This ratio would be

☐ $1Yy:1yy$ . . . . .page **275A.**

☐ $1Yy:3yy$ . . . . .page **267B.**

☐ $2Yy:3yy$ . . . . .page **263A.**

Incorrect. If there were two diseases affecting a community and **271D** 28 persons per 1000 got disease A but only 11 per 1000 got disease B, would not there be more people at the end of a year who had had disease A than had had disease B? Return to page **269B.**

272A You **could** be correct. The lethal allele might disappear, because it became so infrequent that the few individuals having this gene did not mate for one reason or another (they might die off, they might not find a mate, etc.). However, if the only factors operating are those of heredity, it should become less frequent (1 : 100,000 or 1 : 100,000,000 or 1 : 100,000,000,000, etc.) but at least in theory never be completely lost. Return to page **265C**.

272B **Incorrect.** Complete the following checkerboard:

	Y	y	y
Y	YY dies		
y			
y			

What ratio did you obtain? _____. Return to page **270B**.

From page **267A**.

272C **Correct.** Continue.

Where a lethal factor is involved the frequency of the alleles changes. Does this shift in gene frequency follow a definite pattern?

☐ Yes....................................page **265C**.

☐ No....................................page **274B**.

272D **Incorrect.** If there were two diseases affecting a community and 28 persons per 1000 got disease A but only 11 per 1000 got disease B, would not there be more people at the end of a year who had had disease A than had had disease B? Return to page **269B**.

From page **266B.**

Correct. Two of many ways of shifting gene frequencies are selection **273A** by breeders and immigration. If the gene frequency of immigrants is the same as that of the native population, the gene frequency would not be altered.

Suppose a breeder wanted to reduce the frequency of a particular allele to zero (in other words to remove the allele completely from the population) which kind of allele would be easier to remove?

☐ Dominant allele.............................page   **274C.**

☐ Recessive allele.............................page   **269D.**

☐ Either would be of equal difficulty...........page   **266D.**

How could this be? If your rate of learning were the same as your **273B** rate of forgetting then there would be no change in the amount of your knowledge. But if the rate of forgetting were less than your rate of learning would not your knowledge increase? _____.
Return to page **270D.**

From page **271A.**

Correct. The gene frequency for normal color vision would decrease. **273C**
Genes can mutate in both directions. For example genes for normal color vision can mutate to genes that cause total colorblindness, but also genes that cause this type of colorblindness can mutate to genes that cause normal color vision. The mutation from the abnormal to the normal form is called **back mutation.** If both kinds of mutation occur at the same rate what would be the effect on the gene frequencies of the two alleles?

☐ The gene frequencies of both alleles would increase.....................................page   **268A.**

☐ The gene frequencies of both alleles would decrease.....................................page   **263D.**

☐ The gene frequencies of both alleles would remain the same.............................page   **270D.**

274A **Incorrect.** The parents were each Yy. We know this because those with genotypes homozygous for yellow do not live, and these mice were yellow. What is the expected genotypic ratio in this cross, $Yy \times Yy$? _____. So what would be the ratio of the living mice? _____. Return to page **262A**.

274B **Incorrect.** If a lethal gene is involved, as the gene for yellow coat color, there is a shift in gene frequency from generation to generation. It is true that in such a case the Hardy-Weinberg law does not hold, but the worksheet gives evidence that the shift follows a regular pattern. You can predict what the ratio of the genes should be in the 20th generation, can you not? _____. We can only make predictions where there *is* a regularity. Return to page **272C**.

From page 273A.

274C **Correct.** It would be much easier to remove a dominant gene from a population than to remove a recessive one.

We have emphasized that there is stability of genes and the stability of gene frequencies in populations. We have, however, indicated that there are factors which change gene frequencies. The presence of a lethal gene, selection, and migration are all factors affecting gene frequencies. Although genes normally are stable there are occasional sudden changes in genes. Such changes are called **mutations.**

Mutations occur spontaneously. While there is variation in the rate of mutation of any given gene under various conditions, average rates of spontaneous mutation can be determined for particular genes. For example, the mutation rate of the gene for normal color vision to one causing total colorblindness is estimated at 28 mutations per million gametes. If this mutation rate is assumed to be relatively constant what would be the effect on the frequency of this allele for complete colorblindness in a population?

☐ It would increase.........................page **271A.**

☐ It would decrease.........................page **267C.**

☐ It would remain unchanged since the rate is
assumed to be constant....................page **269C.**

☐ No interpretation can be made.............page **264A.**

Incorrect. The ratio for the genes of the gametes produced by the **275A**
M_3 generation was $1Y:3y$, or $\frac{1}{4}Y + \frac{3}{4}y = 1$.

$$\frac{1}{4}Y + \frac{3}{4}y$$
$$\frac{1}{4}Y + \frac{3}{4}y$$

$$\overline{3/16Yy + 9/16yy}$$

(dies)

$$\boxed{1/16YY} + 3/16Yy$$

$$\overline{\qquad\qquad\qquad\qquad\qquad\qquad}$$

$$6/16Yy + 9/16yy = \text{ratio } 6:9 \text{ or } 2:3.$$

Return to page **271C**.

Incorrect. You have discovered that the frequency of the allele for **275B**
total colorblindness should increase. The frequency of an allele is
expressed as a fraction and the sum of the frequencies of all the alleles
must be 1. Therefore if the allele for total colorblindness increases in
frequency the frequency of the allele for normal color vision must
_____. Return to page **271A**.

From page **267D**.

Correct. This is the end of this sequence. Continue with the review. **275C**

REVIEW—Chapter 5, Part III

Under most circumstances gene frequencies (*remain constant, change*)
_____ generation after generation. The dominant gene (*does, does not*)
_____ increase in frequency at the expense of the recessive gene.
There are, however, certain forces which affect gene frequencies. The presence
of a dominant gene which is lethal in the homozygous condition increases the
frequency of the (*dominant, recessive*) _____ gene, and the genotypic
and phenotypic ratios (*are, are not*) _____ changed.

If an animal or plant breeder wishes to eliminate some undesirable characteristic from his stock it is easier to eliminate a (*dominant, recessive*) _____
allele than it is to eliminate a (*wd*) _____ allele. Another factor affecting (*wds*)_____ is immigration of individuals with one of two contrasting characteristics. Gene frequencies can also be altered by the rate of _____
of one gene to another.

To check your responses to the review of Chapter 5, Part III, turn to page
361 and then continue with the summary of Part III.

SUMMARY—Chapter 5, Part III

In Part I of this chapter we developed the idea of gene frequencies and showed that under circumstances where only the normal genetic mechanism is in operation gene frequencies remain constant. In Part II we demonstrated a method of calculating gene frequencies from phenotypic ratios.

In Part III of this chapter we discovered that under certain conditions gene frequencies do change. A lethal gene, which prevents development of individuals whose genotypes are homozygous for the gene, reduces the frequency of the lethal allele, because this gene is constantly being removed from the breeding population. Another method of changing gene frequencies is the intentional removal of individuals from a population. This method is practiced by animal and plant breeders in the improving of stock.

Immigration and emigration can also affect the frequency of a gene in a population providing the gene frequency of those moving in or moving out of a population is different than that of the existing population. Mutations may also affect gene frequencies, the greater the net rate of mutations, the greater the effect upon the gene frequencies of the two alleles.

Continue with the self test for Chapter 5.

SELF TEST—Chapter 5

There is a classification of blood types called the M-N Types. Some individuals are Type M, some are Type N, while others are Type MN. Those individuals who are either Type M or Type N are genotypically homozygous, while those who are Type MN are genotypically heterozygous. Assume that in a certain population 36% of the population has Type M blood. Assume that the frequency for the gene for Type M is represented as the value p. Respond to the next 14 items by using the following key.

KEY: A. p^2 B. q^2 C. $2pq$ D. p E. q
      F. None of these.

__ 1. Which of the symbols represents the fraction of individuals in the population with Type MN blood?

__ 2. Which of the symbols represents the fraction of individuals in the population with Type M blood?

__ 3. Which of the symbols represents the fraction of individuals in the population with Type N blood?

— 4. Which of the symbols represents the frequency of the N gene in the population?

— 5. The value for which of the symbols can be calculated by the expression $1 - p$?

— 6. The numerical value of which of the symbols can be obtained by extracting the square root of .36?

— 7. For which of the symbols would you substitute the value of 36%?

— 8. Which of these should have a numerical value of 64%?

— 9. Which of these should have the numerical value of .60?

—10. Which should have the numerical value of .40?

—11. Which should have the numerical value of 16%?

—12. Which should have the numerical value of 48%?

—13. The sum of which two of these should equal 1?

—14. The sum of which three of these should equal 1?

About 16% of the white population of the United States has Type Rh⁻ blood. Recall that the gene for Type Rh⁻ blood (r) is recessive to the gene for Type Rh⁺ blood (R). Use this information to answer items 15–27.

15. In order to determine the frequency of the gene (R) it is necessary to know one of the following.

  —A. The percent of individuals having the Type Rh⁻ blood.

  —B. Whether the gene for Type Rh⁺ is dominant or recessive.

  —C. Both A and B.

  —D. Neither A nor B.

For the next 4 items use the following key.

KEY: A. .16 C. .40 E. .60 G. .84
      B. .36 D. .48 F. .64 H. None of these

—16. What is the frequency of the gene r in the white population of the United States?

—17. What is the frequency of the gene R?

—18. What fraction of the population would have the genotype RR?

—19. What fraction of the population would have the genotype Rr?

For the next two items use the key and let the frequency of $r = q$.

KEY: A. $p + q = 1$ B. $p^2 + 2pq + q^2 = 1$
      C. either of these   D. neither of these

—20. Which equation did you use to calculate the frequency of the gene r?

—21. Which equation did you use to calculate the frequency of the gene R?

In a certain area in Europe about 25% of the population are Type Rh⁻.

22. What is the frequency of the gene r in this European population?

  —A. .25   —B. .50   —C. .75   —D. None of these.

For the next two items use the following key.

KEY: A. $1R:1r$ B. $2R:1r$ C. $3R:1r$ D. $3R:2r$

              E. None of these.

__23. What is the ratio of the alleles in the white population in the United States?

__24. What is the ratio of the alleles in the area in Europe where 25% of the population is Type Rh^-?

For the next 3 items use the following key.

KEY: A. It would increase.

              B. It would decrease.

              C. It would remain unchanged.

              D. There is no way to determine what would happen.

__25. Assuming that mating is random and that there is no differential selection and that the mutation rate and back-mutation rate are balanced, what would be the ratio of genes in the United States after 10 generations?

__26. What would happen to the gene frequency of the gene r in a town in the United States if a large number of people from the area in Europe having 25% individuals with Rh^- blood moved into the town where the percent was 16% Rh^-?

__27. What would happen to the gene frequency of the R gene in the United States if no other factor than those of the heredity mechanism were in operation in the population?

Try the following problem.

The following problem is difficult but solvable. Recall that there are four blood types (A, O, B and AB) and that there are *three* alleles. The percentages of the blood groups in one population are

$$O — 44\%$$
$$A — 40\%$$
$$B — 12\%$$
$$AB — 4\%$$

What are the frequencies of the three genes? Hint: For two alleles the equation for gene frequencies is represented by the equation $p + q = 1$; for three alleles use $p + q + r = 1$.

    Correct answers to the self test for Chapter 5, Population Genetics, are on page 365.

WORKSHEET 6-A

STRAND I

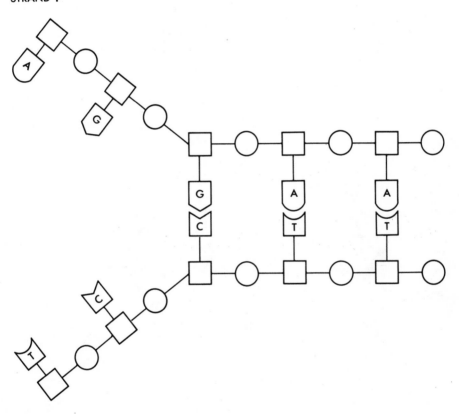

STRAND II

Two Strands of DNA Molecule Separating

WORKSHEET 6-B

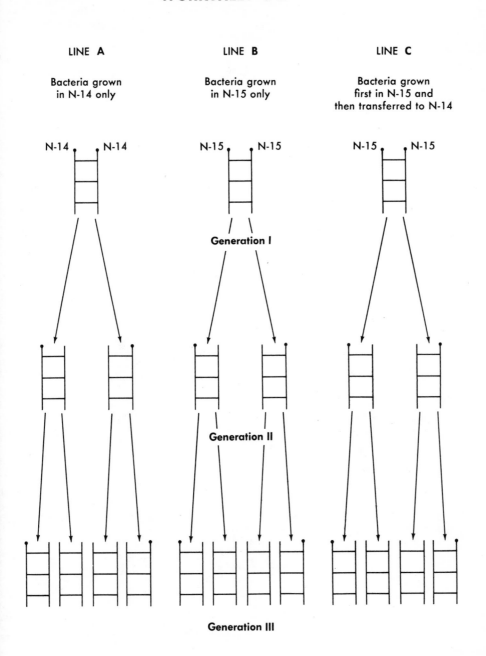

LINE **A**

Bacteria grown
in N-14 only

LINE **B**

Bacteria grown
in N-15 only

LINE **C**

Bacteria grown
first in N-15 and
then transferred to N-14

N-14   N-14

N-15   N-15

N-15   N-15

Generation I

Generation II

Generation III

Bacteria grown in N-14, in N-15, and first in N-15 and then in N-14

chapter 6

THE CHEMICAL NATURE OF THE GENE

PART I

Numerous aspects of the units of heredity — the genes — have been **283A** treated in other volumes of this series. Evidence that the genes are located in nuclei of cells, and that they are arranged in a linear order on chromosomes and that they can change or mutate has also been presented. The regularity with which the genes are transmitted from generation to generation and the mechanisms through which they are parceled out to germ cells to recombine in pairs at fertilization are fundamental concepts of heredity. Knowledge of the behavior of these units (the genes) has been acquired by combining facts obtained from breeding experiments, from an understanding of probability, and from microscopic observations of cells and chromosomes. All of these aspects of genetics are referred to as **classical genetics.** Another branch known as **population genetics** is concerned with gene frequencies in relation to populations.

A new and exciting field that has developed recently is called **biochemical genetics.** This branch of genetics deals with the chemical nature of genes, and their relationship to embryonic development and to the physiology of the adult organism.

The field of biochemical genetics attempts to answer the following questions:

a. What chemical substances are genes composed of?

b. What properties of the chemical substances could be responsible for specific gene action?

c. How are genes duplicated exactly?

d. What is the chemical basis of mutation?

In this chapter we will attempt to give partial answers to the questions listed above.

284A   Certain concepts concerning genes have been implied but not definitely stated in previous volumes. These ideas, which are essential to an understanding of the kinds of evidence which will be presented concerning the chemical nature of genes, will be introduced before we discuss the chemistry of genes.

Consider two individuals, such as identical twins, that have originated from a single zygote. What conclusion could you draw about the genes of one twin compared with the genes of the other twin?

☐ They would be identical................page   **300D.**

☐ They would be different................page   **292B.**

284B   **Incorrect.** It has been assumed that at each cell division each gene duplicates itself, hence each daughter cell is assumed to have the same kind and number of genes as the cell from which it arose. Is not each somatic cell derived from a preceding cell and do they not all go back in a direct line to the zygote? Return to page **296A.**

From page **290A.**

284C   **Correct.** You would expect some similarity in the genes of all human beings because they all have certain inherited characteristics in common, i.e., they all have a head, trunk, two legs, two arms; they walk upright, and have a highly developed brain.

Now compare men, apes, and goldfish. These three kinds of animals have recognizably different inherited characteristics. Would you expect differences in the genes of these three animal types?

☐ Yes..page   **292C.**

☐ No...page   **297B.**

284D   **No.** Bacteria contain many different chemical substances, any one of which might be the genetic substance. In this experiment all of the material of the bacteria was mixed with the living bacteria so there was no way to determine which particular substance was responsible. Return to page **298A.**

If chromosomes are reduced by one-half at gamete formation so that **285A** one-half of them go into one gamete and one-half into the other gamete, and if DNA is the genetic material in the chromosomes, how much of the total amount of the DNA in the immature reproductive cell would go into each gamete? Return to page **293B**.

Correct. You assumed that if two phenotypes were produced such as **285B** taster and nontaster of PTC, two different genes were responsible for this trait. Different kinds of capsules in bacteria are different phenotypes. Therefore, you would conclude that there are different genes involved. If the genes and DNA are either the same or closely related, what assumption would you have to make about the DNA of two bacterial strains that had different capsules? Return to page **291D**.

From page **300D**.

Correct. You would expect more variation in the genes between non- **285C** identical brothers than between identical twins.

Consider all of the individuals in the United States. Compare two brothers with any other two men (not brothers) picked at random, with respect to similarities of their genes.

☐ The genes of the two brothers are likely to be
more similar than those of the two men picked
at random . . . . .page   **290A.**

☐ The genes of the two brothers would have no
more similarity than those of the two men picked
at random . . . . .page   **286B.**

☐ There would be no similarity in the genes of the
two men picked at random . . . . .page   **294D.**

☐ There is no basis for estimating the degree of
similarity . . . . .page   **288B.**

No. Man and mouse belong to different species. Is there a difference **285D** in the DNA per cell of members of different species? Return to page **294B**.

From page 292A.

286A **Correct.** Do these experiments also support the idea that DNA is the genetic material (genes) of bacteria?

☐ Yes . . . . page **291D.**

☐ No . . . . page **289D.**

286B **Incorrect.** Human beings have a wide range of inherited differences. Compare Chinese, Negroes, pygmies, or even tall, short, blond, and brunet types among Caucasians. All of these various types differ in their genetic make-up, so would it not be more likely that brothers who at least would be of the same race would have more like genes in common than two people who were not so closely related? Go back to page **285C.**

From page 292C.

286C **Good.** Because apes and men have many characteristics in common, such as general body structure, upright stature, eyes on the front of the head, arms, and legs, we assume that there is more similarity in the genes of men and apes than there is between these two and fish. We assume that all characteristics which are inherited, such as position of eyes, are controlled by genes. Thus the development of arms and legs is controlled by one kind of gene or genes while the development of fur is controlled by other kinds of genes. Would all animals that have hair (fur) instead of scales (as fish) or feathers (as birds) have genes for the production of hair (fur)?

☐ Yes . . . . page **297C.**

☐ No . . . . page **294C.**

286D Yes you have, or, at least, you should have. You should remember that the chromosomes are reduced in number by one-half during gamete formation so that one-half the number goes into each gamete. If the DNA is a part of the chromosomes what should happen to the DNA during production of gametes? Return to page **293B.**

If DNA is the genetic material and if genetic material refers to all of **287A** the genes of an individual then the DNA molecule should be one or more genes. If two phenotypes are produced such as taster and non-taster of PTC, would you assume that there was only one kind of gene or one kind of genetic material for this trait?

☐ Yes...................................page **293A.**

☐ No....................................page **285B.**

No. The basis of any expectation concerning the position of a specific **287B** chemical substance as the assumed location of the gene is based on classical genetic experiments involving chromosome behavior, linkage, and crossover. In the study of gene theory, where have we assumed the genes to be located? Go back to page **297C.**

From page **296A.**

Correct. If DNA is the genetic material the amount in any single body **287C** cell should be the same as the amount in the zygote from which the individual developed. This conclusion is based on the relation of genes to chromosomes and the behavior of chromosomes during mitosis. It has also been found that the amount of DNA per cell is the same for all of the cells of individuals of the same species.

In which of the following would you expect the average amount of DNA per cell to be the same?

☐ Skin cell of a chicken and red blood cell of the same chicken...........................page **301B.**

☐ Skin cell of one chicken and skin cell of another chicken of the same species................page **291A.**

☐ Both of these............................page **294B.**

☐ Neither of these..........................page **293C.**

No. The man and the woman belong to the same species. Cells of **287D** individuals of the same species have the same amount of DNA. Return to page **294B.**

288A **Incorrect.** Apes and men have hair, fish have scales; apes and men have arms and legs, fish have fins; apes and men have eyes on the front of the head, goldfish have eyes at sides of the head; etc., etc. Start again on page **292C**.

288B **Incorrect.** We know that "like begets like." For example, humans produce human offspring, dogs produce puppies, and fish produce fish. The kind of offspring produced is controlled by inheritance, by genes. Thus parents always produce offspring that are like themselves. From this may it not reasonably follow that those organisms, including humans, that are more alike have many more genes in common? Go back to page **285C**.

288C **Incorrect.** It has been assumed that at each cell division each gene duplicates itself, hence each daughter cell is assumed to have the same kind and number of genes as the cell from which it arose. Is not each somatic cell derived from a preceding cell and do they not all go back in a direct line to the zygote? Return to page **296A**.

From page **293B**.

288D **Your prediction is correct.** Studies have shown that the amount of DNA in sperm cells is one-half of that found in the somatic cells of the same individual.

The number of chromosomes in the body cells of any organism is normally the same. However, occasionally a few cells are found that have twice the normal number or even four times the normal number of chromosomes. A special technique has been developed that makes it possible to determine the amount of DNA in individual cells. This technique is used to determine the amount in the normal nuclei, and in the nuclei with extra chromosomes.

What prediction would you make concerning the amount of DNA in the nuclei containing twice the normal number of chromosomes?

☐ The same amount as in the normal nucleus . . . . . page **300B.**

☐ Twice the amount in the normal nucleus . . . . page **295C.**

☐ One-half of the amount in the normal nucleus . . page **293D.**

Incorrect. Since all human beings have certain characteristics in common, such as two ears, two eyes, eyelashes, and eyebrows, and since we assume inborn characteristics are controlled by genes, all humans must have some genes which are alike. Return to page **290A**.

289A

From page **298A**.

You are correct. These experiments showed only that some material in the dead bacteria was responsible for the change. On the basis of this experiment it would not be possible to say that DNA was the substance.

289B

The problem, now, was to find the important substance in the disintegrated pneumococcus cell which was responsible for these results. The capsular gum was destroyed by an enzyme and the remaining cell debris tested by mixing it with noncapsulate living bacteria. These bacteria again produced some offspring with capsules.

Do the results of this experiment eliminate the capsular gum as a factor in the transmission of the ability to produce capsules?

☐ Yes.......................................page **300A**.

☐ No..page **290D**.

Incorrect. Indirect evidence is like circumstantial evidence. If Mr. X was dressed in a tuxedo and was known to have been in the vicinity of a robbery, and if the person robbed saw that the man who robbed him wore a tuxedo, Mr. X might be accused of the robbery. This would be circumstantial evidence. However, if a reliable witness who knew Mr. X saw Mr. X steal from the man this would be direct evidence. Is the case for DNA more like the former or the latter? _____. Return to page **295C**.

289C

Incorrect. It is true that these experiments do not "prove" that the DNA is the genetic material. However, we have assumed (a) that the ability to produce capsules is hereditary, and (b) that there was a transfer of hereditary material from dead cells to living cells.

289D

We know that the cells were not able to produce capsules in the absence of the DNA. What function of DNA is at least suggested? Return to page **286A**.

From page 285C.

290A **Correct.** We would expect the genes of two brothers to be more similar than the genes of two nonbrothers. The reason for this is that two brothers receive their genetic material (genes) from a single set of parents, while nonbrothers receive theirs from different parents. The chances of receiving the same kinds of genes from one set of parents are much greater than are the chances of receiving the same kinds of genes from different sets of parents.

Would you expect that the genes of the two brothers and those of the two nonbrothers would have any similarity?

☐ Yes . . . . page **284C.**

☐ No . . . . page **289A.**

290B **No.** Here again we have removed something from the material, the protein. We know, therefore, that this cannot be the cause of the genetic change. Return to page **300A.**

From page 297C.

290C **Correct.** Since we have assumed in the gene theory that the genes are in the nucleus, any chemical substance that was identified as genetic material should be in the nucleus.

Where in the nucleus would you expect such a chemical substance would be found?

☐ Throughout the nucleus . . . . page **292D.**

☐ Associated with the chromosomes only . . . . page **296A.**

290D **Why not?** In science and also in everyday life we usually reason that if A causes B, B cannot occur unless A is present. For example, we believe that a rock thrown against a window (A) will cause the window to break (B). Now, if we know in a particular instance that no rock was thrown but that the window broke anyway, would we still insist that a thrown rock broke the window? Wouldn't we, rather, look for some other cause? Start again on page **289B.**

Your answer is not wrong, but there is a more inclusive one. Return **291A**
to page 287C.

How come? The phenotypes of identical twins are the same. The **291B**
genotype causes the production of the phenotype. Identical twins
come from a single zygote, therefore their genotypes must be identical.
We have already discovered that brothers can be different in phenotype, therefore they must differ in genotype. Return to page **300D**.

Your answer is not incorrect, but there is a more inclusive answer **291C**
in the list. Return to page **297A**.

From page **286A**.

Correct. The loss of ability to produce capsules when the DNA was **291D**
destroyed at least suggests that the DNA is the actual genetic
material.

Following this lead additional experiments were performed on
pneumococcus bacteria. There are several strains of capsule-pro-
ducing pneumococci that can be separated on the basis of the kind of
capsule produced. Each strain had a different type of capsule. The
type of capsule is an inherited characteristic. A series of experiments
was performed. In each of these experiments a different strain was
tested by killing the bacteria and mixing them with the living noncapsulated forms to see if each of the killed strains could cause a
noncapsulated strain to produce offspring that had capsules and also
to see what kind of capsule would be produced in each case.

The results of these experiments were (1) that each strain when
killed and mixed with noncapsulated bacteria caused these bacteria to
produce some offspring having capsules and (2) that the kind of
capsule produced in each case was the same as the kind that had
been killed and mixed with the noncapsule-producing bacteria.

The results of these experiments suggest that

☐ the DNA of all capsule-forming bacteria is the
same.......................................page **287A**.

☐ different kinds of pneumococci bacteria have
different kinds of DNA.....:..............page **301C**.

From page **300A.**

292A **Good.** With the elimination of the capsular gum and the protein as possible causes of the production of capsules by these bacteria, the next step was the elimination of the DNA from the cell debris. DNA was removed by an enzyme which destroys only the DNA. It was then found that the cell debris did not have the ability to cause the bacteria to produce some offspring with capsules. Do these experiments as a group suggest that the DNA of the dead capsulate bacteria might be a factor in the hereditary change of the strain that originally did not have capsules?

☐ Yes...page **286A.**

☐ No..page **299B.**

292B **Incorrect.** Identical twins arise from a single fertilized egg and therefore have identical genes. Return to page **283A.**

From page **284C.**

292C **Correct.** You would expect differences. If we compare men, apes, and goldfish as to the degree of similarity among their genes, in which of the following pairs would you expect the greatest similarity of genes?

☐ Apes and goldfish.........................page **300C.**

☐ Men and goldfish..........................page **288A.**

☐ Apes and men.............................page **286C.**

☐ There would be no similarity among any of these....................................page **299C.**

292D **Incorrect.** On the basis of the gene theory where would you expect to find the genes? Return to page **290C.**

Incorrect. You have forgotten some of the most basic assumptions **293A** concerning genes. You assumed that the reason two organisms were phenotypically alike (as both nontasters) was because the genes they had were alike. The differences between tasters and nontasters was assumed to be due to differences in genes. Return to page **287A**.

From page 297A.

Correct. We have assumed that inherited variation among different **293B** kinds of organisms is correlated with differences among genes. Therefore, if DNA is the genetic material, one would expect variation in DNA among various kinds of organisms. The constancy of amount per cell of any one individual is correlated with the assumption that all cells of any one individual have the same kind and number of chromosomes, hence genes.

If DNA, found only in the chromosomes, is the genetic material and if each body cell of all members of a single species contains the same amount of DNA, how much DNA would you expect to find in a sperm cell of this species? Remember what happens to chromosomes during gamete formation.

☐ The same amount as in a body cell......... page   **285A.**

☐ Twice as much as in a body cell............ page   **299D.**

☐ One-half as much as in a body cell.......... page   **288D.**

☐ I have no basis for determining this.......... page   **286D.**

Incorrect. The same average amount of DNA is found in all the **293C** different kinds of cells in any one individual and also in the cells of individuals of the same species. The skin cells and blood cells were taken from the same chicken in the one case and the skin cells from different chickens in the second case. The two chickens belong to the same species. Return to page **287C**.

Did you read the question right? Try this: If I have two pounds of **293D** candy in my room and someone brings me another two-pound box of candy, will the total weight of candy be twice what it was or half what it was? Return to page **288D**.

294A **No.** The basis of any expectation concerning the position of a specific chemical substance as the assumed location of the gene, is based on classical genetic experiments involving chromosome behavior, linkage and crossover. In the study of gene theory, where have we assumed the genes to be located? Return to page **297C**.

294B **Correct.** The amount of DNA should be the same in the cells of organisms of the same species as well as in different cells of the same individuals. However, when cells of individuals of different species are compared, differences are found in the amount of DNA per cell. That is, while the average amount of DNA per cell is constant for any one species, the average amount of DNA per cell for that species is different from the average amount of DNA per cell in another species. In which of the following would you expect the amount of DNA to be different?

☐ In a skin cell of a man and a skin cell of a woman................................page **301A.**

☐ In a skin cell of a man and a skin cell of a mouse................................page **297A.**

☐ Both of these............................page **287D.**

☐ Neither of these............................page **285D.**

294C **How come?** If they do not have genes for the production of hair what does cause the production of hair? Why do pea plants produce new pea plants and not oak trees? What causes the development of all inborn characteristics? _____. Start again, page **286C**.

294D **Incorrect.** We know that "like begets like." For example, human beings produce human offspring, dogs produce puppies, and fish produce fish. The kind of offspring produced is controlled by inheritance, by genes. Thus two organisms, simply by being human, must have some genes that are alike. Return to page **285C**.

Your answer is not incorrect, but there is a more inclusive answer **295A**
in the list. Return to page **297A**.

No. Here again we have removed something from the material, the **295B**
protein. We know, therefore, that this cannot be the cause of the
genetic change. Return to page **300A**.

From page **288D**.

Correct. For any one species the amount of DNA per cell is directly **295C**
proportional to the number of chromosomes per cell.

The chemical analysis of chromosomes has demonstrated that
DNA is a constant and stable part of chromosomes. The chromosomes
contain other chemical substances besides DNA (*e.g.*, various pro-
teins), but none of the other known constituents has the same constancy of amount.

On the basis of knowledge of chromosome behavior in relation to
the hypothetical behavior of genes it is possible to conclude that the
genes are on the chromosomes or are a part of the chromosomes.
Observations of developing organisms show that through mitosis
each body cell receives a full complement of chromosomes, hence each
cell would have the same amount of chromatin material. We also
equated the separation of paired genes with the process of meiosis
where the chromosomes were parceled out so that half of them went
into one gamete and half into another.

On the basis of the above assumed relations of genes and chromosomes plus the observed constancy of amount of DNA in body cells
and the reduction of this amount by one-half in the gametes, it is
reasonable to assume that DNA is the actual genetic material.

The hypothesis that DNA is the actual genetic material is supported
by the observations (1) that DNA is found only in chromosomes,
(2) that the amount of DNA is constant in cells of the same individual
and of the same species, (3) that the amount of DNA differs between
species, and (4) that gametes contain one-half the amount normal for
body cells. All of this evidence is

☐ direct evidence that DNA is the genetic ma-
terial. . . . . .page **289C.**

☐ indirect evidence that DNA is the genetic
material. . . . . .page **298A.**

From page **290C.**

296A **Good.** It is reasonable to assume that the genetic material would be associated with the chromosomes only. A chemical substance called *deoxyribonucleic acid*, or DNA for short, was found only in the chromosomes. Therefore it became a likely candidate as the genetic material.

The investigation of the chemical nature of the chromosomes was done by collecting large numbers of cells and removing all of the cell substance until only the chromosomes were left. Besides being able to identify the chemical substance common to the chromosomes as DNA, it was also possible to determine the amount of DNA in each cell. This information was of particular value in relation to building up indirect evidence of the genetic nature of the DNA.

The determination of the average amount of DNA in each cell was accomplished by counting the number of cells used in the extraction of the DNA of the chromosomes and then, after weighing the total amount of DNA, dividing this weight by the number of cells. This determination was first done in domestic fowl by taking a specimen of blood from a rooster and counting the number of red cells in a given volume. The amount of DNA in that volume was then measured and divided by the number of cells. This gave the average quantity of DNA per red cell nucleus, which was 2.3 hundred-millionths (2.3×10^{-8}) of a milligram per nucleus.

If the number of red cells were 5,000,000 per cu. mm., and if the total weight of DNA per cu. mm. of cells were 0.125 mg., the average amount per cell would be 25 billionths of a mg. The minuteness of the amount of DNA is at least interesting, if it turns out to be true that DNA is the genetic material that carries the hereditary information.

Analysis of the DNA content in various kinds of cells such as red blood cells and kidney cells in a single organism such as fowl has revealed that each of these kinds of cells has the same amount of DNA.

If DNA is the genetic material and if the amount of DNA is the same in all the body cells of an individual organism, with which of the following statements would you agree?

☐ There should be more DNA in a single cell of the lining of the mouth of a human being than in the zygote from which this individual developed . . . . page **288C.**

☐ There should be less DNA in a single cell of the lining of the mouth of a human being than in the zygote from which this individual developed . . . . page **284B.**

☐ The amount of DNA in a single cell of the lining of the mouth should be the same as that in the zygote . . . . page **287C.**

From page **294B.**

Correct. You would expect the skin cells of man and mouse to be **297A** different.

For any chemical substance to qualify as genetic material it must have properties and relationships that correspond with what we know about the properties and relationships of genes. The properties and relationships of DNA that we have presented so far are (1) DNA is found in chromosomes only, (2) all cells of any one organism contain the same amount of DNA, (3) the cells of all organisms of the same species contain the same amount of DNA, (4) cells of different species of organisms have different amounts of DNA.

Which of the following hypotheses concerning genes are in agreement with the properties and relationships of DNA presented above?

☐ Somatic cells of any one organism have the same
number of genes............................page **295A.**

☐ Different species of organisms have different
numbers of genes in their somatic cells.......page **291C.**

☐ Both of these.............................page **293B.**

What? If you had all the genes of a goldfish wouldn't you be a fish? **297B**
Return to page **284C.**

From page **286C.**

Correct. All animals having hair would have genes for the production **297C** of hair. Thus the whole class of animals, known as mammals, which includes dogs, cats, humans, apes, and others, would all have certain kinds of genes in common.

Let us now return to the question of the chemical nature of the gene. If the gene is some specific chemical substance where would you expect to find this substance?

☐ In all parts of the cell......................page **294A.**

☐ In the cytoplasm..........................page **287B.**

☐ In the nucleus............................page **290C.**

From page 295C.

298A **Good.** The fact that the amount of DNA is constant for any species and that there is one-half of this amount in the gametes suggests that DNA is the genetic material. However, the evidence is very indirect. More direct evidence was discovered from investigations of the relation of DNA to inheritance of the bacteria that cause pneumonia.

Originally bacteria, which are single-celled organisms, were thought to be too primitive and simple to need genes for inheritance and the first experiments that opened the way for an understanding of bacterial genetics were not designed for this purpose at all. Instead the experiments were planned to discover something about pneumonia.

In the late 1920's an English bacteriologist was working with two strains of pneumonia bacteria. One strain was virulent and caused pneumonia when injected into mice. Another strain when injected would not cause pneumonia and hence was nonvirulent. These characteristics of virulence and nonvirulence were passed on from generation to generation in the two strains and thus were hereditary. Associated with the disease-producing ability in the two strains was a physical characteristic. The virulent strains had a gummy nonliving capsule (a case or envelope) that grew around each bacterium, that is, around each cell. The nonvirulent strain did not have capsules.

The part of the experiment that was to become so significant to students of heredity was as follows. Both strains of bacteria, the virulent and nonvirulent, were injected into mice at the same time. However, prior to the injection the virulent strain was killed by heat. Thus what was injected was a mixture of dead virulent bacteria and living nonvirulent bacteria.

The results were surprising because the mice developed pneumonia and their blood was found to be teeming with virulent capsulated bacteria. Had the dead capsulated forms come to life again or had the living nonvirulent forms somehow acquired the virulent characteristic from the dead forms? This latter possibility is what intrigued students of heredity and led to further evidence of the relation of DNA to genes.

To discover how bacteria could have obtained a new genetic characteristic from the dead forms of another type, a number of other experiments were tried. In these experiments attention was concentrated on the presence or absence of the capsule rather than on virulence or nonvirulence.

Both virulent and nonvirulent pneumococcus cells will disintegrate and dissolve if placed in a solution containing bile salts. A culture of bacteria having capsules was treated with bile salts to produce a solution of dead and dissolved bacterial cells. The bile salts were removed and the remaining solution was mixed with a culture of living bacteria of the type that did not produce capsules. The living

Continue on page 299A.

bacteria continued to grow and to reproduce. Some of the offspring **299A**
of these bacteria had capsules. These forms with the newly acquired
ability to produce capsules transmitted this ability to their offspring
indicating that the change was an hereditary one.

The results of this experiment suggest

☐ that some substance in the cell rather than the
cell as a whole is responsible for the transmission, from the dead cells to the living cells,
of the ability to produce capsules............page **289B.**

☐ that DNA is the substance transmitted from
the dead to the living cells.................page **284D.**

Incorrect. You apparently did not understand the reasoning involved **299B**
in this series of experiments. First, in science and in everyday life we
usually reason that if A causes B, B cannot occur unless A is present.
In detective stories alibis are most important, because if a suspect
can prove that he was not present when the victim was killed he
could not have been the murderer. We have a somewhat parallel case
in these experiments. The capsular gum was the first suspect. However,
the "murder" (production of capsules by noncapsulated forms)
occurred even when it was known that the capsular gum was absent.
Protein was the next suspect, but here again the "murder" occurred
even though no protein was present. DNA was the last suspect. It
was shown that DNA had to be present in order for the "murder" to
occur. Return to page **292A.**

Incorrect. We assume that all inborn characteristics are controlled by **299C**
genes. There are very evident inborn similarities between man and
apes, therefore we assume there are similarities of some of the genes.
Return to page **292C.**

If chromosomes are reduced by one-half at gamete formation so that **299D**
one-half of them go into one gamete and one-half into the other
gamete, and if DNA is the genetic material in the chromosomes,
how much of the total amount of the DNA in the immature reproductive cell would go into each gamete? Return to page **293B.**

From page **289B.**

300A **Correct.** Since capsular gum was not in the cellular debris that caused the production of capsules, it was reasonable to eliminate capsular gum as a factor. Protein which makes up the bulk of the material in the cell was next removed and the material remaining was still found to cause the bacteria from the noncapsulated strain to produce offspring that had capsules. The results of this experiment indicate

☐ that it was not the protein which was the genetic
material . . . . .page   **292A.**

☐ that DNA was the material affecting the in-
heritance of ability to produce a capsule . . . . . .page   **295B.**

☐ both of these . . . . .page   **290B.**

300B **How come?** If the amount of DNA is related directly to the amount of chromosomes then if the amount (number) of chromosomes is increased would not the amount of DNA increase also? Go back to page **288D.**

300C **Incorrect.** Apes and men have hair, fish have scales; apes and men have arms and legs, fish have fins; apes and men have eyes on the front of the head, goldfish have eyes at sides of the head; etc., etc. Go back to page **292C.**

From page **283A.**

300D **Correct.** Identical twins should have identical genes since identical twins arise from a single fertilized egg, and have identical inherited characteristics.

Nonidentical children born of the same parents differ from each other in hereditary characteristics.

Would you expect more variation in the genes of these children than you would expect in the genes of identical twins?

☐ Yes . . . . .page   **285C.**

☐ No . . . . .page   **291B.**

No. The man and the woman belong to the same species. Cells of **301A**
individuals of the same species have the same amount of DNA.
Return to page **294B**.

Your answer is not wrong, but there is a more inclusive one. **301B**
Return to page **287C**.

From page **291D**.

Correct. This is the end of the sequence. Continue with the **301C**
review.

REVIEW—Chapter 6, Part I

In the introductory questions of this chapter certain ideas were presented
about the relation of genes and genetic make-up to phenotypic characteristics.
Since identical twins arise from a single zygote their genes should be (*identical,
different*) _____. Brothers should have (*more, fewer*) _____
genes in common than two men (nonbrothers) picked at random. All men
have many characteristics in common; they (*should, should not*) _____
_____ have many genes in common.

Since all organisms have some characteristics in common, for example all
are composed of protoplasm, all organisms (*should, should not*) _____
have some genes in common.

The question posed at the beginning of this section was, *Of what chemical
substance or substances are genes composed?* We now believe that genes are
composed of _____, because there is constancy of amount of this
substance in the chromosomes of cells of individuals of the same species, and
because the sperm cells contain _____ the amount. Additional evidence
is provided by the experiments on pneumococci. When the capsular gum and
the protein in the cell debris of a capsule form were destroyed and the remaining material mixed with bacteria of a noncapsular strain, the strain (*did,
did not*) _____ produce offspring having capsules, but when the
_____ was destroyed by an enzyme the strain (*did, did not*) _____
produce offspring having capsules.

Check your responses to the review of Chapter 6, Part I, on page 361 and
continue with the summary of Part I.

SUMMARY—Chapter 6, Part I

The idea that a certain chemical substance (deoxyribonucleic acid, or DNA) might be the genetic material came when it was discovered that this substance was found only in chromosomes, that the amount of DNA per cell was the same in all body cells of an organism, that the gametes produced by the organism had half this amount, and that abnormal cells with twice or four times the normal number of chromosomes had twice or four times the normal amount of DNA.

A series of experiments with the bacterium that causes pneumonia gave added support to the idea that genes and DNA were the same thing. It was accidentally discovered that when killed pneumococci of one type (encapsulated) were mixed with living bacteria of the noncapsulated type, some offspring of the noncapsulated forms had the ability to develop capsules. This represented a change in the heredity of the noncapsulated bacteria. In terms of the gene theory, genes from the killed capsulated forms entered the living noncapsulated pneumococci cells and caused their offspring *to produce capsules*.

A series of experiments designed to discover the substance in the killed cells that could cause a change in the heredity of the living cells led to the discovery that DNA was the only substance that when destroyed also destroyed the ability of the dead capsulated cells to change the heredity of the noncapsulated bacteria. This supported the idea that DNA was the genetic material.

One section of this chapter was introduced to review certain implications of the gene theory in relation to different races and species of organisms. This was necessary because we needed these ideas later to understand some of the evidence supporting the idea that DNA was the genetic material. The implications follow:

Identical twins develop from single fertilized eggs, hence have the same kinds of genes. Identical twins also have identical phenotypes. Children of the same pair of parents have fewer genes in common than identical twins, but they have more in common than people picked at random having different parents. However, all humans have some similar genes. We assume this is so because we assume similar genes cause similar characteristics. Thus the similarity of inherited characteristics can be used as a rough indication of the presence of similar genes. For example, because apes are more like humans than they are like fish it is assumed that apes and men have more genes in common than apes and fish or than men and fish. Different species of organisms thus can have some similar genes, but one would expect that they also would have different genes.

Continue with Part II of this chapter.

302

PART II

What Properties of DNA Could be Responsible for Gene Action?

The chemical substance that was later to be known as deoxyribonucleic acid (DNA) was discovered by Miescher in nuclei of cells in 1869, about the same time that Mendel was developing the gene theory on the basis of experiments with pea plants. At that time no relation was seen between these two events. It was not until 1924 that the discovery was made that all of the DNA of cells was located in the chromosomes. Thirty more years elapsed before it was discovered that the amount of DNA in nuclei was constant for organisms. At about this same time the experiments with pneumococci linked the DNA with genetic material and thus finally joined the original discoveries of Miescher and Mendel. This union of chemical and genetic concepts was of much importance both to geneticists and to biochemists. For the geneticist it gave a partial answer to the question, *What is the nature of the gene?* and for the biochemist it gave a new possibility for investigations in his specialty.

If the DNA molecule carries genetic information, then there must be something about its structure which parallels what we have assumed to be the characteristics of genes.

Which of the following assumptions about genes must be reflected in the structure and behavior of the DNA molecule, if the DNA molecule is genetic material (the genes)?

☐ Each gene comes from a pre-existing gene.....page **312C.**

☐ Genes are arranged in a linear order on chromosomes, as evidenced by linkage and crossing over...................................page **306A.**

☐ There is some difference in the genes of different kinds of organisms........................page **311B.**

☐ Two of these.............................page **304D.**

☐ All of these.............................page **308A.**

Incorrect. Look at the diagram on page 314B. Which base is symbolized in such a way that it "fits" the symbol for adenine? _____.
Now answer the question on page **315A.**

304A **Incorrect.** The four bases are symbolized in such a way that the complementary base pairs can be easily recognized. Adenine is symbolized as ⌐A⌐ or ⌐A⌐ and thymine is symbolized as ⌐T⌐ or ⌐T⌐ . Return to page **311D**.

304B **No.** This is assumed to be the way in which nucleotides are joined in a single chain. The entire DNA molecule is assumed to be made of two single chains. Think about a ladder. If the two sugar-phosphate chains represented the two side pieces of a ladder what would represent the rungs? _____ . Return to page **306B**.

From page **318A**.

304C **Correct.** In an earlier question the configuration

[S]----(P)----[S]----(P)

was presented. You recognized that this was not a nucleotide. However, it does represent the way in which the sugar and phosphate components are assumed to be joined.

Many nucleotides join together to form a long chain molecule. The phosphate component of one nucleotide joins the sugar component of another nucleotide to form a single chain as follows:

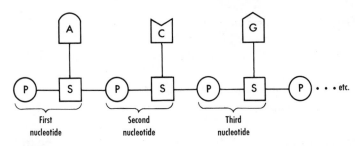

The chainlike nature of the DNA molecule is a consequence of

☐ joining of a series of sugars and phosphates . . . page **306B**.

☐ joining of the bases to the sugars . . . . page **315C**.

304D **Your answer is correct but incomplete.** Return to page **303A**.

Good. You had no sound basis for making a prediction. The data **305A** concerning this are as follows: In the chicken the molecular proportions are:

Guanine	Cytosine	Adenine	Thymine
21	21	29	29

Continue on page **309D**.

From page **315A**.

Correct. 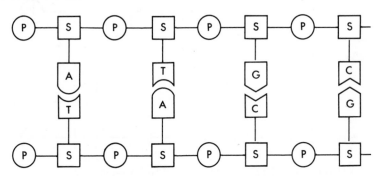 represents one base pair arrangement and **305B** represents another arrangement, as in the following segment of a DNA molecule.

How many different arrangements of base pairs are possible, considering all four bases?

☐ Two...page **307A.**

☐ Three..page **316C.**

☐ Four...page **311D.**

Incorrect. If the DNA molecule is a code then different arrangements **305C** of the "letters" of the code should have different meanings. We know that species differ in their hereditary traits, so if we assume that a molecular code is responsible for these differences would not the code have to be different in the different species? _____ . Return to page **310D**.

306A Your answer is correct but incomplete. Return to page **303A**.

From page **304C**.

306B **Right.** While it is known that the serial arrangement of the sugar and phosphate components produces a long unbranched chainlike molecule, the detailed organization of the DNA molecule is not known for sure. However, on the basis of the known chemical facts a theoretical model was developed to represent the possible structural organization of the total molecule.

According to this model the complete molecule of DNA consists of a double chain. Each single chain consists of nucleotides as described above. The double chain is produced by the attachment of the bases of one strand or chain to the bases of another as shown below.

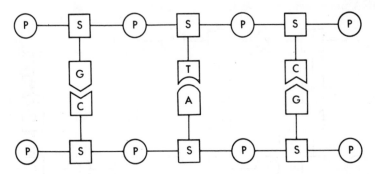

The two chains of DNA are assumed to be joined by

☐ a sugar to a phosphate.....................page   **304B.**

☐ one base to another.......................page   **314B.**

306C **How come?** If you do not accept the idea of a difference in DNA as the cause of hereditary differences between species then you must hypothesize some other substance than DNA that differs and is the genetic material. A difference in the genetic material seems essential and at the present time DNA seems to have the properties required for genetic material. Return to page **309D.**

306D Your answer is correct but incomplete. Return to page **313A**.

Incorrect. Did you forget the guanine-cytosine base pair? If adenine **307A** and thymine can make two different arrangements how many more would guanine and cytosine make? _____. Return to page **305B**.

Return to page **305B** and study the model. Does this model suggest **307B** anything about the ratio of molecules of adenine to those of thymine? Then continue from that page.

From page **310D**.

Correct. If the arrangement of base pairs represents a genetic code **307C** then the arrangement of base pairs should be different in different species. A code is a language consisting of a finite number of symbols that can be arranged in a variety of orders. For example, our alphabet contains 26 letters that can be used over and over again in various combinations that produce words. Each of the different combinations has a different meaning, and the same combination repeated would have the same meaning. By analogy, if the DNA molecule is a code, one might expect that various combinations of base pairs would produce different meanings. Because there are four different arrangements possible of the base pairs it is assumed that the DNA code is written in a language with four letters. These four letters would be analogous to the 26 letters of our alphabet, where instead of 26 different letters in various combinations producing different words, the various combinations of the four letters would produce different words. For example, if the four letters were *e, r, a,* and *n* different meanings could be produced as *near* and *earn,* or if one letter could be used more than once then *nearer* and *earner* are possible. In the genetic code the different meanings would be expressed as different hereditary traits. Thus, because different species have different hereditary traits, the base pairs of the different species should be in different arrangements.

In which of the following should the order of base pairs be exactly the same?

☐ Members of same species....................page **309B.**

☐ Members of the same family................page **310C.**

☐ Identical twins............................page **313A.**

☐ None of these............................page **316A.**

From page **303A.**

308A **Correct.** All of these assumed properties must be explained by the structure of the DNA molecule, if this molecule is the genetic material.

The next problem therefore is: What is the chemical nature of the DNA molecule?

To attempt to discover the relation of the DNA molecule to genes, chemists first analyzed this substance to discover its chemical components, and then they developed a theoretical model of its probable structure.

They found that DNA contained three primary components — a sugar, a phosphate, and a base. Because our concern here is with heredity and not primarily with the detailed chemical structures we are going to ask you to think of the components of DNA as three different kinds of building blocks. The sugar component is one kind of block, the phosphate is a second kind of block and the base is a third kind.

All of the sugar components and all of the phosphate components in the DNA molecule are alike in chemical structure, but there are four different kinds of bases. They are adenine, thymine, guanine, and cytosine.

Let us symbolize the building block which is the sugar component (deoxyribose) as $\boxed{S}$

the phosphate component as $\left(P \right)$

and the four bases as

$\boxed{G}$ guanine

$\boxed{A}$ adenine

$\boxed{C}$ cytosine

$\boxed{T}$ thymine

It must be constantly kept in mind that the squares, circles, and other graphic symbols used here for the sugar, for the phosphate, and for the bases are purely symbolic and do not represent the actual structure of these substances. They are used to help you to conceptualize the relationship of the three components.

Continue on page 309A.

Incorrect. If the compound were the same for all kinds of organisms, **311A** the amounts of each of the bases should be the same for all kinds of organisms. You have evidence that this is not the case. Return to page **315D.**

Your answer is correct but incomplete. Return to page 303A. **311B**

Incorrect. The symbols $\boxed{S}$ and (P) were used to represent the **311C** sugar and the phosphate. A chain of sugars and phosphates is not a nucleotide. Each nucleotide is composed of all three of the kinds of building blocks — sugar, phosphate, and base. Return to page **308A.**

From page 305B.

Correct. Four different arrangements are possible, because and **311D** represent two different arrangements.

If in a DNA molecule one strand contains the following sequence of bases (in this diagram the sugar and phosphate molecules are indicated by a straight line)

which of the following would represent the complementary sequence of bases on the other strand?

...page **312B.**

...page **316D.**

...page **304A.**

From page **309D.**

312A **You are correct.** It is reasonable to expect that the DNA of different species would be different. Analysis of DNA from different kinds of organisms has shown that the ratio of guanine plus cytosine to adenine plus thymine is the same in any one species but varies between species.

In each of the following organisms the molecular proportions of bases were distributed as follows:

	Guanine	Cytosine	Adenine	Thymine
Chicken	21	21	29	29
Sea urchin	18	18	32	32
Bacillus (T.B.)	35	35	15	15
Another bacterium	30	30	20	20

Compare the proportion of guanine for the four different species. Note that the amount varies from 18 to 35. Also examine the differences among the other bases. Do these data confirm your prediction concerning variation of the DNA molecule of different species?

☐ Yes......................................page **315D.**

☐ No......................................page **318B.**

312B **Incorrect.** The four bases are symbolized in such a way that the complementary base pairs can be easily recognized. Adenine is symbolized as or and thymine is symbolized as or . Return to page **311D.**

312C **Your answer is correct but incomplete.** Return to page **303A.**

312D **Your expectation is confirmed** by actual data collected on various organisms. For example, in the chicken the molecular proportions are:

Guanine	Cytosine	Adenine	Thymine
21	21	29	29

Continue on page **309D.**

From page 307C.

Good. Identical twins are assumed to have identical genes. There- **313A**
fore, one might expect that they would also have identical DNA
molecules. Members of the same family or the same species presumably
have many of the same kinds of genes, but because they have hereditary differences they also have different kinds of genes. Hence, their
DNA should differ also.

The assumed identification of DNA with the genetic material
raises the question of what the gene actually is in terms of the DNA
molecule. Is a gene one base pair, several, or the entire molecule?
Because the complete DNA molecule is a very long chain of base
pairs it seems reasonable to assume that the whole molecule consists
of many genes, and therefore a single gene would be some segment of
the entire molecule.

The base pairs of a DNA molecule are arranged in a linear order as
an unbranched molecule consisting of two strands. This linear
unbranched structure is important to the hypothesis that DNA is
the genetic material.

Why?

☐ Because genes are assumed to be located in a
   linear pattern on the chromosome, as beads on
   a string...............................page   **316B.**

☐ Because crossover could not occur if the units of
   the molecule were not arranged in a linear order.page   **306D.**

☐ Both of these............................page   **318D.**

What are the constituents of a nucleotide? Does a nucleotide include **313B**
the sugar? _____. Does it include a phosphate? _____.
Does it include one of the four kinds of bases? _____. Are
there any of the diagrams on page **309A** which include one each of
these? _____. Return to page **308A**.

Incorrect. Look at the diagram on page **314B**. Which base is symbol- **313C**
ized in such a way that it "fits" the symbol for adenine? _____.
Now answer the question on page **315A**.

Your answer is correct but incomplete. Return to page **316D**.   **313D**

314A **Your answer is correct but incomplete.** Return to page **316D**.

From page **306B**.

314B **Correct.** The two chains of DNA are assumed to be joined by the bases.

The four different kinds of bases are assumed to be important in the connection of one strand or chain to the other. Adenine on one strand attaches only to thymine on the other strand and guanine attaches only to cytosine. A portion of a DNA molecule would have this type of relationship.

phosphate — sugar — adenine . . . thymine — sugar — phosphate
phosphate — sugar — cytosine . . . guanine — sugar — phosphate
phosphate — sugar — guanine . . . cytosine — sugar — phosphate
phosphate — sugar — thymine . . . adenine — sugar — phosphate
etc.   etc.

This double strand molecule of DNA can also be represented with block symbols as

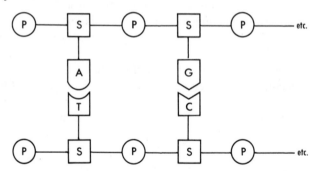

Note that the four bases have been symbolized by different shaped

blocks and that the block for adenine ⎡A⎤ is complementary to the

block for thymine ⎣T⎦ and that the block for guanine ⎡G⎤ is comple-

mentary to the block for cytosine ⎣C⎦. One pair of these comple-

mentary blocks represents a supposed linkage between the adenine and the thymine; the other pair represents a linkage between guanine and cytosine. These pairs, adenine-thymine and guanine-cytosine, are called **base pairs**. Adenine supposedly pairs only with thymine because of the "fit" of the molecules, and guanine supposedly pairs only with cytosine.

Continue on page 315A.

In any double chain DNA molecule if one nucleotide of one chain contains an adenine base, which base on the other chain of the pair would the adenine be attached to?

☐ Guanine. G .... page **313C.**

☐ Cytosine. C .... page **303B.**

☐ Thymine. T .... page **305B.**

☐ Any of these.............................. page **317A.**

Incorrect. The symbols S and P were used to represent the **315B** sugar and the phosphate. A chain of sugars and phosphates is not a nucleotide. Each nucleotide is composed of all three of the kinds of building blocks — sugar, phosphate, and base. Return to page **308A.**

No. In a charm bracelet, is it the attachment of the charm to the link **315C** which makes the chain, or the attachment of one link to another which makes the chain? The charm would be analogous to the base and the phosphate and sugar would be analogous to two different types of links. Return to page **304C.**

From page **312A.**

Correct. As you probably know, a molecule of a single kind of **315D** chemical compound is composed of atoms combined in a definite proportion. For example, water is composed of twice as many atoms of hydrogen as of oxygen, and for this reason the formula for a molecule of water is written H_2O. The molecules of any particular compound are always assumed to have their components combined in a definite proportion which is always the same. The data on molecules of DNA as presented for the four different species give evidence

☐ that DNA is not the same wherever it is found, but rather that it differs in various kinds of organisms................................ page **317B.**

☐ that DNA is a specific compound which is the same in all kinds of organisms.............. page **311A.**

316A **Incorrect.** It is generally assumed that identical twins have identical sets of genes. Return to page **307C**.

316B **Your answer is correct but incomplete.** Return to page 313A.

316C **No.** If adenine and thymine can make two different arrangements how many more can guanine and cytosine make? _____. Return to page **305B**.

From page **311D**.

316D **Correct.** The complementary strand of any single DNA strand must contain the bases which complete the base pairs of the molecule; thus adenine of one strand unites with thymine of the other strand and guanine unites with cytosine.

The DNA molecule probably is composed of thousands of nucleotides (the phosphate-sugar-base unit) strung in a double chain. In this chain one of the four bases adenine, thymine, guanine, and cytosine, makes up a part of each nucleotide, hence there would also be thousands of the bases.

If the model of the DNA molecule is correct so that adenine always connects to thymine and guanine to cytosine, which of the following predictions could you make?

If pure DNA molecules are broken down into their component units and a chemical analysis made of the quantity of the four different bases in the sample

☐ the proportion of molecules of guanine would be the same as the proportion of molecules of cytosine.................................page **313D.**

☐ the proportion of molecules of adenine would be the same as the proportion of molecules of thymine.................................page **314A.**

☐ Both of these............................page **310B.**

☐ There is no basis for making any prediction concerning proportion of bases in base pairs....page **307B.**

Incorrect. Look at the diagram on page **314B.** Which base is symbol- **317A** ized in such a way that it "fits" the symbol for adenine? _____.
Now answer the question on page **315A.**

From page **315D.**

Correct. The difference in the proportion of the four bases in different **317B** DNA molecules plus the theoretical model of the DNA molecule in which the bases join in certain specific ways suggested the possibility that the differences between DNA molecules should be due to different orders in which the base pairs are arranged. Thus one sequence theoretically could be:

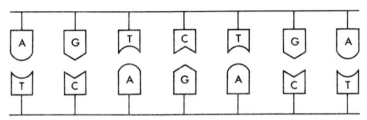

another could be:

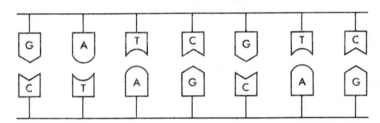

If such differences in the order of base pairs were significant in terms of the genetic control of organisms, the base pairs would constitute a kind of code in which one arrangement of the base pairs would have one meaning and another arrangement another meaning.

Such a code would be a four symbol code in contrast to our alphabet which has 26 symbols (A to Z), or the Morse code used in telegraphy which has only two symbols, a dot and a dash.

Why is the genetic code referred to as a four symbol code?

☐ Because each genetic word has four letters . . . . . page **309C.**

☐ Because the genetic alphabet has four "letters,"
guanine, adenine, thymine, cytosine . . . . page **310D.**

From page **308A.**

318A **You are correct.** The nucleotide was symbolized as

The positional relations of these three components are important. The base is always attached to the _____ and never to the _____. Complete the above blanks. What do you have recorded?

☐ Sugar; phosphate . . . . .page   **304C.**

☐ Phosphate; sugar . . . . .page   **310A.**

318B **Incorrect.** Presumably you predicted that since genes of one organism differ from genes of another organism, the DNA of one organism should vary from the DNA of another. If DNA did not vary from one organism to another, then shouldn't the amount of each base be the same in all organisms? _____. Does the amount vary? _____. What effect does this have on your prediction? Does it agree with it? _____. Confirm means *agree with*, contradict means *disagree with*. Return to page **312A.**

318C **This is not an unreasonable expectation,** but the data on various organisms is contrary to such a prediction. For example, in the chicken the molecular proportions are:

Guanine	Cytosine	Adenine	Thymine
21	21	29	29

Continue on page **309D.**

From page **313A.**

318D **Correct.** If the DNA molecule is the genetic material and is a code that gives directions for the construction of organisms, it must also be able to reproduce itself exactly, and it must be transmitted essentially unchanged from parents to offspring.
     Continue with the review of Part II.

REVIEW—Chapter 6, Part II

In Part II of this chapter we were concerned with the problem of the chemical nature of the DNA molecule. We found that the DNA molecule was thought to be composed of complex structures called nucleotides, and that each nucleotide was composed of a phosphate and a (*wd*) _____, which were always the same in all nucleotides, and of one of (#) _____ different _____. The base of the nucleotide was always attached to the (*wd*) _____; chains (strands) of nucleotides are assumed to be formed by attachment of the sugar of one nucleotide to the (*wd*) _____ of another nucleotide. It is also assumed that (*few, many*) _____ nucleotides join to form a long chain. A single long chain (*does, does not*) _____ constitute a DNA molecule. A DNA molecule is assumed to be a (*single, double*) _____ chain. According to the theoretical model of a DNA molecule, two strands of nucleotides join by the attachment of one base to (*wds*) _____. The theoretical model also suggests that there are specific combinations which are called (*wds*) _____. It is assumed that adenine can join only with thymine and that guanine can attach only to (*wd*) _____. Evidence, which supports the belief that there are specific base pairs, is found in analysis of the molecular proportions of the bases. It was found that the molecular proportion of cytosine (*was, was not*) _____ equal to that of guanine. However analysis revealed that the molecular proportions of thymine and cytosine (*were, were not*) _____ equal. It was also found that in different species of organisms the molecular proportions of the various bases were (*the same, different*) _____; thus all DNA (*is, is not*) _____ the same. It has been assumed that the base pairs represent a code, with (#) _____ symbols; thus differences in inherited characteristics could be explained by assuming that in different species the order of the base pairs should be (*the same, different*) _____. It can also be assumed that in identical twins, developing from a single zygote, the order of the base pairs should be (*the same, different*) _____. In terms of DNA, the gene can be defined as (*all, part*) _____ of a DNA molecule. Linkage and crossing over of genes can be explained by the idea that the DNA molecule is a long and (*wd*) _____ structure.

To check your responses to the review of Chapter 6, Part II, turn to page 362 and then continue with the summary of Part II.

SUMMARY—Chapter 6, Part II

In Part II we examined a theoretical model of a DNA molecule, compared its structure with the assumptions we had made concerning genes to see if the DNA molecule might, in fact, be the genetic material (the genes).

The DNA molecule is composed of nucleotides made up of three components, a sugar, a phosphate, and a base. The sugar and phosphate components are attached alternately to each other to form a long unbranched chain or strand. The bases are attached to the sugars and stick out at an angle to the chain.

A complete DNA molecule consists of two chains of nucleotides connected together by their bases.

There were four bases, adenine, thymine, guanine, and cytosine. In forming the double chain of the DNA molecule the bases were assumed to combine only in certain ways. Adenine combined with thymine to form one base pair, and guanine attached to cytosine to form another base pair. Thus the model of the double stranded DNA molecule consisted of two chains of sugar and phosphate components connected by pairs of bases. This formed a ladderlike molecule with the uprights being composed of the sugars and phosphates, and the rungs of base pairs.

The chainlike nature of the DNA molecule compares favorably with the idea of genes arranged in a linear order like beads on a string. Thus the chainlike structure of the DNA molecule matches the assumed arrangement of genes on a chromosome.

Genes, in addition to being arranged in a linear order on chromosomes, are supposedly different in different species of organisms. Because the differences between species are inherited it is necessary to assume that different species have different kinds of genes. DNA molecules were also found to differ in different species. This difference was in the relative amounts of the base pairs adenine-thymine and guanine-cytosine. For every adenine component in a DNA molecule there was a thymine, and for every guanine component there was a cytosine, but the ratio of the base pairs adenine-thymine to guanine-cytosine was not the same in all species. It differed in different species.

This difference in the relative amounts of base pairs in different species suggested that the base pairs are related to genetic differences.

The base pairs were compared to letters of an alphabet, and because four different arrangements of base pairs were possible in the DNA molecule it was suggested that the DNA alphabet was composed of four letters. Different arrangements of these four letters would have different meanings in terms of directions for the development of hereditary characteristics.

Thus the DNA molecule by virtue of the differences in base pairs could conceivably function as genes are supposed to function in heredity. This supported the idea that DNA was actually the genetic material.

One aspect of the DNA molecule model that we have omitted mentioning is that the chain is in the form of a helix. We have described the DNA molecule as though it were a ladder. For the purposes of understanding the relation of DNA to heredity this was sufficient. To make a helix out of a ladder one would have to hold the ladder at both ends and twist it. Another analogy to describe a helix is a circular staircase with the railings on two sides analogous to the uprights of the ladder and the stairs analogous to the rungs of the ladder.

Continue with Part III.

PART III

322A   In Part I of this chapter we presented evidence that DNA is the genetic material. This belief is based on the facts that DNA is found only in chromosomes and that for any one species the amount is directly proportional to the number of chromosomes in the cell and upon evidence obtained from experiments on pneumococcus. In Part II a theoretical model of a DNA molecule was presented. It is believed that DNA is a double-stranded molecule each strand of which is comprised of a sugar-phosphate chain with bases attached. The two strands are assumed to be joined by specific pairing of bases. The assumption that genes are in a linear order like beads on a string can be correlated with the chainlike structure of the molecule.

If the DNA molecule is the genetic material, one of its features must be the ability to reproduce itself. Genes duplicate themselves somehow, and any chemical substance that is presumed to be genetic material must also duplicate itself. One of the most exciting features of the theoretical model of the DNA molecule is that this model suggests a way in which such duplication might take place. The ideas which follow are highly theoretical. In addition they are probably oversimplifications of the biochemical reactions which take place. They are presented here as possible solutions to the problem of how DNA molecules might duplicate.

First, let us assume that the two strands of the DNA molecule can separate, beginning at one end and proceeding along the length of the molecule, much as a zipper opens. This process of separation is diagramed on Worksheet 6-A. Second, assume that sugar, phosphate, and base molecules are available in the medium surrounding the separated DNA strands. If these three kinds of molecules join to form nucleotides such as the one illustrated

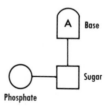

then separate nucleotides can attach to one or the other of the separated DNA strands and eventually two new strands would be formed — one for each of the original DNA strands.

Continue on page 323A.

NOW EXAMINE WORKSHEET 6-A. Recall that base pairs are composed of either adenine and thymine or of guanine and cytosine. If the free nucleotide illustrated (p. 322) were attached to one of the diagramed bases (Worksheet 6-A), to which of the strands, I or II, would the free nucleotide attach?

☐ I . . . . .page   **339D.**

☐ II . . . . .page   **334A.**

☐ Either of these . . . . .page   **330C.**

Incorrect. In order to make this error you must have (1) failed to understand the details of the experiment, or (2) failed to understand the relation of the experiment to the hypothetical model of DNA, or (3) not understood the meaning of support or confirmation of an hypothesis. If you did not understand the details of the experiment or did not understand the relation of the experiment to the DNA model, return to the beginning of Part III, page **322A**.

If your error was due to not understanding the nature of supporting data, read the following. The supposed structure of the DNA molecule suggests a method by which the molecule duplicates itself. On the basis of this idea certain results can be predicted concerning the relation of N-14 to N-15 in the DNA of the second and third generation. The actual results of an experiment involving N-14 and N-15 agreed with the predicted results. This agreement is what we mean by support or confirmation. Had the results not agreed with the prediction they would not have supported the hypothesis. Return to page **325A**.

From page **329C**.

Correct. There would be two nucleotide strands (chains) in each molecule of DNA.

After the two strands of the original DNA molecule have separated and after each has served as a template, or pattern, on which new complementary strands have been formed, how many molecules of DNA would there be?

☐ One . . . . .page   **330A.**

☐ Two . . . . .page   **345C.**

☐ Four . . . . .page   **326B.**

324A Incorrect. You must have misinterpreted the question. Line B was grown in N-15 only. The construction of new DNA could only utilize heavy nitrogen (N-15) because that was all that was available. Return to page **335A.**

324B No. You have failed to understand the relation of the DNA molecule to the chromosome, and you have confused the double strand nature of the DNA molecule with the double nature of paired chromosomes. Examine the following diagrams.

When this chromosome duplicates we have:

or,

a. Two chromosomes

b. Two double-stranded DNA molecules

c. Four single strands of nucleotides.

Think about the duplication of a single DNA molecule. Would two new chromosomes result? _____. In what process are new chromosomes produced? _____. Return to page **347A.**

From page **331B.**

324C Correct. One nucleotide containing thymine and one containing cytosine would attach to the bases of Strand I, to begin the formation of a second new strand. This process of adding of nucleotides is assumed to continue all the way along the strand until a new double strand DNA molecule is formed.

The new strand formed on Strand I would then be

☐ complementary to the original Strand I and identical to the original Strand II . . . . page **329C.**

☐ complementary to the original Strand II and identical to the original Strand I . . . . page **332B.**

From page **348B.**

Good. When this experiment was performed the third generation cells **325A**
were of two types. One-half of the DNA molecules were of the same
density as that of the control cells grown in N-14, while the other
half produced DNA which was intermediate in density between those
grown in N-14 and those cultured in N-15. Do these results support
the hypothesis that DNA is a double chain molecule which can separate and produce two DNA molecules by building new complementary
strands?

☐ Yes....................................page **333B.**

☐ No.....................................page **323B.**

Incorrect. If two of the bases on one of the original strands were **325B**
thymine and cytosine as presented in the diagram, would another
thymine attach to the original thymine and another cytosine to the
cytosine? _____. Return to page **326A.**

Wrong. At first we diagramed the DNA molecule as **325C**

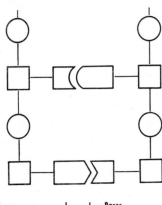

We abbreviated this as

and then diagramed them as

Return to page **326C.**

From page 334A.

326A **Right.** A nucleotide containing guanine could attach to cytosine on Strand II. ON THE DIAGRAM ON WORKSHEET 6-A, SKETCH THIS NUCLEOTIDE IN THE PROPER PLACE.

If the phosphate of the nucleotide containing adenine joins with the sugar of the nucleotide containing guanine, this would be the beginning of a new strand. The newly formed strand when completed

☐ would be a complement of the strand to which it is attached.............................page **331B.**

☐ would be exactly like the strand to which it is attached................................page **325B.**

326B **Incorrect.** It is true that there would be four strands of nucleotides. But how many strands have we assumed each DNA molecule to be composed of? _____. So how many completed DNA molecules would there be? _____. Return to page **323C.**

From page 329A.

326C **Correct.** The ladder represents a double-stranded DNA molecule. What is represented by the two vertical, or upright, lines of the diagram?

←Upright

☐ The bases................................page **347B.**

☐ The base pairs............................page **325C.**

☐ The phosphate-sugar chain................page **340C.**

How many cells are represented by

_____ . How many of these contain one of the original strands?
(#)_____ . This is (#)_____ out of (#)_____ ,
which is _____ percent. Return to page **337B**.

From page **336B**.

Correct. Each chromosome could contain a double strand of DNA. **327B**
Examine the following diagram of a double-stranded DNA molecule.

```
·Strand I        S—P—S—P—S—P—S— etc.
                 |    |    |    |
                 A    T    G    A
                 T    A    C    T
                 |    |    |    |
   Strand II     S—P—S—P—S—P—S— etc.
```

If one strand of the DNA molecule before duplication be designated I
as above and the other strand as II, what would you expect to find in
chromosomes of the two daughter cells resulting from the mitotic
division?

☐ Strand I with a copy of Strand II in one cell and
 Strand II with a copy of Strand I in the other
 cell. . . . . .page   **329A.**

☐ Strand I and Strand II in one cell and a copy of
 Strand I and a copy of Strand II in the other
 cell. . . . . .page   **347C.**

☐ Parts of Strand I and parts of Strand II in one
 cell and the other parts of Strands I and II in
 the other cell. . . . . .page   **341C.**

Incorrect. You must have misinterpreted the question. Line B was   **327C**
grown in N-15 only. The construction of new DNA could only utilize
heavy nitrogen (N-15) because that was all that was available. Return
to page **335A**.

328A How many cells are represented by

_____. How many of these contain one of the original strands? (#)_____. This is (#)_____ out of (#)_____, which is _____ percent. Return to page **337B**.

From page **345C**.

328B **Correct.** There would be two complete DNA molecules which would be exactly like each other and also like the original molecule.

Strand I   Strand II

phosphate — sugar — adenine . . . thymine — sugar — phosphate

phosphate — sugar — cytosine . . . guanine — sugar — phosphate

phosphate — sugar — guanine . . . cytosine — sugar — phosphate

phosphate — sugar — adenine . . . thymine — sugar — phosphate

Now examine the sequence of base pairs above. If the sequence of the base pairs on a part of the DNA molecule were as shown, and the two strands separated, what would be the order of the bases added to Strand I?

☐ Adenine, cytosine, guanine, adenine..........page **334D.**

☐ Thymine, guanine, cytosine, thymine........page **339B.**

☐ Either of these.............................page **349A.**

328C **No.** You have already answered that 50% of the cells have N-15 in their molecules while the others have only N-14 in their molecules. What would this mean with respect to the density of these two classes of DNA molecules? Remember that density is mass (weight) per unit volume and that the N-15 molecule is slightly heavier than the N-14 molecule. Return to page **348B**.

328D **Correct, but incomplete.** Return to page **344D**.

From page **327B.**

You are correct. Strand I would act as a template to build an exact **329A** copy of Strand II. This DNA molecule would be expected to go into one cell while Strand II plus its complement would go into the other cell.

If a DNA molecule duplicated itself by the separation of the strands and the building of a complement of each strand there would be two identical DNA molecules, one of which would be contained in one of the duplicated chromosomes and the other in the other duplicated chromosome. In order to mentally follow the fate of the two strands of a single DNA molecule through several generations, let us represent the double-stranded molecule of DNA in a chromosome as follows:

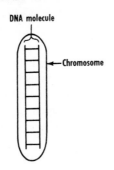

The ladder represents

☐ a single strand of a DNA molecule.........page   **339A.**

☐ a double-stranded DNA molecule...........page   **326C.**

Your answer is correct but incomplete. Presumably you did not **329B** know that it would be possible for a cell to lose parts of chromosomes and hence some of its DNA. Return to page **343A.**

From page **324C.**

Correct. The new strand formed adjacent to the original Strand I **329C** would be complementary to Strand I and identical to Strand II.

How many strands of nucleotides attached in linear order are there in a complete DNA molecule?

☐ One.....................................page   **346A.**

☐ Two.....................................page   **323C.**

☐ Four....................................page   **338A.**

330A **Incorrect.** In a certain type dance where the intention is to have many people meet, one couple starts dancing and after a minute or two the music stops and each of the partners chooses another partner who has not been dancing. How many couples would there be on the floor just after the music started again? _____. If the first couple of dancers were analogous to the double strand of DNA, the male of the first couple would be analogous to one strand and the female to the other strand. Try again on page **323C**.

From page **340C**.

330B **Correct.** Each horizontal line of the diagram represents a base pair. When the DNA molecule and the chromosome containing it duplicate, each new chromosome will contain one of the strands of the original DNA molecule plus a new complementary strand. Let the original strand be represented as ⌡, and the new strand as |. The knob on the line representing the original strand has no significance except to distinguish one strand from the other. At the end of the first duplication of the DNA molecule and the chromosome there would be two chromosomes each containing a DNA molecule as illustrated.

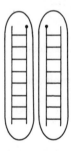

At mitosis one of these two chromosomes, each containing a complete DNA molecule, would go into one cell and one into another cell. What percent of the two daughter cells containing the chromosomes diagramed above would contain a strand of the original DNA molecule?

☐ 50%. . . . . .page   **334B.**

☐ 100%. . . . . .page   **337B.**

330C **Incorrect.** The free nucleotide contained the base adenine. Adenine combines only with thymine to form a base pair. Return to page **322A**.

330D **Your answer is correct but incomplete.** Return to page **341B**.

No. Examine the diagram below.   **331A**

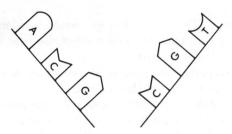

Place the proper symbols on the two halves of this separating molecule
to produce the complement for each. Compare the two resulting DNA
molecule diagrams. Are they the same? _____. Now answer
the question on page **339B**.

From page 326A.

Correct. The newly formed strand would be a complement of Strand   **331B**
II. Which two nucleotides would attach to Strand I of the diagram on
Worksheet 6-A to begin the formation of a new strand? The first
nucleotide (at the left on the diagram) would contain _____
and the second would contain _____.
    What bases do you have recorded in the above blanks?

☐ Adenine, cytosine . . . . page   **342C.**

☐ Adenine, thymine . . . . page   **345B.**

☐ Thymine, guanine . . . . page   **338C.**

☐ Thymine, cytosine . . . . page   **324C.**

☐ None of these . . . . page   **340B.**

Incorrect. The idea of variation among individuals of a species and   **331C**
between various species can be explained on the basis of the assumed
code contained in the DNA molecule, but this variation of sequences
of bases does not help to explain gene duplication. Return to page
333B.

From page **339B.**

332A **You are correct.** The two molecules should be identical, because each base acting as a template would select the base which was the other member of that base pair.

This is the hypothesized process of producing new molecules of DNA that are exact copies of the original.

We have agreed that if the DNA molecule is the genetic material of an organism, the DNA must be a part of the chromosomes. You have just learned of a hypothetical method by which the DNA molecule could duplicate itself, thus producing two identical molecules where only one existed before.

Which of the following statements correlates the DNA with the observed chromosomes?

☐ Each strand of a DNA molecule is in a separate
chromosome..............................page **336A.**

☐ Each chromosome contains a double-stranded
DNA molecule...........................page **347A.**

332B **Incorrect.** The new strand of nucleotides is constructed by the selective action of the bases attached to one of the original strands of the DNA molecule. The bases of the original strand do not select bases for attachment that are identical to themselves. Instead adenine selects only thymine and guanine selects only cytosine. Hence, the new strand can be only complementary to the strand which formed it. However, because each strand of the original DNA molecule was complementary to the other, the newly formed strand would be complementary to the strand on which it was formed and identical to the other original strand. Return to page **324C.**

332C **No.** Are you confusing the two strands of the DNA molecule with paired chromosomes? It is true that only one-half of each molecule would contain N-14, and hence 50% of the strands would incorporate N-14, but keep in mind that we are talking about the double-stranded molecule, and that we assume that each chromosome is largely made up of this double-stranded molecule. Return to page **340A.**

332D LOOK AT THE DIAGRAM ON WORKSHEET 6-A. Aren't Strand I and its complement like Strand II and its complement? _____. Return to page **345C.**

Consider the word *lead*. The four letters of the code are *l, e, a, d*. **333A**
Suppose that a mistake is made in typing and an *e* replaces the *a*. It
becomes *leed*. Does this have the same meaning as *lead*? _____.
But if an *a* were to replace an *e*, the word would be *laad*. Does this
have meaning in English? _____. Return to page **343C**.

From page **325A**.

Correct. In Part II of this chapter we presented (1) a hypothetical **333B**
model for a DNA molecule, (2) some of the evidence which was used
as a basis for constructing the model of the molecule, (3) predictions
from the theoretical model, and (4) experiments which confirmed
these predictions. We also stated that if the DNA molecule was the
genetic material (the genes), it would have to have several unique
properties which would account for the assumed properties of genes
as developed in classical genetics. The properties of the genes which
were to be accounted for were (1) each gene comes from a pre-existing
gene, (2) genes are arranged in a linear order on chromosomes as
evidenced by linkage and crossover, and (3) genes of different organisms differ from each other, that is, there is variation in phenotypes
and genotypes of organisms.

The theoretical model of DNA incorporates the following ideas:
(1) an unbranched chain formed by sugars and phosphates with bases
attached to the sugars, (2) the bases arranged in different sequences
and combinations in different kinds of organisms, and (3) the complete DNA molecule consisting of a double chain of two complementary strands which can separate and each assemble a new complementary strand.

Each of these hypothetical aspects of the model accounts for one
of the above mentioned assumed properties of genes. Which property
of the DNA molecule would account for the belief that genes come
only from pre-existing genes and are exactly like the ones from which
they came?

☐ The idea that the chain is unbranched . . . . page **337A.**

☐ The idea of the variation of the sequence of the
bases . . . . page **331C.**

☐ The idea of a double chain with complementary
bases, which separates into two strands with
each strand assembling a new complementary
strand . . . . page **338B.**

From page **322A**.

334A **Correct.** The nucleotide containing the base adenine could attach to Strand II, with the adenine attaching to the thymine. SKETCH THIS NUCLEOTIDE AT THE PROPER POSITION ON WORKSHEET 6-A.

AGAIN EXAMINE WORKSHEET 6-A. If a nucleotide containing guanine were free in the medium surrounding the DNA molecule, to which of the diagramed bases could it attach?

☐ Thymine...................................page **346D.**

☐ Cytosine..................................page **326A.**

☐ Adenine...................................page **339C.**

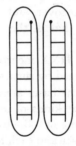

334B **No.** The diagram was

It represents two new chromosomes that went into separate cells. ↑ represented one of the original strands. In how many of the new cells is there a ↑?_____. What percent is this?_____. Return to page **330B.**

334C LOOK AT THE DIAGRAM ON WORKSHEET 6-A. Keep in mind that Strands I and II were attached to each other prior to the beginning of duplication. What were the base pairs of the original DNA molecule before it started to duplicate? _____. Go back to page **345C.**

334D **Incorrect.** If the two strands of a single DNA molecule were compared to a couple dancing and if the dancing partners each chose a new partner, would the male dance with another male? You have said that the new partner can be like the original. Remember that each base joins with its complement, A to T, C to G. Return to page **328B.**

From page **337B.**

Correct. 50% of the cells of the 3rd generation should contain a strand of the original DNA molecule. Chromosomes are small and can be seen only through a light microscope. DNA molecules are much smaller than chromosomes and cannot be seen at all through a light microscope. Consequently we cannot look at a chromosome, follow through its duplication during mitosis, and see what happens to the strands of the DNA molecule. We need other methods if we are to discover the way in which strands of DNA are duplicated and passed on to daughter cells.

The model of the DNA molecule as a double-stranded structure consisting of sugar, phosphate, and base-pair components is theoretical and is based on data obtained from chemical and X-ray analysis. We know that chromosomes duplicate because we can see the process. Also, if the gene theory is correct, genes must duplicate. The proposed duplication of DNA strands as described above would explain the duplication of genes providing that various sequences of base pairs actually represent the genes and providing that duplication of the DNA molecule takes place as hypothesized.

The following experiment is one of the various methods of testing the DNA model. This method depends upon the fact that the DNA molecule contains nitrogen. There are two isotopes (kinds) of nitrogen. The common one has an atomic weight of 14. The other has an atomic weight of 15. Because of the difference in the weight of these two isotopes, molecules of DNA containing N-14 can be separated by centrifugation from molecules of DNA containing N-15.

Bacteria (single-celled organisms) will grow in a medium containing either the nitrogen having an atomic weight of 14 (N-14) or in a medium containing the heavy nitrogen (N-15). When bacterial cells are grown for many generations in a medium containing heavy nitrogen (N-15) only, the nitrogen of the DNA molecule in the cells is N-15.

EXAMINE WORKSHEET 6-B. Notice that the type of *nitrogen* in the DNA molecule is indicated for only the first generation. COMPLETE THE LABELING OF THIS DIAGRAM FOR LINE A, GROWN IN N-14 ONLY, AND FOR LINE B, GROWN IN N-15 ONLY.

What percent of the cells of Generation II of line B would contain DNA with N-14?

☐ 100% . . . . page **324A.**

☐ 50% . . . . page **327C.**

☐ 0% . . . . page **340A.**

336A Incorrect. However, your confusion is understandable. You know that chromosomes sometime occur in pairs and that during early mitosis they are double. However, do not confuse the occasional double nature of chromosomes with the double strand nature of the DNA molecule. Each chromosome contains the complete DNA molecule, that is, it contains both strands. (See diagram below.)

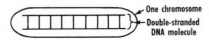

Return to page **332A**.

From page **347A**.

336B Correct. Duplication of DNA would be involved in the duplication of chromosomes prior to mitosis. The chromosome as seen during mitosis is not the DNA molecule only. The chromosome contains protein molecules as well as DNA. Also the chromosome at the time of mitosis is much shorter than the DNA molecule. Apparently, during the changes that occur during prophase the DNA molecule is folded so that it shortens.

In order to be sure you understand the relation of the double strand molecule of DNA to the structure of the chromosome, read the follow in and respond to the question.

At one stage of mitosis duplicated chromosomes align on the equatorial plane and separate. In each of these separated chromosomes is the DNA molecule a single-stranded molecule or a double-stranded molecule?

☐ Single-stranded............................page **342A**.

☐ Double-stranded..........................page **327B**.

336C Incorrect. The idea that the DNA molecule is a double chain is not a necessary concept to explain linkage and crossing over. Are you confusing pairing of chromosomes with the double strand of a single DNA molecule? How many strands of DNA do we assume there would be in a pair of homologous chromosomes? _____.
Return to page **338B**.

336D Your answer is correct but incomplete. Return to page 343C.

Incorrect. Would a single unbranched chain help to account for the **337A** belief that genes of new cells are exact replicas of the genes of the cell from which they arose? _____. It is the template aspect of the model of the DNA molecule which is important in gene duplication. Return to page **333B**.

From page **330B**.

Correct. 100% of the daughter cells resulting from one cell division **337B** would contain one of the original strands of the DNA molecule of the cell which divided.

Now consider the division of these two daughter cells. The chromosomes and the DNA molecules of these two cells are represented as Generation II in the diagram below.

Consider the next generation of cells (Generation III below). Each of the two sets of DNA molecules would again duplicate. The two divisions are represented here.

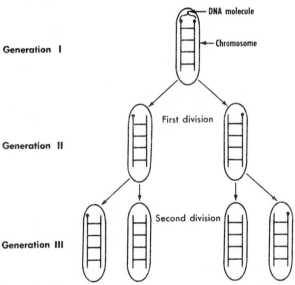

Recall that the knob indicates one of the original strands of a DNA molecule. What percent of the cells of Generation III would contain a strand of the original DNA molecule contained in a chromosome of Generation I?

☐ 25%. . . . . .page   **327A.**

☐ 50%. . . . . .page   **335A.**

☐ 100%. . . . . .page   **328A.**

338A **Incorrect.** A DNA molecule is believed to be composed of strands (chains) of nucleotides attached by base pairs. If the base of one strand attaches to the base of another strand, how many strands are there in one complete DNA molecule? _____. Return to page **329C**.

From page **333B**.

338B **Correct.** The duplication of genes can be explained by assuming that the DNA molecule is a double strand and that because of the complementarity of the bases on these two strands, exact replicas of DNA can be constructed.

If we assume that the genes are arranged in linear order, like beads on a string, and if we assume that a single DNA molecule represents many genes, then crossing over might take place as shown below.

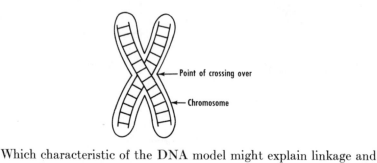

Which characteristic of the DNA model might explain linkage and crossover?

☐ The idea of a long unbranched chain . . . . page **343C**.

☐ The idea that the DNA molecule is a double
chain . . . . page **336C**.

☐ The idea that there is variation in the sequence
of bases . . . . page **349B**.

338C **No.** Look at the diagram on Worksheet 6-A. What is the base indicated at the left on Strand I? _____. The base pairs are thymine-adenine and guanine-cytosine. What base would attach to the adenine? Now look at the second base of Strand I. What is this base? _____. What base would attach to it? _____.
Return to page **331B**.

No. At first we diagramed the DNA molecule as follows: **339A**

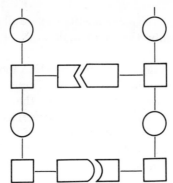

Then, in order to consider several DNA molecules, we simplified the diagram as

We put these two together as

to form the ladder. Return to page **329A**.

From page **328B**.

Good. Would the two resulting DNA molecules, each composed of   **339B**
two strands, be the same with respect to the order of the base pairs or
would they be different?

☐ The same.................................page   **332A.**

☐ Different.................................page   **331A.**

Incorrect. The two base pairs are guanine-cytosine and thymine-   **339C**
adenine. To which base would a guanine attach? _____.
Return to page **334A**.

Incorrect. The free nucleotide contained the base adenine. Adenine   **339D**
combines only with thymine to form a base pair. Return to page **322A**.

From page 335A.

340A **Good.** All of the cells grown in a medium where all of the nitrogen was N-15 should have only the N-15 and no N-14 incorporated into their DNA.

Such bacteria containing N-15 in their DNA molecules were transferred to a medium containing N-14 only. These bacteria were grown just long enough in the N-14 medium for the cells to divide once. NOW LABEL THE DIAGRAMS OF THE DNA MOLECULES (WORKSHEET 6-B) FOR GENERATION II OF LINE C. What percent of the cells of Generation II of line C would contain chromosomes having DNA molecules with N-14 in one of the strands?

☐ 100%. . . . . page   **346B.**

☐ 50%. . . . . page   **332C.**

☐ 0%. . . . . page   **344C.**

340B **No.** Look at the diagram on Worksheet 6-A. What is the base indicated at the left on Strand I? _____. The base pairs are thymine-adenine and guanine-cytosine. What base would attach to the adenine? Now look at the second base of Strand I. What is this base? _____. What base would attach to it? _____. Return to page **331B.**

From page 326C.

340C **Correct.** The upright lines represent the phosphate-sugar chain. What is represented by each horizontal line, or rung of the ladder, connecting the two upright lines as shown in the diagram?

☐ One base, as thymine. . . . . page   **344A.**

☐ A base pair. . . . . page   **330B.**

☐ Both of these. . . . . page   **348C.**

Incorrect. The question asked what percent of cells would contain **341A**
DNA with N-15. Did you answer another question, *i.e.*, "What
percent of DNA strands would contain N-15?" Or did you make an
error in labeling the DNA strands? Note that the new DNA strands
produced after Generation I would contain only N-14. Correct any
error and return to page **342B**.

From page **343C.**

Correct. Throughout our discussion of genes in relation to inheritance **341B**
and of DNA as the genetic material we have emphasized the stability
and constancy of the genes. We have assumed that the phenotypes
of organisms varied but the genes themselves did not. The genes
changed partners and sometimes moved, through crossing over, from
one chromosome to another, but they did not themselves change.
Now it is necessary to modify this concept of changelessness. Genes
occasionally do change. The change is called a **mutation.** Such
mutations cause a change in the phenotype and are thought to be
the source of new alleles. It must be emphasized that we can be aware
of the existence of a gene only when more than one allele of that gene
is recognized on the basis of contrasting phenotypes. Thus without
mutation to produce new alleles there could be no science of heredity.
Most mutations arise spontaneously, but X-rays, mustard gas and all
kinds of ionizing radiations cause mutations.

A change in the genetic message could result in the production of

☐ a new allele................................page **349C.**

☐ a mutation................................page **330D.**

☐ Both of these................................page **343A.**

☐ Neither of these................................page **344B.**

Incorrect. You have failed to understand the explanation of the **341C**
duplication of the DNA molecule and its relation to the duplication of
chromosomes. It would be best to return to page **322A** and try again.

Correct, but incomplete. Return to page **344D.**   **341D**

342A No. When does duplication of the chromosome occur, before the chromosomes align on the equator, or after? _____. Do we assume a complete DNA molecule to be a single or a double strand? _____. Would the DNA molecule be duplicated before or after the chromosomes are on the equator of the spindle? _____. Return to page **336B**.

From page **346B**.

342B **Correct.** You would predict that the DNA of all of the second generation cells of line C would have a density intermediate between those grown in N-15 and those grown in N-14. This is because one-half of the DNA of each cell should be derived from the cell of the first generation grown in N-15, and the other half should be constructed from materials containing N-14. When this experiment was performed the prediction was confirmed. It was found that this second generation had DNA intermediate in density between those taken from line A and those from line B.

COMPLETE THE LABELING OF THE DIAGRAM ON THE WORKSHEET FOR LINE C. Each ladder represents the DNA of a single chromosome of a single cell.

What percent of the cells in Generation III in the culture started in an N-15 medium and transferred to an N-14 medium would contain DNA with N-15?

☐ 25% . . . . .page   **346C.**

☐ 50% . . . . .page   **348B.**

☐ 100% . . . . .page   **341A.**

342C No. Look at the diagram on Worksheet 6-A. What is the base indicated at the left on Strand I? _____. The base pairs are thymine-adenine and guanine-cytosine. What base would attach to the adenine? Now look at the second base of Strand I. What is this base? _____. What base would attach to it? _____. Return to page **331B**.

342D **Correct, but incomplete.** Return to page **344D**.

From page **341B.**

Correct. A mutation, or change in the genetic message, or code, **343A** might be caused by

☐ loss of part of the DNA molecule of the cell...page   **348A.**

☐ substitution of one base pair for another.......page   **329B.**

☐ Either of these.............................page   **344D.**

Incorrect. Have you completed the diagram on Worksheet 6-A as **343B** instructed? _____. If not, return to the beginning of Part III. If you have completed it, examine it. Don't you have a nucleotide containing adenine and one containing guanine attached to Strand II? _____. Do you have a nucleotide containing thymine and one containing cytosine attached to Strand I? _____. Now compare the two strands. Are they alike or are they different? _____. Try again on page **345C.**

From page **338B.**

Good. If we assume that the genetic material is arranged in linear **343C** fashion, and if we assume that a single molecule of DNA represents many genes, then this molecule would probably have to be long and unbranched to explain linkage and crossover.

The variation among organisms can be accounted for on the basis of this model by assuming that the sequence of base pairs (A-T, T-A, C-G, and G-C) constitutes a code written in four letters.

If the genetic message is a sequence of the base pairs, what might be the effect of a change in the sequence of the base pairs?

☐ It could change the genetic message to some
other message that has meaning.............page   **345A.**

☐ It could change the genetic message so that the
message had no meaning..................page   **336D.**

☐ Either of these.............................page   **341B.**

☐ Neither of these; it would have no effect.....page   **333A.**

344A **No.** Because two bases come together to connect the two strands of the DNA molecule, the rungs in the diagram represent two bases or a base pair. Return to page **340C.**

344B **Incorrect.** We have equated the DNA molecule with the genetic code. We have also equated the genes with the genetic code. We have assumed that the code is written in some way by the base pairs which we equated with the letters of an alphabet. If you change some of the letters the message would be changed. Would this not produce a change in the gene? _____. Return to page **341B.**

344C **Look at your worksheet.** Do you have one strand of each molecule labeled with N-15 and the other with N-14? _____. If not, correct your error. Return to page **340A.**

From page **343A.**

344D **Correct.** In earlier volumes of this program we stated a number of assumptions of the gene theory. Which of the following represents a new assumption or new assumptions which can be added to the gene theory on the bais of ideas presented in this volume?

☐ Genetic information is carried from generation to generation by a chemical substance known as DNA . . . . .page **341D.**

☐ The genetic information is coded in the DNA so that the sequence in which the four kinds of nucleotides occur constitute an alphabet which spells out the genetic information . . . . .page **347D.**

☐ Occasional errors in replication of the base pairs may occur at the time of gene replication; such errors are mutations . . . . .page **342D.**

☐ Two of these . . . . .page **328D.**

☐ All of these . . . . .page **349D.**

Your answer is correct but incomplete. Return to page 343C.

No. Look at the diagram on Worksheet 6-A. What is the base in- **345B** dicated at the left on Strand I? _____. The base pairs are thymine-adenine and guanine-cytosine. What base would attach to the adenine? Now look at the second base of Strand I. What is this base? _____. What base would attach to it? _____. Return to page **331B**.

From page 323C.

Correct. There would be two molecules of DNA formed. These two **345C** molecules of DNA would be exactly like

☐ each other. . . . . page **334C.**

☐ the original molecule. . . . . page **332D.**

☐ Both of these. . . . . page **328B.**

☐ Neither of these. . . . . page **343B.**

Incorrect. You have already stated that the original strands of DNA **345D** would be equally distributed in daughter cells after the first division.

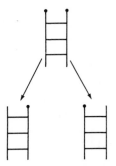

Density is defined as mass (wt.) per unit volume. So a quart of sawdust would be less dense than a quart of sand, because a quart of sawdust would weigh less than a quart of sand. If equal volumes of sawdust and sand were mixed, would the density of the mixture be the same as that of the sand? or the same as that of the sawdust? or would it be intermediate? Return to page **346B**.

346A **Incorrect.** A DNA molecule is believed to be composed of strands (chains) of nucleotides attached by base pairs. If the base of one strand attaches to the base of another strand, how many strands are there in one complete DNA molecule? _____. Return to page **329C.**

From page **340A.**

346B **Correct.** All of the cells of Generation II of line C would also contain N-14.

After the cells of each of these lines (A, B, and C) had divided just once to produce Generation II, samples were taken from each line and the DNA of the cells of the sample was extracted.

All three samples of DNA were placed in a centrifuge to compare their respective densities. The DNA containing N-15 would have a greater density than that containing N-14.

The DNA extracted from the bacteria that had grown in N-15 and which were then transferred to a medium containing N-14 (line C) and allowed to reproduce once should have a density

☐ the same as those grown only in N-15 . . . . .page   **345D.**

☐ intermediate between those grown in N-15 and
   those grown in N-14 . . . . .page   **342B.**

☐ the same as those grown in N-14 only . . . . .page   **348D.**

346C **Incorrect.** The question asked what percent of cells would contain DNA with N-15. Did you answer another question, *i.e.,* "What percent of DNA strands would contain N-15?" Or did you make an error in labeling the DNA strands? Note that the new DNA strands produced after Generation I would contain only N-14. Correct any error and return to page **342B.**

346D **Incorrect.** The two base pairs are guanine-cytosine and thymine-adenine. To which base would a guanine attach? _____. Return to page **334A.**

From page **332A.**

Correct. Each chromosome would contain a DNA molecule made up **347A** of two strands.

   With which of the following biological processes would duplication of the DNA molecule be associated?

☐ Duplication of chromosomes prior to mitosis . . . page   **336B.**

☐ Pairing of homologous chromosomes during
   meiosis . . . . page   **324B.**

Incorrect. At first we diagramed the DNA molecule as   **347B**

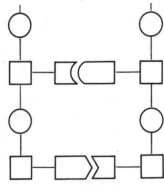

We abbreviated this as

and then diagramed them as

Return to page **326C.**

Incorrect. You have failed to understand the explanation of the **347C** duplication of the DNA molecule and its relation to the duplication of chromosomes. It would be best to return to page **322A** and try again.

Correct, but incomplete. Return to page **344D.**   **347D**

348A Your answer is correct but incomplete. Return to page 343A.

From page 342B.

348B **Correct.** 50% of the cells in Generation III of line C would contain N-15.

Which of the following predictions could you make concerning the density of the DNA molecules of Generation III?

☐ One-half of the DNA molecules should have the same density as those grown in N-14 only, and the other half of the DNA should be intermediate in density between those grown in N-14 and those grown in N-15..................page **325A.**

☐ All of the DNA molecules would have approximately the same density....................page **328C.**

348C **No.** Because two bases come together to connect the two strands of the DNA molecule, the rungs in the diagram represent two bases or a base pair. Return to page 340C.

348D **Incorrect.** You have already stated that the original strands of DNA would be equally distributed in daughter cells after the first division.

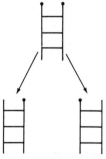

Density is defined as mass (wt.) per unit volume. So a quart of sawdust would be less dense than a quart of sand, because a quart of sawdust would weigh less than a quart of sand. If equal volumes of sawdust and sand were mixed, would the density of the mixture be the same as that of the sand? or the same as that of the sawdust? or would it be intermediate? Return to page 346B.

No. If the two strands of a single DNA molecule were compared to a **349A** couple dancing and if the dancing partners each chose a new partner, would the male dance with another male? You have said that the new partner can be like the original. Remember that each base joins with its complement, A to T, C to G. Return to page **328B**.

Incorrect. While variation of DNA would be necessary to produce **349B** different genes which could be linked, it does not help to explain why there is linkage nor how crossover could occur. Return to page **338B**.

Your answer is correct but incomplete. Return to page **341B**. **349C**

From page **344D**.

Correct. The following represent new assumptions of the gene theory. **349D** (1) **Genetic information is carried from generation to generation by a chemical substance known as DNA.** (2) **The genetic information is coded in the DNA so that the sequence in which the four kinds of nucleotides occur constitute an alphabet which spells out the genetic information.** (3) **Occasional errors in replication of the base pairs may occur at the time of gene replication; such errors are mutations.**

In Chapter 1, Volume I, we introduced the idea of a gene, and defined it as a "thing" which determines hereditary characteristics. At first the gene was thought of as a separate unit particle. When linkage was discovered the concept of gene evolved to one of beads on a string. With the identification of genes with a DNA molecule the answer to the question "What is a gene?" became more difficult, rather than easier! We have assumed that a word in the genetic code consists of several letters of the base pair alphabet. Is the gene a single letter (a base pair), a word (probably several base pairs) or is it a sentence (several or many words)?

At the present time no answer can be given to these questions, or rather, different geneticists give different answers. Before a final answer to the question "What is a gene?" can ge given, the gene must be defined operationally. Several different operational definitions have been suggested, but so far there has not been agreement as to which of the operational definitions is the most satisfactory. This is the end of this sequence. Continue with the review of Part III.

In order for DNA to be a candidate for the genetic material it would have to have certain characteristics. The idea that the molecule is long and un-branched helps to explain (*wd*) _____ and (*wd*) _____. The variation of characteristics of organisms could be explained by various se-quences of (*wds*) _____. Another aspect of the genes, which would have to be reflected in the DNA molecule, is the capacity of genes to reproduce themselves. That the DNA molecule model is pictured as a (*double, single*) _____ strand helps to explain how the DNA molecule could duplicate itself. A second important aspect of the model, which accounts for the idea that each of the strands can build a new strand which is (*identical to, comple-mentary to*) _____ itself, is the idea that each base can join with (*any, only one*) _____ other base. Thus the two resulting new molecules would be like the (*wd*) _____ DNA molecule and also (*like, different from*) _____ each other. The two resulting DNA molecules should have the same order of (*wd*) _____ pairs, since each strand acts as a template (mold) to build a new strand. This process of duplication is assumed to take place at the time that the (*wd*) _____ duplicate themselves in the process of (*wd*) _____; thus when the chromatids align on the equator of the cell, each of the chromatids would contain (*#*) _____ strand of the original chromosome and (*#*) _____ strand which had been built up prior to the cell division. Thus each daughter cell resulting from mitosis would contain one of the original strands with a copy of (*that, the other*) _____ strand. In chromosomes of the daughter cells (*#*) _____% would contain one strand from the original DNA mole-cule (First Generation). At the next cell division (*#*) _____% of the cells would contain chromosomes which had one strand of the original (first generation) DNA molecule. This hypothetical model of the manner in which DNA duplicates itself was (*confirmed, contradicted*) _____ by experi-ments where bacteria were grown in a medium containing heavy nitrogen (N-15) and then transferred to a medium containing N-14.

If DNA is the genetic material (genes) then mutations (spontaneous ap-pearance of new phenotypes) should be explicable in terms of DNA. Mutations can be explained by assuming that occasionally a part of the DNA molecule is lost from the cell, and by assuming that occasionally there is an error in the duplication of DNA, and that the wrong (*wd*) _____ is incorporated into the new strand.

To check your responses to the review of Chapter 6, Part III, turn to page 363 and then continue with the Summary of Part III.

SUMMARY—Chapter 6, Part III

One of the assumptions of the gene theory is that genes duplicate themselves producing identical copies that can be passed on to daughter cells in mitosis or to gametes in meiosis. If DNA is the genetic material the DNA molecule must be of such nature that it can explain gene duplication. The fact that the theoretical model of the DNA molecule suggested an explanation of gene duplication was one of the reasons why this model was hailed with enthusiasm. The manner in which the model of the DNA molecule explained gene duplication was as follows.

The DNA molecule presumably consists of a double strand, held together by the attachment of the bases of one strand to the bases of the other strand. The two strands would begin to separate at one end and continue to separate, much as a zipper opens. Separation of the strands occurs between the bases; thus each strand would have bases attached at one end to the sugar molecule of the strand, but the other end would be free. If nucleotides consisting each of one sugar, one phosphate, and one base molecule were available in the surrounding medium the base of the free nucleotide could become attached to one of the bases of the original intact but separated strand. A sequence of such additions of free nucleotides would eventually build up a new strand to replace the strand that had initially been attached.

Since this addition of free nucleotides presumably would occur on both of the original strands, the end result would be the production of two new strands, one along each original strand, thus the production of two new DNA molecules where there was only one before.

The two new DNA molecules would be identical to each other and also to the original molecule. It is assumed that only certain bases attach to certain other bases. There are four bases, adenine, thymine, guanine, and cytosine. Adenine will only attach to thymine and guanine will only attach to cytosine. Thus when free nucleotides attach to the bases of the intact strand only nucleotides containing the base thymine will connect with the nucleotides containing the base adenine, and so on. The result is that the newly formed strand is a complement of the intact strand on which it forms. However, it is identical to the other original strand. As both strands produce new strands that are identical to their former partners the two new double strand molecules produced are identical.

Each double strand DNA molecule is associated with one single chromosome, and the duplication of the DNA molecule presumably coincides with the duplication of chromosomes.

If the duplication of the DNA molecule actually represents the duplication of chromosomes then daughter cells after mitosis should contain one of the original strands of the DNA molecule and one newly formed strand. Experiments with N-14 and N-15 in bacteria confirmed this prediction.

The theoretical duplication of DNA molecules offers an explanation for the duplication of genes. Also the structure of the DNA molecule as a long unbranched chain supports the idea of genes arranged in a linear order like beads on the string, and it fits the conditions necessary for linkage and crossing over to take place. Furthermore, mutation can be explained by assuming that during the duplication of the DNA molecule errors could occur so that some rearrangement of bases might change the base pairs and thus change the genetic information.

Continue with the self test for this Chapter.

SELF TEST—Chapter 6

For items 1 through 8 use the following key.

> KEY: A. DNA
> B. Chromosomes
> C. Both of these
> D. Neither of these

— 1. Composed entirely of nucleotides, each nucleotide being made up of one sugar, one phosphate and a base.

— 2. Is assumed to be a double-stranded molecule.

— 3. Produces a copy of itself prior to cell division.

— 4. The sequence of bases on a strand is complementary to the sequence of bases on the other strand.

— 5. Composed in part of protein.

— 6. Associated with genetic material (or genes).

— 7. Assumed to be the genetic code.

— 8. Visible through an optical microscope.

Recall that guanine and cytosine represent one base-pair and adenine and thymine represent the other base-pair. For items 9 through 20 use the following key.

KEY: A. The amount of the substance or the numerical value of the ratio in Column A is greater than that in Column B.

B. The amount of the substance or the numerical value of the ratio in Column A is the same as that in Column B.

C. The amount of the substance or the numerical value of the ratio in Column A is less than that in Column B.

D. There is insufficient information to permit a comparison.

Column A	Column B
__ 9. Adenine in all DNA molecules	Thymine in all DNA molecules
__10. Cytosine in one cell of an organism	Cytosine in another cell of the same organism
__11. Adenine in a sperm cell of a cat	Adenine in the zygote of a cat
__12. Cytosine in a cell of one organism	Guanine in another cell of the same organism
__13. DNA in a cell of a poodle	DNA in cell of a Great Dane
__14. Ratio of adenine to cytosine in zygote of an individual	Ratio of adenine to cytosine skin cell of the same individual
__15. Ratio of adenine to cytosine in man	Ratio of adenine to cytosine in a mouse
__16. Ratio of adenine plus guanine to cytosine plus thymine in man	Ratio of adenine plus guanine to cytosine plus thymine in a mouse
__17. DNA in a single cell just before cell division	DNA in a single cell just after cell division
__18. DNA in one cell of one identical twin	DNA in one cell of the other identical twin
__19. Thymine in one cell of one identical twin	Thymine in one cell of the other identical twin
__20. Adenine in gene that determines that an individual will be a taster	Adenine in gene that determines that an individual will be a nontaster

For items 21 through 26 use the following information.

Bean seedlings were grown in a medium containing nucleotides with thymine labeled with radioactive hydrogen. Photomicrographs of cells show these atoms as dark spots on the chromosomes. After being allowed to divide once in this medium all of the chromosomes showed radioactivity along the entire chromosome. The cells were then removed to a medium without radioactive hydrogen. After this division only one of each pair of chromosomes showed radioactivity.

For items 21 through 26 use the following key.

KEY: A.   The experiment gives evidence for this statement.
              B.   The experiment gives evidence against this statement.
              C.   The experiment gives no evidence for or against this statement.

__21. Thymine is not restricted to any particular segment of DNA molecule.

__22. Each strand of DNA remains intact during mitosis.

__23. Each strand of DNA produces a complement of itself during mitosis.

__24. In the production of new DNA, Strand I breaks up and part of this is incorporated into the new strand.

__25. The DNA molecule is a molecule that extends from one end of the chromosome to the other without folds or bends.

__26. The DNA molecule is a double strand.

Correct answers to the self test for Chapter 6 are on page 365.

APPENDIX

Correct Responses to Reviews

REVIEW—Chapter 2, Part I

Individuals can have any one of four blood types: Type A, Type B, Type O, or Type AB. These blood types are (*genotypes, phenotypes*) **phenotypes** The inheritance of blood types is assumed to be controlled by (#) **3** genes; any one individual, however, can have only (#) **2** of these genes. This situation where there are more than two alleles is called (*wds*) **multiple allele** inheritance. The genotype of a Type A individual can be (*lts*) **AA** or (*lts*) **Ao**. The genotype of a Type B individual could be (*lts*) **BB** or (*lts*) **Bo**. All Type O individuals would have the genotype (*lts*) **oo** and all of the Type AB individuals would have the genotype (*lts*) **AB**. There are (#) **2** classes of families where both parents are Type A, those that produce all Type (*lt*) **A** individuals and those that produce both Type A individuals and Type (*lt*) **O** individuals. The offspring of two Type O parents would be Type (*lt*) **O**. If one parent is Type O and the other is Type AB, (#) **2** types of offspring can be produced; they are: (*wds*) **Type A, Type B.**

REVIEW—Chapter 2, Part II

Each person can be classified on the basis of his A, B, O blood type and also on the basis of his Rh blood type. The two contrasting characteristics with respect to this latter trait are (*wd*) **Rh positive** and (*wd*) **Rh negative** The gene for Rh+ is dominant to the gene for Rh−; therefore, the genotype of anyone who is Rh− is (*lts*) **r r**, while the person who is Rh+ has the genotype (*lts*) **R R** or (*lts*) **R r**.

REVIEW—Chapter 3, Part I

In a cross between two F_1 individuals where there is dominance the ratio of the dominant characteristic to the recessive characteristic is 3:1. If the genes for this particular trait are carried on the autosomes the ratio of males to females for those with dominant phenotypes will be **3** : **1**, and the ratio of males to females for those with the recessive phenotype will be **3** : **1**.

Some genes are sex-linked, that is, some genes are located on (*autosomes, sex chromosomes*) _sex chromo-somes_. It is assumed that the X-chromosome (*does, does not*) _does_ carry genes and that the Y-chromosome (*does, does not*) _does not_ carry sex-linked genes.

By assuming that the genes for red and for white eye color are located on the (*X, Y*) _X_ chromosome, the sex ratios of individuals of the F_2 generation of a cross between two F_1 flies can be explained. In this cross there were no (*males, females*) _females_ with the (*dominant, recessive*) _recessive_ characteristic. The genotype of the original red-eyed female parent (P_1) was (*lts*) _WW_ while the genotype of the white-eyed male parent (P_1) was (*lts*) _wr_. The F_2 females had the genotype (*lts*) _Ww or WW_ and the F_2 males had the genotype (*lts*) _wr or Wr_. There were no white-eyed females in the F_2 generation, but white-eyed females could be produced by crossing a white-eyed male with a female having the genotype (*lts*) _Ww or ww_.

Sex-linked inheritance differs from other types of inheritance in that the (*male, female*) _male_ has but one gene for the trait. Thus the assumption of the gene theory that genes always occur in pairs must be modified. The assumption can be modified as: Genes occur in (*wd*) _pairs_ on all (*autosomes, sex chromosomes*) _autosomes_ and on the sex chromosome of the sex that has (*one, two*) _two_ sex chromosomes. Thus a single recessive gene (*can, cannot*) _can_ be expressed in the sex which has but one X-chromosome.

REVIEW—Chapter 3, Part II

If a characteristic is sex-linked (1) it is more frequent in (*males, females*) _males_ (2) it is transmitted through a (*son, daughter*) _daughter_ to (*½, all*) _½_ of (*her, his*) _her_ (*sons, daughters*) _sons_ and (3) it should appear in father and son only if the characteristic had appeared in the family of the (*father, mother*) _mother_. The family showing red-green colorblindness exhibited all of these three points, therefore colorblindness was assumed to be due to a recessive and (*wd*) _sex-linked_ gene; the gene being located on the (*X, Y*) _X_ -chromosome. The genotypes of (*all, some*) _all_ of the males could be determined from the phenotypes because the males are assumed to have (*#*) _1_ X-chromosome(s), so any gene on that chromosome (*would, would not*) _would_ be expressed since there is no other gene to "mask" its effect. The genotype of the one colorblind female (*could, could not*) _could not_ be completely determined from her phenotype, because colorblindness was assumed to be (*dominant, recessive*) _recessive_. If the sperm fertilizing an egg contains an X-chromosome the resulting child will be a (*male, female*) *female*, therefore if a normal-visioned female has a father who is colorblind, her genotype (*can, cannot*) *can* be completely determined. The X-chromosome of a male comes from the (*father, mother*) *mother* so if a normal visioned female has a colorblind son her complete genotype (*can, cannot*) *can* be determined.

REVIEW—Chapter 4, Part I

If a backcross is made between an individual with a genotype heterozygous for two traits and an individual recessive for both traits (*AaBb* × *aabb*), when there is independent assortment gametes are produced by the individual with the genotype *AaBb* in the ratio of (#) *1:1:1:1*. Therefore the ratio of the offspring should be (#) *1:1:1:1*. In such a cross this random assortment of the two pairs of alleles is explained by assuming that two pairs of alleles are located on (#) *2* pair(s) of homologous chromosomes. If, however, the ratio of the offspring is 1:1 we assume that only (#) *2* types of gametes were produced. Such a condition is called (*wd*) *linkage* and can be explained by assuming that the two pairs of alleles are located on (#) *1* pair(s) of homologous chromosomes.

REVIEW—Chapter 4, Part II

If an individual with the genotype *AaBb* is crossed with one having the genotype *aabb*, the ratio of offspring should be (#) *1:1:1:1* if the alleles are on two pairs of homologous chromosomes, but should be (#) *1:1* if there is complete linkage. If instead of a ratio of 1:1:1:1 or 1:1 we obtained a ratio of 4:1:1:4, we could assume that the two pairs of alleles were located on (#) *1* pair(s) of homologous chromosomes but that there had been a break and recombination of the (*wd*) *chromo-somes* between the (#) *2* pair(s) of alleles. This type of recombination of genes is called *crossing-over*. The crossover percent is the (*sum of, difference between*) *sum of* the percents of the types which would not occur if there were complete linkage. Thus if the ratio of offspring were 4:1:1:4 the crossover percentage would be *20%*. The percent of crossover was found to be (*the same, different*) *different* for different pairs of alleles, such as vestigial cinnabar and kidney-shaped short.

As a result of the discovery of linkage and crossing-over, one of the assumptions of gene theory had to be modified. The assumption which was modified was that of (*wds*) *independent assortment*. It was assumed that (*wd*) *chromosomes* rather than (*wd*) *genes* assort independently.

Also as a result of the discovery of linkage and crossing-over three new assumptions were added to the gene theory. They were (1) that genes are located in a (wd) _linear_ order on the chromosomes (2) alleles occupy corresponding positions (loci) on (wd) _homologous_ chromosomes and (3) alleles line up side by side when homologous chromosomes (wd) _pair_ during meiosis.

REVIEW—Chapter 4, Part III

The discovery of linkage and crossing-over led to the concept of genes as being located in linear order on a chromosome. The closer two alleles are to each other on a chromosome the (larger, smaller) _smaller_ will be the crossover percentage. If the crossover percent between genes a and b is 5%, and between genes b and c is 3%, the crossover percent between genes a and c might be _8_ % or it might be _2_ %. To discover which of these is correct we would have to make the actual cross. If it is 8% it means that c is (closer to, farther from) _farther from_ a than b is. On the basis of crossover percents it has been possible to construct chromosome maps. If the crossover percentage between gene a and gene b is known, and between gene b and gene c is known, it (is, is not) _is_ necessary to know the crossover percent between gene a and gene c in order to construct a section of a chromosome map.

REVIEW—Chapter 5, Part I

A population of fruit flies in a bottle was studied for several generations. Of the two original flies of this population one had a homozygous genotype for black body (bb) the other had a homozygous genotype for gray body, (lt) _B B_. All of the F_1 individuals had the genotype, (lt) _Bb_ and were (wd) _gray_ bodied. These F_1 individuals would produce gametes in the ratio of 1 (lt) _B_ :(#) _1_ b. Thus the ratio of the alleles in the individuals of the F_1 generation was _1_ : _1_ . Expressed as a decimal fraction the frequency of the gene B was (#) _.5_ , and the frequency of the gene b was also (#) _.5_ . In a population of gray flies all with homozygous genotypes the frequency of the gene B would be (#) _1.0_ and in the same population the frequency of the gene b would be (#) _0_ . When the F_1 individuals, considered as a population, mated, they produced offspring in the ratio of (#) _3_ gray:(#) _1_ black; the genotypic ratio would be (# and lt) _1BB_ : _2Bb_ : _1bb_ . If a total of 4000 gametes were produced by the individuals of this generation (#) _2000_ should contain the gene B and (#) __2000__ should contain the gene b. Thus the ratio of the gametes and hence the ratio of the genes in this generation would be __1__ : __1__. Hence again the frequency of the gene B and the gene b would be (#) __.5__; therefore the ratio of genotypes for the F_3 generation should be __1BB__ : __2Bb__ : __1bb__, which would yield a phenotypic ratio of (#) __3__ gray : (#) __1__ black. This ratio of alleles would remain constant generation after generation providing mating (*is, is not*) __is__ random; thus the recessive allele (*will, will not*) __will not__ be reduced in frequency. If the ratio of two alleles (A and a) in a population is 1:1, this ratio can be expressed as the probability equation (#) __½__ $A + ½$ (*lt*) __a__ = (#) __1__. Since gene frequencies are usually written as decimal fractions this equation can be expressed as (#) __.5__ $A +$ (#) __.5__ $a = 1$. The equation for the genotypes of the population can be developed from this equation by multiplication of the binomials of two such equations to give the genotypic ratio for the population; this equation, expressed in decimal fractions is (#) __.25__ $AA +$ (#) __.5__ $Aa + .25$ (*lt*) __aa__ = 1.

REVIEW—Chapter 5, Part II

Population genetics is concerned with the entire "pool" of genes in a population and not with specific crosses or with selected families. The proportion of any one allele in a population is referred to, as the (*wds*) __frequency__ of that allele, and is expressed as a (*wds*) __decimal fraction__. The ratio of the genes in the gametes reflects the (*wds*) __ratio__ of the alleles in the entire population. When the gene frequencies of two alleles are both .5 and there is dominance the phenotype ratio of the entire population will be __3:1__; therefore if any characteristic due to a recessive gene is present in more than 25% of the population, the recessive allele must be (*more, less*) __more__ frequent than the dominant allele.

In any population, if the only factors in operation are those of heredity, the frequency of any allele (*will, will not*) __will not__ change; therefore a recessive allele (*would, would not*) __would not__ decrease in successive generations.

Since the general equation for gene frequencies in a population is $p + q =$ (#) __1__, the equation $p^2 + 2pq +$ __q^2__ = 1 expresses the proportion of the various genotypes in the population. The p^2 represents individuals who are (*homozygous, heterozygous*) __homozygous__ for the dominant gene. The proportion of individuals having the characteristic due to

the recessive gene is represented by ___q^2___ of the equation. If 19%
of a population has a particular characteristic due to a dominant gene, the
value of q^2 would be (#) __.81__. The gene frequency of the recessive
allele can be calculated by taking the square root of ___.81___; therefore for the above mentioned trait in which 19% of the population had the
characteristic due to the dominant gene, the frequency of the recessive allele
would be (#) __.9__, while the frequency of the dominant allele would
be (#) __.1__.

REVIEW—Chapter 5, Part III

Under most circumstances gene frequencies (*remain constant, change*)
remain constant generation after generation. The dominant gene (*does, does not*)
does not increase in frequency at the expense of the recessive gene.
There are, however, certain forces which affect gene frequencies. The presence
of a dominant gene which is lethal in the homozygous condition increases the
frequency of the (*dominant, recessive*) *recessive* gene, and the genotypic
and phenotypic ratios (*are, are not*) *are* changed.

If an animal or plant breeder wishes to eliminate some undesirable characteristic from his stock it is easier to eliminate a (*dominant, recessive*) *dominant*
allele than it is to eliminate a (*wd*) *recessive* allele. Another factor affecting (*wds*) *gene frequencies* is immigration of individuals with one of two contrasting characteristics. Gene frequencies can also be altered by the rate of *mutation*
of one gene to another.

REVIEW—Chapter 6, Part I

In the introductory questions of this chapter certain ideas were presented
about the relation of genes and genetic make-up to phenotypic characteristics.
Since identical twins arise from a single zygote their genes should be (*identical,
different*) *identical*. Brothers should have (*more, fewer*) *more*
genes in common than two men (nonbrothers) picked at random. All men
have many characteristics in common; they (*should, should not*) *should*
_____ have many genes in common.

Since all organisms have some characteristics in common, for example all
are composed of protoplasm, all organisms (*should, should not*) *should*
have some genes in common.

The question posed at the beginning of this section was, *Of what chemical
substance or substances are genes composed?* We now believe that genes are
composed of __DNA__, because there is constancy of amount of this
substance in the chromosomes of cells of individuals of the same species, and

because the sperm cells contain ___*half*___ the amount. Additional evidence is provided by the experiments on pneumococci. When the capsular gum and the protein in the cell debris of a capsule form were destroyed and the remaining material mixed with bacteria of a noncapsular strain, the strain (*did, did not*) ___*did*___ produce offspring having capsules, but when the ___*DNA*___ was destroyed by an enzyme the strain (*did, did not*) *did not* produce offspring having capsules.

REVIEW—Chapter 6, Part II

In Part II of this chapter we were concerned with the problem of the chemical nature of the DNA molecule. We found that the DNA molecule was thought to be composed of complex structures called nucleotides, and that each nucleotide was composed of a phosphate and a (*wd*) *sugar*, which were always the same in all nucleotides, and of one of (#) *4* different *bases*. The base of the nucleotide was always attached to the (*wd*) *sugar*; chains (strands) of nucleotides are assumed to be formed by attachment of the sugar of one nucleotide to the (*wd*) *phosphate* of another nucleotide. It is also assumed that (*few, many*) *many* nucleotides join to form a long chain. A single long chain (*does, does not*) *does not* constitute a DNA molecule. A DNA molecule is assumed to be a (*single, double*) *double* chain. According to the theoretical model of a DNA molecule, two strands of nucleotides join by the attachment of one base to (*wds*) *another base*. The theoretical model also suggests that there are specific combinations which are called (*wds*) *base pairs*. It is assumed that adenine can join only with thymine and that guanine can attach only to (*wd*) *cytosine*. Evidence, which supports the belief that there are specific base pairs, is found in analysis of the molecular proportions of the bases. It was found that the molecular proportion of cytosine (*was, was not*) *was* equal to that of guanine. However analysis revealed that the molecular proportions of thymine and cytosine (*were, were not*) *were not* equal. It was also found that in different species of organisms the molecular proportions of the various bases were (*the same, different*) *different*; thus all DNA (*is, is not*) *is not* the same. It has been assumed that the base pairs represent a code, with (#) ___*4*___ symbols; thus differences in inherited characteristics could be explained by assuming that in different species the order of the base pairs should be (*the same, different*) *different*. It can also be assumed that in identical twins, developing from a single zygote, the order of the base pairs should be (*the same, different*) *the same*. In terms of DNA, the gene can be defined as (*all, part*) *part* of a DNA molecule. Linkage and cross-

ing over of genes can be explained by the idea that the DNA molecule is a
long and (wd) *chainlike* structure.

REVIEW—Chapter 6, Part III

In order for DNA to be a candidate for the genetic material it would have
to have certain characteristics. The idea that the molecule is long and unbranched helps to explain (wd) *linkage* and (wd) *crossing-over*. The
variation of characteristics of organisms could be explained by various sequences of (wds) *base pairs*. Another aspect of the genes, which would have
to be reflected in the DNA molecule, is the capacity of genes to reproduce
themselves. That the DNA molecule model is pictured as a (*double, single*)
double strand helps to explain how the DNA molecule could duplicate
itself. A second important aspect of the model, which accounts for the idea
that each of the strands can build a new strand which is (*identical to, complementary to*) *complementary to* itself, is the idea that each base can join with (*any,
only one*) *only one* other base. Thus the two resulting new molecules
would be like the (wd) *original* DNA molecule and also (*like, different
from*) *like* each other. The two resulting DNA molecules should
have the same order of (wd) *base* pairs, since each strand acts as a
template (mold) to build a new strand. This process of duplication is assumed
to take place at the time that the (wd) *chromosomes* duplicate
themselves in the process of (wd) *mitosis*; thus when the chromatids
align on the equator of the cell, each of the chromatids would contain (#)
one strand of the original chromosome and (#) *one* strand
which had been built up prior to the cell division. Thus each daughter cell
resulting from mitosis would contain one of the original strands with a copy of
(*that, the other*) *the other* strand. In chromosomes of the daughter cells
(#) *100* % would contain one strand from the original DNA molecule (First Generation). At the next cell division (#) *50* % of the
cells would contain chromosomes which had one strand of the original (first
generation) DNA molecule. This hypothetical model of the manner in which
DNA duplicates itself was (*confirmed, contradicted*) *confirmed* by experiments where bacteria were grown in a medium containing heavy nitrogen
(N-15) and then transferred to a medium containing N-14.

If DNA is the genetic material (genes) then mutations (spontaneous appearance of new phenotypes) should be explicable in terms of DNA. Mutations
can be explained by assuming that occasionally a part of the DNA molecule is
lost from the cell, and by assuming that occasionally there is an error in the
duplication of DNA, and that the wrong (wd) *base* is incorporated
into the new strand.

Answers to Self Test on Chapter 1

1.	C	6.	C	11.	B
2.	B	7.	C	12.	D
3.	C	8.	C	13.	C
4.	C	9.	C	14.	C
5.	A	10.	A		

Answers to Self Test on Chapter 2

1.	B	16.	C	31.	C
2.	A	17.	C	32.	D
3.	D	18.	E	33.	E
4.	B	19.	B	34.	E
5.	C	20.	B	35.	A
6.	B	21.	C	36.	A
7.	A	22.	D	37.	B
8.	D	23.	E	38.	B
9.	E	24.	C	39.	D
10.	E	25.	A	40.	A
11.	D	26.	D	41.	B
12.	A	27.	D	42.	D
13.	C	28.	C	43.	C
14.	B	29.	A	44.	D
15.	E	30.	B	45.	C

Answers to Self Test on Chapter 3

1.	C	16.	D	31.	E
2.	D	17.	C	32.	A
3.	B	18.	B	33.	B
4.	D	19.	E	34.	A
5.	C	20.	D	35.	C
6.	E	21.	A	36.	C
7.	B	22.	E	37.	A
8.	B	23.	C	38.	C
9.	B	24.	D	39.	D
10.	B	25.	B	40.	C
11.	B	26.	B	41.	D
12.	A	27.	D	42.	C
13.	C	28.	C	43.	C
14.	B	29.	A		
15.	A	30.	C		

Answers to Self Test on Chapter 4

1.	B	15.	D	29.	B
2.	A	16.	A	30.	D
3.	B	17.	D	31.	C
4.	A	18.	D	32.	D
5.	E	19.	D	33.	D
6.	B	20.	A	34.	D
7.	B	21.	C	35.	C
8.	B	22.	B	36.	D
9.	D	23.	D	37.	D
10.	A	24.	B	38.	D
11.	B	25.	B	39.	C
12.	C	26.	D	40.	D
13.	D	27.	B	41.	D
14.	A	28.	B		

Answers to Self Test on Chapter 5

1.	C	10.	E	19.	D
2.	A	11.	B	20.	B
3.	B	12.	C	21.	A
4.	E	13.	D and E	22.	B
5.	E	14.	A, B, and C	23.	D
6.	D	15.	C	24.	A
7.	A	16.	C	25.	C
8.	F	17.	E	26.	A
9.	D	18.	B	27.	C

The approximate frequencies of genes:

$$A - 25\tfrac{1}{2}\%$$
$$B - 8\tfrac{1}{2}\%$$
$$O - 66 \ \%$$

Answers to Self Test on Chapter 6

1.	A	10.	B	19.	B
2.	A	11.	C	20.	D
3.	C	12.	B	21.	A
4.	A	13.	D	22.	A
5.	B	14.	B	23.	A
6.	C	15.	D	24.	B
7.	A	16.	B	25.	C
8.	B	17.	A	26.	A
9.	B	18.	B		

The Gift of Light
Is here for all to see.
The Joy of Love
Gives light to those who need;
Contribute to the Light.
BLS

ABOUT THE AUTHOR

Brian Luke Seaward is an associate faculty member of the Center for Human Caring at the University of Colorado-Denver and executive director of Inspiration Unlimited & Rocky Mountains Stress Management Seminars, a health promotion consulting company in Longmont, Colorado. He is also an adjunct professor at the University of Northern Colorado. He teaches courses in stress reduction, health and wellness, behavioral medicine, humor and health, and exercise physiology. Dr. Seaward received his B.A. in journalism from the University of Maine at Orono, his M.S. in exercise physiology from the University of Illinois at Champaign-Urbana, and his Ph.D. in health promotion and wellness (an interdisciplinary program) from the University of Maryland in College Park. He is a certified stress management educator through the Association for Applied Psychophysiology and Biofeedback. Dr. Seaward has been invited to speak on the topic of stress management and wellness to such organizations as IBM, AT&T, Conoco Oil, Kodak, Amoco Oil, the Olympic Biathlon Team, the American Cancer Society, the American Heart Association, the United States Postal Service, and the National Safety Council. When not instructing, consulting, or counseling stress management programs, Dr. Seaward relaxes back home in the Colorado Rocky Mountains.